Where The Huckleberries Grow

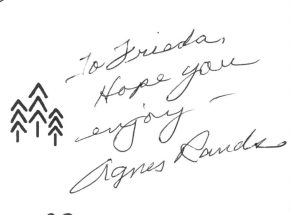

*To Frieda,
Hope you
enjoy —
Agnes Rands*

Agnes Rands

Linden Press   Sisters, Oregon

august 2007

*Mom,
Happy Birthday! I met the author
at the scandinavian festival.
she reminded me a lot of you.
love, Kide*

LINDEN PRESS
P.O. Box 8251
Sisters, OR 97759

©2000 by Agnes Rands

ISBN: 0-9675827-0-9

Library of Congress Card Number: 99-091120

First edition, Fourth printing

Cover photo of Lake Cushman,Washington, by Agnes Rands

Layout and design by DIMI PRESS

Cover design by Bruce DeRoos

Typeface-12 pt. Palatino

DEDICATION

To my late husband Ralph, who saw a
story in the lives of my immigrant
parents and their experiences in
the logging camps, and who
gave me the encouragement
I needed to write
that story.

And to my supportive daughters
Debbie Cullen, Lisa Wysel,
Julie Mikula, and Shelley Jorgensen
for keeping me on task by persistently asking,
"When you going to finish your book, Mom?"

BOUNTIFUL THANKS

To my sister Thelma Banner for sharing with me
her memories of growing up in the logging
camps;

To my cousin Art Carlson, Marietta, Georgia, for
responding so fully to my questions about his
parents, Ida and Charlie;

And to my *små-kusin* Ralf Häggqvist, Ivar's
grandson, Närpes, Finland, who sent me
the information about the Häggqvist
family and the times in which they lived.

ALSO

Thanks to the Mason County Historical Society, Shelton, Washington, for the use of the photo of the speeder.

The author has made every effort to obtain the permission of those whose logging photos are reproduced. In some cases it proved impossible to locate them. The author thanks those anonymous individuals and urges them to contact the author or publisher so that they can receive appropriate credit in the next edition.

AUTHOR'S FOREWORD

During the same week in February, 1980, my father, my remaining parent, died at age 91, and Sarah, my first grandchild, was born. Sadness and joy joined hands. Then came melancholy.

Lost forever to Sarah and our future grandchildren was the opportunity to know their great-grandparents and to hear them tell in their delightful Swedish accent about coming to America and living in the logging camps. I decided that even if I could not record on paper the music of their mother tongue, I could at least retell some of their stories.

Those who remember the camp days might say I didn't get all the facts straight or that I fictionalized too much. It's true that for the sake of story, I combined some separate events into single episodes and that I changed the names of some of the people. Also, I wrote the letters that appear in the book because no letters were preserved.

But aside from these alterations and additions, I have, to the best of my ability, knowledge, and research, presented the way the camp was, the way the people were, and the way things happened. My hope is that you will find something of value here, some interesting information, a few laughs, and a glimpse of a time and place you would otherwise never know.

PHOENIX LOGGING COMPANY

CAMPS ● 1920 to 1939

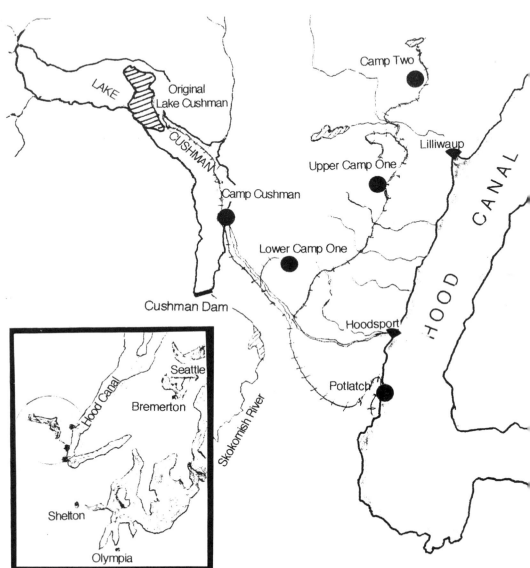

In 1920 Tacoma Power and Light awarded Phoenix Logging Company a six year contract to clear the heavily-timbered land bordering Lake Cushman and the Skokomish River in anticipation of the construction of Cushman Dam and the flooding of the valley. After completing this contract, Phoenix continued its railroad logging primarily in the area between Lake Cushman and Hood Canal. In 1939 the company closed down its logging operation. (Only a few of the many railroads appear on this brief map.)

CONTENTS

PART VI - CAMP TWO, 1931-1936

PART VI - POTLATCH, 1936-1939

AFTERWORD - SHELTON, 1990

INTRODUCTION

Tilda and Charlie grew up in neighboring communities in the Swedish-speaking section of Finland, but they meet for the first time at a Swedish dance in Portland, Oregon. A year later, 1917, they marry and move to Seattle.

Tilda doesn't know what she's getting into when she marries a logger. He tries other work for her sake, but the call of the outdoors is too great. He convinces her that the woods is where they should live and rear their children.

When Tilda first sees the logging camp, its grey-weathered shacks lining an oil-soaked railroad bed, its scorched snags and black stumps, she is ready to leave. "Give it one year," Charlie coaxes. "Then if you still want to go, we'll go."

Nathaniel Hawthorne in his short story, "The Ambitious Guest," tells of a family who live at the base of a mountain that forever trembles and rocks, threatening their very existence. Families who live in the logging camps of the Olympic Mountains have no fear of avalanche from the fir-carpeted hills and mountains around them, but Tilda soon experiences other fears just as pernicious—the fear of logging accidents and forest fires and the dread of isolation when the snow and spring thaws make roads and trestles impassable. Tilda agrees to one year, little dreaming that it will be seventeen years before she leaves the logging camps.

This book is about those years, the ordinary events that fill the lives of the Lind family and their community. But these episodes—some of which are told through the voices of the children—reveal a larger story, that of an extraordinary spirit. The people in the early logging camps—primarily young, hard-working, Scandinavian immigrants—struggle against harsh and uncertain circumstances but are sustained by an inner strength and **joie de vivre**, even in the face of tragedy.

PART 1 - FINLAND 1912

CHAPTER 1: AMERICA BECKONS

The Letter

"Ida! Ida! Father! It came! The letter from Ivar!" Tilda shouted, waving the envelope above her head, racing through the wild grass that separated the road from the house. "August picked up our mail at the store and here it is. Ivar's letter!"

Spring was early and their foreroom door was open. Before her foot touched the large, flat stone that was their doorstep, her father and her sister Ida were at the door. Ida was holding their tin dinner plates and Father was drying his hands for the noonday meal.

"Tilda, don't run like that!" Ida scolded. "Remember your leg!"

Father reached out and took the letter from Tilda's hand and retreated into the house. Her stepmother slipped back into the shadows of the room.

In all her sixteen years, Tilda had never been so excited and knew that Ida felt the same way. This had to be the letter her brother promised. Neither dared speak as Father read aloud from the front of the envelope.

"'Herr Erik Edvard Kull Häggqvist, Narpes, Finland.'" He glanced up at the girls and then back at the envelope. "It's postmarked, 'Portland, Oregon, U.S.A.'"

He picked up the knife Ida had used to cut their bread and carefully slit open the top of the envelope. Tilda sank into the chair by the stove and felt Ida move around behind her, still holding their dinner plates. The table could wait, but Tilda wasn't sure she and her sister could. Tilda rubbed her leg, more out of habit than need. She watched her father unfold the letter from their brother, and then move to the window for better light. Still standing, he began to read, this time silently.

In the years since Ivar left for America, he had never failed to write home every few months. In the next village, Ester Alskog, the girl he promised to marry, lived for his letters and his return, but one year moved into another until now five years had gone by. He had written that as soon as he saved enough money to buy the farm they lived on in Finland, as soon as he could pay for their freedom from indenture, he would come home.

But he delayed. The railroad he worked for paid well, but it was expensive to live in America. Two years ago when he learned of Tilda's sick leg, he sent money from his savings to pay for a doctor and medicine, and then he had to keep working to rebuild his savings.

Tilda touched the sunken spot on the top of her foot where the poison had drained out. It was still tender but had finally healed.

Then Ivar had written in his last letter that there was something he wanted to do for his two younger sisters. He would need to work another year to get the money, but he felt it was worth it. While he was a resident of the United States, he could "sponsor" his sisters. Ivar was making it possible for them to move to America.

The possibility made Tilda weak. She reached for her older sister's hand and found that it, too, was trembling. When would Father finish reading the letter!

Edvard

Edvard dropped his arm to his side. The weight of the letter in his hand was too much. He knew his daughters were watching him from across the room even though his back was to them. Ida, the elder of his last two children, stood tall, straight, strong. She could run like the wind and thresh and clean the grain as well as Ivar. And then there was Tilda—a little shy and unsure, fairer of skin and not as strong, but wanting to keep up with her sister. Both had thick, glistening, brown hair that challenged their combs, and eyes that vied with the blue of the Bothnia Sea. Was it possible he'd lose these children, too?

Tilda had been only six and Ida eight, when Edvard's beloved Maria died of the terrible coughing disease. Alma, his first born, tried to be mother to her young brother and sisters, but was impatient with Tilda's headaches and leg pain and Ida's mischief and Ivar's independence. Four years later she married Karl John Haga. A year after that when their son Eskil was born, his first grandchild, they moved to America. The next year Ivar, Edvard's only son, left, too.

To help the family at home, Ivar said. A year or two at the most, he had said. He'd earn enough money to buy the land they worked, so they would be free of their indenture, he said. He was twenty-one then, when a young man thinks he can do anything. But Ivar was still gone. And now Edvard's last two children might leave.

America was a siren song. It lured away the best of Finland's youth by promising them riches and independence. It swallowed them up. Gave few back. Perhaps Ivar, too, would stay in America as others had, forgetting his promises and coaxing his sisters to join him.

Edvard had to admit that times were bad now, but it hadn't been bad in the beginning. When he married Maria Karlsdotter, they had done what most of the common people did. They'd indentured themselves to a landholder. It meant giving all they grew and earned four days a week to the landowner. In return, the landlord allowed them to have a barn of their own where they could keep their cow and pig and a few chickens, and they could work for themselves in the fields around the barn the rest of the week. The landlord provided for certain family needs like a pair of shoes a year for each child.

Edvard accepted this, and he and Maria felt fortunate. They had a good cow. They could sell enough milk to build up their savings. Even though they would need to work seven days a week for many years, the day would come when they could buy the land from the landowner and build a better life for themselves.

Before he started his day's work for the landowner, Edvard milked his own cow and carried the milk in its container four miles to a place where the milk company picked it up. After the company had separated the milk, Edvard could buy back the skim milk at a cheap price for his animals and for themselves. At the end of Edvard's workday in the fields, he would walk again to the pick-up place and carry the container of skim milk home. In the winter it was easier to make this trip in spite of the terrible cold because he could push the container on a wide ski. But summer or winter, it was hard. Still, they were getting ahead a little, he and Maria, and then it happened.

Ivar was twelve, old enough to help his father with the milking. They had just turned the cow out to pasture when they saw the threatening black clouds roll in over the pine forest that separated them from the sea. Thunder clapped and lightning split the fields and sky. When the storm was over, Edvard and Ivar ran to find their cow.

Ivar saw her first under a spruce tree where she had huddled for shelter. Their fine cow, their pride, their hope for a better life, lay dead under the tree. The traitorous spruce had conducted the lightning bolt into the heart of this fine animal.

Ivar, as well as Edvard, understood what had happened that day. Hope for a better life was gone. Struggle for enough to eat and wear would increase. When the pair of shoes the landowner gave him was worn out or outgrown, there would be no other until the next year. The indenture system allowed for survival and no more and without their cow, they were without hope.

Edvard leaned against the window frame, shaking his head to rid himself of the memory. He tried to slip Ivar's letter back into the envelope, but his big hands were clumsy, and he swore under his breath. He understood why Ivar couldn't accept the poverty and servitude that followed that day, why he had looked for a way out by going to the United States. But why did he have to send for Ida and Tilda?

Edvard turned from the window and sat down heavily on the chair by the table where he always took his meals. He was proud of this table with its heavy pine boards. He'd cut down a tree at the far end of the field and carefully hewn the boards. The benches and chair, too, he'd made.

Edvard's eyes traced the edges of the tiny room. Kajsa Stina had been his wife now for six years, but the lace curtains Maria had sewn still hung at the windows here in the center-room and in the inner-room where they all slept. He wanted it that way. The narrow sideboard still held the same dishes on its shelves and the tin basins for washing them. The same cooking pot sat on the stove for their midday meal. Maria's rag rugs, so carefully plaited, lay like pressed flowers on the wide, time-polished planks of the wood floor. The worn, stark plainness of his home was, to him, soft with memories, but to his daughters, this house was just two cramped rooms with a boarded-in foreroom for coats and boots, a house full of icy drafts in winter and endless work in summer. How could he ask his girls to stay?

Edvard felt his daughters' eyes on him as he placed the letter face down on the table and turned to look out the window again, out toward the Bothnia Sea and the ocean and America. He never talked about it much, but he himself had been to America before Ida was born. It was a grand country, the United States. High mountains, wide rivers, giant pines and firs and mile after mile of rich, virgin soil.

But Finland had its own beauty, too, fragile as it was. The gentle landscape of soft, green fields was fringed with deep-green forests; white-barked birches stood guard over clear streams, and 10,000 emerald-blue lakes dotted his homeland. Though his country was not as grand as America, and though it still lived under the paw of the Russian bear, Edvard loved it and wondered how his children could leave it so easily.

Certainly Edvard knew well Finland's hardships, but he understood without blame why it was such a poor country. The growing season in this far-north land was short and the winters long. When the world was young, glaciers had scoured the best soil from the land and left too many rocks and bare outcroppings to make farming easy. Over the centuries the armies of Sweden and Russia had marched across Finland, claiming it for their own, using its resources to feed and clothe their armies. In his own time, he had seen the young men of the nation conscripted to fight the Russians, and then he'd heard those Finnish boys who made it home, maimed and defeated, talk only of emigrating to America.

Edvard knew about the better life, the free life waiting there in America for the young, the ambitious and adventuresome. He could have stayed, but he came back when some men with families in Finland chose not to. He could never have left Maria and the two children, Alma and Ivar, to face the hardships at home by themselves. It was hard enough to survive in Finland when the man was present.

Their neighbor, Josef Carlsen, had left his family for America. When he hadn't been able to make a living on the farm, he'd traveled to the city to find work. When he couldn't find work, he lost his self-respect and started to drink. He returned to the farm, but could speak of nothing but America.

Edvard would never forget the day Josef rode his horse to the shore of Kristinestad to meet the big, white ship. Edvard brought Josef's wife, Anna Elisabet, and their five young children in his wagon to see him off. Edvard watched as Josef gave August, his ten-year-old son, a taste of his beer to let his eldest know that he would now be taking the role of the man of the house. Edvard and Anna and all who stood silently and watched knew that they would never see Josef again.

Anna and her children huddled and cried until the ship was out of sight. And Anna cried all the way back to their home and for weeks and months after. Josef had left his family without a stick of wood to heat the house and with a pasture fence in need of repair. He'd been gone three years now and his family had had no word from him.

Edvard sighed. He himself had returned to Finland to provide for his family. He'd kept food on the table through the hard years, and now this was the thanks he got!

Edvard was tired. How long could he work seven days a week, fourteen hours a day, just to survive? And when he couldn't work any longer and needed help in his old age, where would his children be then? And where would be the grandchildren to hold on his knee? To bring life meaning? Make a man feel complete? A father deserved this much.

Edvard turned the letter over and studied it, tracing the round postmark with his work-scarred finger. It was all there. The date the letter was sent. City. State. A circle of information. A circle of life across the world. But he loved his comely, spirited, warm-hearted daughters and wanted them to be a part of his own circle. How could he let them go!

Edvard pushed his chair back from the table and looked around, startled for a moment by the silence in the room. Then he was back in the present.

"Still standing there, Ida?" he asked. "Holding your work in your hands? Get the table set, and Tilda, get up and help your stepmother put the midday meal on the table. There's work to be done before we have time to talk."

Ida scurried to the table and set the plates at their places. Tilda ran to the sideboard for a bowl for the potatoes and then they sat up to the table. Father blessed the potatoes and fish. They ate silently. Then Father took his hat and coat from the hook by the door and left for the barn. Stepmother followed. Ida picked up the kettle of boiling water from the stove and poured it into two tin basins on the sideboard while Tilda carried the dishes to her to be washed and rinsed.

"What do you think?" Tilda whispered to Ida, though they were now alone in the house. She grabbed the sun-bleached flour sack from its hook on the wall, picked up a dish from the rinsing basin, shook off the water, and patted it dry. "Is Father going to let us go?"

"I don't know," Ida whispered back. "He did say we'd talk later." Ida brushed a wisp of hair from her cheek with the back of her sudsy hand and then rested both hands on the edge of the basin. "Tilda," she began, and then paused. "Tilda, there is something we must think about. We must be very sure we want to go to America more than anything in the world." Ida was no longer whispering. "Think if we never saw our home or Father again. Ever!"

Tilda stared at her sister. "I guess I was too excited to think about that," she said. "It would be terrible never to see Father again, or Anna Carlsen."

Tilda's thoughts raced back. Anna Carlsen had been a second mother to her when her own mother died. When Father remarried, and Stepmother treated Tilda and Ida badly, Tilda had escaped to Anna's kitchen. On days her leg ached so badly that she knew she wouldn't be able to sit in school and concentrate, she walked the six miles to Anna's house. Anna let her sit with her foot on a chair and watch while she cooked and sewed and tended the children. At the end of the day, Tilda returned home reluctantly, knowing that Stepmother would scold and maybe switch her for coming home late. Later, when Anna's husband Josef left her, Tilda tried to help. She watched the little ones while Anna and her eldest boy August worked in the fields.

At first Tilda and Ida had been happy for Father. His new wife was pretty with yellow curls and pink cheeks. She was good to Father, cooked the food he liked and did everything he asked of her. But when Father was working in the fields, Stepmother turned on Tilda and Ida and treated them like intruders.

Once when she and Ida were taking the cows to pasture, the cows turned and ran back to the barn, beating the girls home. Stepmother knew what had happened, but she called the girls lazy and disobedient for not doing as she had ordered.

Tilda was remembering how Stepmother never believed her when she said her head hurt so badly she saw spots and whirling lights. Only when the headache made Tilda throw up, did Stepmother let her stay home from school, but even then she made Tilda get out of bed and work for her all day. Tilda loved school, but Stepmother accused her of pretending to be sick to stay home or get out of work.

Tilda remembered not too long ago Schoolmaster had closed his eyes long and hard and told them how the streets in America were paved with gold, and Tilda and Ida told Father what he said. Stepmother huffed, "What difference does it make if the streets are paved with gold? You girls are too ignorant and uncultured to get anywhere. Stay on the farm where you belong."

Once Ida brought a friend home from school. Stepmother sent the friend away and told them they were not to bring friends to the house. She had enough to do without extra people making extra work for her and keeping Ida and Tilda from doing their chores. And the first Christmas of their new marriage, the girls were told they couldn't bring a tree into the house. Trees were dirty and too much bother, she said. There would be no Christmas trees while she lived there!

Tilda sighed deeply. "I'd miss Father, and Anna Carlsen, but I would never miss Stepmother!"

"Neither would I!" Ida said. "And, Tilda, I wouldn't miss being so poor either. I wouldn't miss going to bed hungry. Or not having warm clothes to wear in the winter when the temperature gets below zero."

Tilda remembered walking home from school in shoes too cracked to hold out the snow, and peeing on her own feet to keep them from freezing.

"No, Ida, I would not miss being poor!" Tilda exclaimed. "And maybe we'd marry rich Americans and could buy tickets to come home and visit Father as often as we wanted."

"You're right, Tilda," Ida said, her hands again busy in the dishpan. "And our rich husbands will be handsome and will buy us fine clothes and jewelry and big houses with maids to do all the work!" she finished, flipping soapy water at the rafters.

"Yes, but now, Ida, we must do the hard part," Tilda said. "We have to talk Father into letting us go to America."

Father looked tired. He'd worked until dark as always, and now that the days were getting longer, so was his workday. Supper was out of the way, but this time Stepmother cleared the table. Father must have told her he needed to talk to his daughters.

Father leaned his elbows on the table and wrapped both hands around his coffee cup. Tilda had seen him do this other times when he had something very serious to talk about.

"Daughters," he began, "do you know how long and how hard this trip to America would be?"

Tilda and Ida shook their heads because they knew Father wanted to tell them.

"You have to ride our horse to the port of Kristinestad. You must take a boat from there to the port town Åbo and from there to Liverpool, England. Now you get on a huge ship, but you will never see the upper deck, never see the blue sky. You will travel steerage, two decks below the main deck, the part of the ship reserved for our class of people. You know why they call it 'steerage'?"

He didn't wait for an answer.

"They call it steerage because this is where they used to haul cattle."

Edvard waited for this to be really understood.

"Yes, Father, we have heard that," Ida responded. "We know that we are packed into a tiny space, that we have to take some of our own food, and that if we get sick, there may be no one to help us."

Father went on. "You'll spend over a week in the bottom of this ship, short of fresh air and fresh food, fighting seasickness, hoping and praying you will not come down with a bad disease because of the filthy conditions. When the ship docks in New York, you will be herded into little boats and rowed to Ellis Island where you will be checked for disease and for proper papers to enter the United States. If you pass, you are taken to Battery Park in New York City and turned out to find your own way."

Tilda stepped closer to her sister.

"Now you must find the railroad station," Father said, "and

buy your tickets to Oregon. You must not let go of your bags at any time because they could be stolen. But as young, immigrant girls, a greater danger threatens you. White slave traders acting like immigration officers or people wanting to help, have kidnapped young women and sold them to evil men who use them for prostitution until their health breaks. Then they throw them out on the street. Do you know what I am talking about?"

"Yes, Father, we have heard about this danger," Tilda answered, and waited for what he would say next.

"And knowing all this," Father said more quietly than he usually spoke, "do you still want to go to America?"

Tilda slipped her hand into Ida's hand so Ida would have the courage to speak out for both of them.

"Yes, Father," Ida answered. "We've talked about it and we want to go to America more than anything in the world."

Father wasn't through. "And what will you do in America to support yourselves? Ivar doesn't have money to take care of you, you know."

Ida spoke first. "We can work as maids until we learn the language, and then we'll get better jobs. We've heard that that is the way it is done in America."

"And soon we will have money to buy things," Tilda added. "Fine dresses, fancy hats, and shoes—a pair for summer and a pair for winter..."

Edvard looked at Tilda's dress. It had been Ida's, and Alma's before that. Patches on patches. A torn hem. It had once been blue, but the color was mostly gone. Ida, too, wore a dress that had been washed too many times and hung limp at the top of her broken boots, but still both girls stood tall in front of him as if they were wearing elegant finery. They should be wearing finery, or at least something new, crisp, fresh, to match their good looks. His daughters deserved something better than he could ever give them.

Edvard dropped his head into his hands. He felt the girls watching him. Waiting. Today all day as he worked—stirring the ground, repairing the wagon wheel, tending the pigs—the same question turned round and round in his head like the arms on the windmill behind the barn, 'How can I let them go?' But now he knew. How could he not let them go!

He fumbled for Ivar's letter in his pants pocket and when he found it, handed it to Ida. "The money for your passage is here," he said. "Divide it with your sister."

He pulled himself to his feet and moved slowly to the door that led outside. He opened it and paused. He spoke softly to the stars, but his daughters heard him, too.

"Have a safe voyage—and a good life," he said, and walked out toward the barn in the dark.

Ellis Island

They'd been squeezed in among strangers in the hold of the ship for over a week. With fifty other women, they had eaten stale bread and stringy meat and slept on straw mattresses in narrow bunks in a room the size of their little house in Finland. But the body odor, rancid wool, stale vomit, all the smells of sea-sickness and confinement in steerage, were forgotten now as Tilda and the others pressed toward the open hatch and a new life in America.

Ida started up the ladder-like stairs first. Tilda followed in the press of people, holding on to the hem of her sister's skirt so they wouldn't get separated. Already she could smell fresh salt air as it misted around them from the opening above their heads. Feet felt for steps hidden by skirts and long coats as they climbed toward the square of daylight and finally tumbled out onto the shiny, wet deck of the ship.

She and Ida wrapped their arms around each other for protection from the sharp wind and waited for their eyes to become accustomed to the unfamiliar daylight. With the hundreds of other immigrants, they huddled and waited, wondering what would happen next, and then they saw her.

They had read about her in their history books and heard about her from their teacher, but nothing had prepared them for her size and beauty. Rising out of the ocean, torch in hand, looking out at them from above the mists, shining like silver in the moist air of the grey day, she became at once their protecting angel and welcoming mother.

"It's the Statue of Liberty," Ida whispered.

"I know," Tilda answered.

They couldn't stop looking at her, even when crewmen herded them into little boats and began rowing them across the choppy water toward a small, low-lying island weighted down by a mammoth building.

"That must be Ellis Island," Ida said, wiping the splashing sea foam from her face with one hand while hanging on to the edge of the boat with the other. "Father told us that immigration officers here check to see that we have the right papers and that we don't have any contagious disease. A lot of people are sent back."

"They wouldn't send us back, would they?"

"No, of course not. Father said he would make sure our papers were in order. And we're both healthy. We have nothing to worry about."

Tilda believed her sister, but, still, the huge, square building with its tiers of dark windows and four giant towers looked as cold and threatening in the grey light as the waves that churned around its wharf. Someone in steerage had said it was called "Devil's Isle," Tilda remembered, and reached out for her sister's hand. Soon they and the hundreds of others disembarked on the island and, like the ants that sometimes trailed across their threshold at home, they wound their way into the shadowy interior of the building and up a long flight of stairs.

"Have your green health cards ready," they were told as they reached the top of the stairs. The people juggled luggage, gripped the hands of their children, and dug for their health cards. Then they moved into the registry hall where they were directed to find a place at the long benches that filled the cavernous room. They were out of the wind now, but babies cried and people talked nervously as they waited to be ushered in groups to the table of uniformed men at each end of the room.

Two of the immigration officers stood in front of the table as Tilda and Ida approached with their group. One sat behind the table leaning back in his chair. All three studied them as they walked up and stood stiffly before them.

"Ida," Tilda whispered, "is that officer pointing at us?"

"I think he is. I think he's beckoning to you."

Tilda stepped back. Her heart raced. The uniformed inspector behind the table jumped up, tipping his chair as he darted out from behind the table. He strode down the hushed line and stood in front of Tilda. His voice was harsh as he spoke to her in English. Not understanding, Tilda shook her head and stepped back.

The officer shook his head then, grabbed Tilda by the arm and pulled her out of the line. Still talking, he gestured to a door in the wall behind the table. Tilda thought of Father's words—white slave traders acting like immigration officers. Her knees shook. She braced her feet, but he was too strong. He tightened his grip on her arm and led her toward the door.

"I'm coming, too," Ida said, and the officer nodded.

The room behind the door was tiny, its only light from a narrow window near the ceiling. The officer pointed to a bench next to a table, closed the door, and left.

"What did I do?" Tilda choked. "Are they sending me back to Finland?"

"I don't know, but if they do, I'm going, too."

Minutes passed slowly. Finally the door opened again. A man in a white coat entered carrying a lighted lamp. He glanced at Ida and then turned to Tilda. He brought the lamp up close to her face and squinted. He leaned closer until his nose nearly touched hers and she could feel his breath. With his free hand, he poked and squeezed her skin. Then he nodded at her and left. More minutes passed before a young woman entered with a pad and pencil in her hand.

"I interpret for the doctor," she said, speaking to Tilda in Swedish. "He wants me to tell you that you do not have measles or smallpox. The rash on your face is acne, possibly caused by poor diet on the ship, or maybe nervousness about moving to a new country. You and your sister can go ahead and register your papers," she smiled, "and then you are free to go. And, oh yes, **snälla flickor**, welcome to America."

PART II - SEATTLE 1922

CHAPTER 2: UNSETTLED

Ballard

"I da, come sit down and we'll have a **på tår**," Tilda said, carrying the coffeepot to the table. "Stop doing dishes now when you are company."

"Sisters aren't company, and I like to help," Ida said. "But now that we finally got the children down for their naps, a second cup of coffee would taste good."

Tilda could see that Ida's one-year-old Arthur was wearing his mother out, and Tilda felt ready to sit down, too. Thelma was four, now, but she ran as wild as her two-and-a-half year old brother Leonard and their little cousin when they were together, especially when they hadn't seen each other for a while.

Ida brushed a crumb from the table, sliding her hand across the polished surface. "Tilda, your new table is really nice. The smooth wood makes me think of our table at home that Father made."

Tilda flinched a little at the mention of home. She missed Father and Ivar, even though her new world brimmed with good things, the good life Father had wished for them.

"We paid only a dollar for this table at the secondhand store," Tilda said. "It's sturdy and the sides fold down like the fancy tables in the furniture store windows. The man who sold it to us said this table would still be around for our grand-children to use."

"One generation at a time," Ida laughed. "I have all I can do to keep up with Artur!"

Tilda sipped her coffee. "We've missed you since you moved from Seattle. We have good neighbors, but I have to talk English with them, and you know how hard that is, even after living in this country for ten years. I guess we spend too much time with old-country friends talking nothing but Swedish."

"Ya," Ida said, "it's hard to think of the right English words and when we do, we can't say them. 'W' comes out 'V' and 'V', 'W'. I get the 'J' and 'Y' sounds backwards, too."

"And when we have so much trouble with the 'th' sound, we name our first born 'Thelma' and 'Arthur'," Tilda said, ex-aggerating the "th" in the names by pressing the tip of her tongue hard against her upper teeth. "That sound is really hard to make," she laughed. "I guess we weren't thinking when we decided on names for our children."

"I guess not," Ida agreed, sitting back in her chair and look-ing around. "I see Charlie painted all the cupboards since we were here last."

"Ya, he painted the window frames in the front room, too," Tilda said. "Our rented houses won't ever look like the big houses in Portland where we worked as maids, but I never expected that. We're rich enough when we have electricity and running water and a modern wood stove to cook on."

"Don't forget the inside toilets!" Ida smiled.

"Remember, we were going to marry rich American men so we would never be poor again? Instead we meet and marry Swede-Finn boys from the old country. Two Charlies," Tilda laughed.

"But my Charlie Carlson and your Charlie Lind sure know how to work and make us comfortable," Ida said. "We have it good now."

"Ya, they're **duktiga pojkar**," Tilda agreed. "I was so glad when my Charlie took the mill job here in Ballard. I like the paved streets and sidewalks, and being close to a streetcar when we want to go to downtown Seattle. And now the Ballard city council is making a rule that every time a new saloon is built, there has to be a new church. This will be a good place to raise a family."

"What about Charlie?" Ida asked. "Is he liking Ballard by now?"

"Charlie has always liked Ballard," Tilda said, concentrating on stirring her coffee. "He likes being part of a city like Seattle, but he'll tell you he liked this part of Seattle best when he logged here. Before we were married, he helped fall and buck trees next to the university that were as big around as this table." Tilda glanced up at her sister. "Ya, I know," she said. "He acts restless sometimes. It's hard for him to be locked up in a mill all day."

Tilda wanted her sister to understand. Ida's Charlie was a draftsman and was content to work inside, drawing blueprints for new mills like the one in Shelton where he was working now. But Tilda's Charlie was a logger. He started working in the woods in the old country when he was fourteen. He emigrated to Canada when he was eighteen and logged there for a short time before he moved to the United States and started logging around Seattle and Astoria and Portland.

He knew when they married that she didn't want to live in a logging camp, that she worried about logging accidents and forest fires, and being alone in the mountains. Tilda had told him shortly after they met at a Runeberg dance in Portland, that she didn't move to America, the "land of opportunity," to live in the woods with a bunch of rough lumberjacks! So he took the mill job for her.

"Now I wash the dishes," Ida said, stacking their plates and carrying them to the sink. Tilda jumped up to help, glad for the interruption to her thoughts.

"Have you heard from Father or Ivar lately?" Tilda asked, wanting to change the subject.

"Ya," Ida said. "From Ivar. I almost forgot to show you the letter. Everything goes well for them. Ester is busy with their three little boys, and Father and Ivar work their farm."

"I know Ivar was anxious to get back to Finland," Tilda said, "but I wish he could have stayed in Portland a little longer after we came. I still miss him."

"Ya, but when he finally had the money to buy their land," Ida said, "there was no holding him back. Now he and Father work together, and Father has time on long winter evenings to play with his grandchildren, to tell them stories—"

"I bet he tells them how the bear lost its tail," Tilda smiled. "I loved that story when I was little."

"I know he'll tell them how the Russian bear finally pulled back its paw," Ida said, "and let Finland go free."

"My Charlie says that Finland won its freedom the same year he lost his," Tilda laughed. "That was 1917, the year we were married, you know." Tilda studied her sister's face. "He is joking, isn't he? He doesn't mind working in the cedar mill?" Tilda asked, searching for reassurance.

"Tilda," Ida replied, sounding a little impatient, "he has steady work and a comfortable house in a good neighborhood. What more can he ask?" She dried her hands on the dishtowel and tip-toed to the bedroom door to listen for Arthur.

"He's still sleeping," Ida said, sitting back down at the table. "You know, Tilda, when you think about it, we are lucky we even made it to America. Remember how disappointed we were when we couldn't buy tickets on that beautiful new ship, the *Titanic*? They sold the last ticket three days before we tried to buy ours."

"I remember," Tilda said. "Only a third of the passengers were rescued when the ship hit the iceberg and sank. They say almost no one in steerage even made it to the deck."

"But the worst was yet to come, remember?" Ida smiled.

"Yes," Tilda said. "Getting through immigration with my bad skin. And then thinking we'd starve to death on the train to Portland. I remember we were too scared to leave our seats and our suitcases to go to the dining car."

"Remember how that woman at the train station in New York scared us?" Ida asked. "She wanted to carry our grips. And she kept motioning us to follow her. We hung on tight to our bags all the way from New York to Portland."

"Lucky we bought all those bananas at the train station," Tilda said, "but I didn't think I'd ever eat another banana."

"Me, either," Ida said. "But Artur loves them. My, he's sleeping a long time today. I guess he was tired from playing so hard. Wondering where my Charlie is. He just went for a walk."

"I guess he likes to be on his own when he gets a day off," Tilda said. "He probably walked down to the Ballard Locks. They finished those locks the year we moved to Seattle and my Charlie never gets tired of watching the boats go through."

"I know," Ida said. "The locks are like magic. The operator sends the boats through a gate at one end of the locks and the water lifts them up, and then another gate lets them out at the lake. And when the boats want back out to the ocean, the water lets them down, and away they sail—"

"Listen," Tilda interrupted. "I think I hear your Charlie on the porch now. Oh, my! I'll bet he hasn't had lunch and we didn't even leave him a cup of coffee!" She hurried to the sink and began rinsing out the coffee pot. She heard the door open.

"Tilda," a familiar voice said, "I have something to tell you."

Tilda froze. This wasn't Ida's Charlie. It was her own Charlie who spoke. But he wasn't supposed to be home from work for three hours. She set the pot down on the stove and slowly turned around to face her husband. He was tall and strong, filling the doorway. He stepped toward her then, his clear-blue eyes locking onto hers. She loved her handsome husband, but why was he home in the middle of the afternoon? She waited.

"Tilda," he said, "maybe you better sit down."

She reached for a chair without taking her eyes off her husband.

"Tilda, I quit the mill. I signed up with Phoenix Logging Company. We're moving to a logging camp in the Olympic Mountains at the end of the month."

"Telma, don't run into the street!" Tilda called.

"I'm just waving goodbye to Art," Thelma answered, stepping back onto the sidewalk in front of their house.

Leonard would have waved, but he saw something in the grass that interested him. He dropped to his knees and parted the tender spring blades with his fingers to see if he could find whatever little creature had caught his eye.

Tilda waved from the porch until the car turned the corner at the end of the block. Her brother-in-law was really proud of his first car and honked the horn as he drove away. Tilda's own Charlie had been saving for an automobile, but they hadn't really needed one. Charlie could walk to work and if they wanted to go to town, they could take the streetcar.

"I thought they were staying all night," Thelma complained.

Tilda touched her hand to her stomach. She felt like she'd eaten something that didn't agree with her, but she knew that wasn't the problem.

"Tilda," Charlie said, startling her. She thought he'd gone in to change out of his work clothes. He was always careful not to spread sawdust all over the house when he came home from the mill. He was thoughtful in so many ways, so why had he quit his job without talking it over with her first?

"Tilda, sit down on the step," he said. "I want to tell you what happened."

She smoothed her skirt under her with her hands and then gathered the fullness around her knees as she sat down. She had been glad when dress styles changed and women could be more comfortable. No more skirt hems dragging in the dirt. She never did understand why a lady couldn't show her ankles. Some changes were sensible, she thought, but not what Charlie had done today.

Thelma was helping her little brother now. Her brown curls bobbed next to his hair of ripe wheat as the two sat on the lawn combing the grass. The children liked playing in the grass, and Tilda knew there were no lawns in logging camps. But neither were there busy streets with traffic to worry about when the children were out playing. She'd try to think of that.

"Tilda, a man from Phoenix Logging Company at Potlatch came through the mill," Charlie began. "He heard about labor strikes and layoffs here in Seattle and was looking for men who wanted a change. Phoenix needs men right now. Two years ago they signed a six-year contract with Tacoma Power and Light to log trees around Lake Cushman on the Skokomish River."

Charlie looked at her to see if she was listening. Then went on. "The power company is going to build a dam across the river and flood the whole valley. Phoenix Logging is under pressure to get all the trees out before the deadline."

Tilda watched Leonard pluck a June bug out of the grass and gently pet its shiny shell, but she was listening.

"They're offering good wages to get the job done on time. Much more than they pay here at the mill," he said, studying the sawdust on the toes of his shoes.

She wished Ida hadn't been in such a hurry to leave. When Ida's Charlie came back from his walk, Ida said they had to get back to Shelton before dark in case the car lights didn't work. She guessed Ida knew Tilda and Charlie needed time to talk.

"Where is Lake Cushman?" Tilda made herself ask.

"It's in the Garden of Eden," Charlie exclaimed and turned again to look at her. "Lake Cushman is at the foot of Mount Elinor, one of the most beautiful peaks in the Olympic Mountains. And between the lake and the mountains are miles and miles of giant firs and cedars and hemlock. Streams and waterfalls tumble down from the mountains year round and run into the Skokomish River and the lake."

He jumped to his feet. "Tilda, the man from the logging company said Lake Cushman's been a vacation spot for years. The Antlers Hotel and Cushman House bring people in from Seattle and Portland and even as far away as New York to fish and to hunt deer and bear and elk. Some come just to walk in the woods or sit by the lake, the man said. Tilda, the logging camp is right in the middle of all this, not at the end of the world like you think."

"But where is it on a map?" Tilda persisted, squeezing the words out past the lump in her throat.

"You drive sixteen miles north from Shelton," Charlie said, "to the little town of Hoodsport on Hood Canal. Then you go five miles west into the mountains. You'll live about twenty-one miles from Ida."

Tilda became interested now.

"The creeks that run into the Skokomish River are full of trout, the man told me. I can teach Leonard to fish, and we can go out after work and drop our lines into the stream—"

"Teach me, too," Thelma called as she ran up to the porch. Tilda wasn't surprised she was listening. She never missed a thing.

"Sure, I take you fishing, too," Charlie said. "We all go. Mama can pack a picnic and take a blanket to sit on, and we'll fish till we catch our limit. What you think of that now, Tilda?"

Tilda hadn't seen her husband so excited. He made the move sound better all the time.

"And you know, Tilda, we live free in company houses so the rent we save we can put in the bank for a trip to the old country. We'll visit your father and brother and my family, and old friends, and you can show off Telma and Leonard—"

"Watch me!" Thelma called as she hopped down the sidewalk on one foot. "Step on a crack and break your mother's back," she chanted.

Leonard crawled into his father's lap and held out the June bug for him to admire. He was everything they'd ever wanted in a boy. He could roughhouse, but still be gentle with any little bird or animal or bug, like now. Leonard would like living where there was beautiful, deep woods next to the house, and she knew Thelma would like it. She was always ready for adventure.

"All right, Charlie," Tilda said, brushing her skirt as she stood up. A small sigh escaped her. "I'll go in and start packing."

Charlie carried the kitchen table and chairs, his wooden rocker with the comfortable wide arms, and Tilda's new Eldredge rotary sewing machine to the covered front porch where it would be handy for the movers. Tilda filled the bottom of their steamer trunk with sheets and towels and table scarves. She wrapped the dishes in newspaper and placed them next to the linens. The packing was going well until she started sorting through the bottom drawer of the bureau.

Letters, pictures, souvenirs. What to keep and what to throw away! She decided to keep only the latest letters from Father and Ivar, and she'd part with her Runeberg Lodge dance programs. She'd keep all their photographs, of course, and the memories that went with them...

Their wedding picture. Charlie sat so tall, so serious, in his three piece suit, his white shirt and white bow-tie, and with the sprig of lily of the valley in his lapel. On one arm Tilda cradled a bouquet of white roses so resplendent it nearly touched the single rose corsage pinned to her shoulder. Her necklace was her engagement present. Three little diamonds hanging from a gold chain. Charlie had really splurged to buy that for her.

When they were married in Portland, Ida and Charlie stood up for them. The next year, she and her own Charlie stood up for Ida and her Charlie in Seattle. They had good times together when they all lived in Ballard, and now, with this move, they would again live close to each other. Tilda had to admit she was getting excited.

Here was Thelma's baby picture. They worried about the big, ugly birthmark on the edge of her face. She was two years old before they could be sure her hairline would cover the mark. A year later she came down with whooping cough. She was so sick they thought she would die, like so many people were dying that year from influenza. They were thankful to God that little Leonard didn't get sick, too. How could they have stood it if they had lost one of their children?

A special snapshot. Leonard wearing his sailor suit and sitting on the woodpile behind the house. He pretended to smoke his daddy's pipe, puffing and blowing invisible smoke, acting grown up. And then the snapshot of the four of them standing by the big bushes at the side of the house. She'd be sure to mail that one to Father. •

More portraits. Her and Ida posing together in their wedding dresses. Families back home expected these pictures so they would know their children were well. My, how clothes had changed in ten years. From gathered voile and lace to simple, short dresses. Tilda wondered if it was more than a coincidence that dresses became practical and comfortable when women were given the right to vote—

"Tilda, did you forget the movers are coming today?" Charlie fussed. "Are you going to sit there on the floor all day looking at old pictures?"

Tilda hurriedly stacked the letters and pictures and tied them together with a string. She placed them in the trunk next to the dishes. Charlie was right. No use looking back. They had their future to think about. And a ferry to catch first thing in the morning.

A seagull swooped and squawked, startling Tilda. She and Charlie and the children stood on the passenger deck of the ferry waiting for the motors to start up to shuttle them from Seattle to Bremerton. Through the early morning mist, she could see the pale outline of the beautiful Olympic Mountains in the distance. Any moment the ship's horn would sound and they would leave the harbor to sail into their new and exciting life.

"Look, Mama! Daddy!" Thelma called from the railing. "Look at all the boats!"

"Telma! Leonard! Get away from the edge! You want to fall overboard?" Tilda exclaimed, running to grab them. "Now stand by Daddy and me," she ordered, giving them each a shake. Leonard took her hand, but Thelma dashed away again to look over the edge. Tilda decided it would be best if they all stood by the rail and looked at the water together.

Seattle was a busy harbor in 1922. Tug boats pulled booms of logs to waiting mills. Fishing boats returned from their night's work, riding low in the water, their nets heavy with seawater, and their holds throbbing with salmon. Freighters were carrying goods to waterfront warehouses where department stores and grocers picked up their orders. Smells from seafood grills blended with the stench of discarded clam and oyster shells piled high on the beach next to the restaurants.

"When will we get there?" Leonard asked.

"We haven't left yet," Tilda laughed. "Watch the seagulls. They're looking for something to eat."

"Me, too," Leonard said. "I'm hungry."

Tilda reached into her satchel and broke off a piece of the rye bread she'd baked for the day's trip. "Don't feed it all to the seagulls," she warned, knowing he would give them at least half.

Finally the ship's horn blew—a long blast and two short. Thelma and Leonard covered their ears, looked up for the source of the strident noise, and then grabbed the rail for balance. The ferry had slowly begun to move, caroming gently between mussel-crusted, sentinel-like pilings on each side until it was free of the pier. In a little while they would dock at Bremerton. A car and driver would be waiting, Charlie told her, to take them to their new home on Lake Cushman.

Squawking seagulls swooped and crisscrossed behind them, diminishing in size and blending with the sea mist as the ferry moved ahead. Tilda watched, suddenly uneasy. Her happy, secure life in Ballard was now behind her and was, like the seagulls, vanishing in the wake of the ship.

PART III - CAMP CUSHMAN
1922-1924

CHAPTER 3: INTRODUCTION TO CAMP

The Hollow Stump

C harlie was shaking her. She had fallen asleep on the warm deck of the ferry and they were docking.
Bremerton. Known for its shipbuilding. A large town, but not as big as Seattle. Tilda led the children down the steep stairs from the passenger deck to the car level and across the lowered ramp to the shore.

"Over here, Missus," a tall, skinny man in heavy boots and red shirt called. He already had Charlie's attention and was holding the back door of the dusty, banged-up automobile open for her and the children.

"Name's Gabe," he said, "and this here's your 'taxi'," he grinned, banging the side of the car with the flat of his hand. Dust flew. "Good road to Hoodsport. Be there in an hour or so," he added, boosting Tilda into the car before she had time to put her foot on the running board. Thelma and Leonard scrambled in after her. "Hoodsport's where we turn onto the camp road, you know."

The man slid behind the steering wheel and spat on the ground before slamming the door shut. He wiped his mouth on the sleeve of his shirt.

"I'm still spitting dust from the camp road," he explained. "Either have to swallow the dust or spit it out, but, hell, a little dust don't hurt. Better than mud or snow. That road used to be a wagon trail, so, wet or dry, it's a damn sight better now than it was. But it'll still be five miles of bumps and curves. Hope you're up to it," he grinned, putting the car in gear and spraying rocks behind them. "Hope the young'uns don't get carsick."

Gabe was slowing down. Hoodsport. A few houses, a building with a red and white striped roof advertising "Auto Repairs." A lumber mill on the water's edge. They were turning off the highway.

"See the sign there, next to the road?" Gabe shouted over his shoulder.

Tilda looked but had trouble seeing through the dust.

"'Lake Cushman—Doorway to the Olympics'," Gabe read to them without looking at the sign. "Yes, sir, with both resorts closing down because of the dam flooding the valley, the fishing and hunting will be better than ever. You're mighty lucky to be moving into this spot."

Tilda hung on to the children as they slid around a sharp curve.

"Guess you folks heard about the accident," Gabe said after a few minutes of concentrating on the road. "Joe Pulsifer, brakeman on the Phoenix train, got his leg smashed last week when a log rolled on it. They took him to the new hospital in Shelton, but they couldn't save his leg."

Dust was sifting in through the floorboards and the edges of the doors. Tilda covered her nose and mouth and coughed into her handkerchief.

"Joe was luckier than Kneeland though," he went on. "Allen Kneeland was logging at Webb Hill earlier this spring when a log broke loose. He was crushed to death." Gabe rolled down the window to spit again. "I'd say just losing a leg was pretty lucky, wouldn't you?"

Charlie nodded, glancing over his shoulder at Tilda.

"Accidents happen all the time in the woods, you know," Gabe said, pulling a can of snoose out of his shirt pocket. "They used to say that a man's life expectancy as a logger was seven years. Read somewhere that from 1870 to 1910 one logger died every other day, on average. Close to seventy-five hundred loggers killed during that period, the article said, and I can believe it. I once saw a man cut in half when a two-inch guy wire snapped loose and whipped through the brush. His brother drove from Tacoma to claim the pieces." He worked the can open with the thumb of one hand. "Guess he should have ducked," he said under his breath.

"So what'll you be doing?" he asked, turning to Charlie as he stuffed a wad of the chewing tobacco behind his lower lip.

"Setting choker," Charlie answered. "Used to tend hook around Portland."

"You're no greenhorn then," Gabe said. "You know how to jump out of the way when the donkey starts reeling in a log. Hell, I guess we both know that, or we wouldn't be here today," he laughed. "Just so we don't get to daydreaming on the job and think it's a fish instead of a log dancing on the end of the line. You never know..."

Charlie interrupted abruptly. Asked Gabe about the fishing. Tilda looked out the window and tried to enjoy the scenery.

Fir trees on the sides of the road reached up like maypole dancers, their boughs nearly touching across the roof of the car. Soft-green ferns blanketed the ground under the trees. Tilda was aware of the beauty around her, but as they burrowed deeper into the woods, all she could see were those wild guy wires snapping through the air and giant logs rolling loose, out of control.

"We're here," Gabe finally announced, pulling on the brake. Dust swirled through the crack in the back window. Thelma and Leonard scrambled out of the car ahead of her.

"As you can see," Gabe said, meeting Tilda at the front of the car, "the road ends here at the railroad track. Just a short walk across the railroad trestle now, and you'll be in camp."

Tilda had seen pictures of trestles with their network of weather-bleached beams straddling deep ravines, weaving canyon walls together like laces on a boot. But she had never stood on one, nor walked across one. She held Thelma and Leonard back and peered down between the ties at the thread of a river far below.

"Me and Charlie'll carry the kids," Gabe said. "Watch how you step now, Missus. Don't want to lose you before you even move in."

Tilda held her breath, stepped onto the first tie, and the second. Then, without looking between the ties, she scurried ahead, hurrying to keep up with the long strides of the men.

"We're high enough to see the whole camp from here," Gabe said when they reached the far end of the trestle. "Ten family houses on one side of the railroad tracks, and two bunkhouses for the single boys on the other side. That's the cookhouse next to the bunkhouses." He waved his arm as he spoke. "You can see the filing shack and some tool sheds this side of the bunkhouses. The roundhouse and water tower for the lokey are down there at the end of the tracks. Even got a school-house, but it don't look like you need one yet," he said, sizing up the children.

Thelma and Leonard ran to the nearest stump and climbed to the top. Tilda stared where Gabe had pointed. Identical, unpainted, weathered shacks, each resting high on two huge, rough-hewn logs, were lined up in a row before her.

"The houses are so small," Tilda whispered.

"That's so they'll fit on the flatcars," Gabe said. "When a place is logged out, the company moves the houses to the next camp. Those logs under the houses are called 'skids.' They work like runners on a sled. Makes it easy for the locomotive to pull the houses on and off the flatcars."

Tilda blinked back the tears. "There's no trees in the camp," she said, her voice rising. A sea of black stumps, scorched snags, and ripped-up logs encircled the houses. The clear-cut wasteland spread all the way to the logged-off hillsides.

"And everything's been burned!" she choked.

"You're right, Missus," Gabe said. "There's reasons for that, too. Before a logging company sets up camp, it has to log and burn everything clean to make room for the houses and buildings. Makes the camp safer from wild fires, too. It don't look very pretty to newcomers, I guess," he said, looking sideways at Tilda."

"It's just not what I expected," Tilda said. What she expected was a house in the woods by a lake...

She felt her face get hot. Something else was terribly wrong, and she suddenly realized what it was. "Where's the lake?" she blurted out, angry, feeling for a moment that all this must be Gabe's fault.

"Lake Cushman's another three miles up the track," Gabe said. "They couldn't put the houses any closer to the lake because that's where they're logging now. The men ride to work on the speeder or a flatcar behind the train— Tarnation, I almost forgot," he said, interrupting himself. "Ed Johnson that oversees the living arrangements asked me to tell you he's sorry, but he doesn't have a house for you right now. Said to tell you he'd find you a hollow stump somewhere—"

"A hollow stump?" Tilda wiped her eyes with her handkerchief.

Gabe grinned and patted Tilda on the shoulder. Then he turned and followed Charlie down the track toward the houses. Thelma and Leonard skipped along behind the men, trying to jump every other tie between the tracks. Thelma could do it, but Leonard kept landing on the oily gravel between the ties, so he tried walking on a track instead. Tilda held one of Leonard's balancing hands, but he tired of slipping off the rail and ran to catch his sister.

"Sorry about your house," Tilda could hear Gabe telling Charlie. "Ed thought the people living in it would be out by now, but the man's upset about being laid off, so he's taking his own sweet time about leaving. Ed figures him and his family will be gone in another week." Gabe turned to find Tilda. "Ed's taken care of you until you can get into the house, you can be sure of that."

"Ya, you told me," Tilda said. "A hollow stump!"

"Better than that," Gabe laughed. "Hold up, Charlie," Gabe said, grabbing Charlie's arm and pointing left. "This first house in the row is your place. The mattresses and the kitchen stove are furnished, like they told you. But you have to come up with the rest yourself."

"I know," Charlie said. "We have what we need, and what we don't have, I can make."

"Well, that's the spirit," a cheery voice interrupted. A large woman with yellow hair pulled back into a thick bun walked up beside them. Her wide smile dimpled her bright cheeks.

"I'm Mrs. Nelson," she said. "You and the family are going to sleep at my house right next to your house. That way we get acquainted in a hurry," she smiled. "Our little girl Edit' is eight years old and can hardly wait to meet your children. And you'll be eating at Jacobson's. She's a good cook, like all Norwegians. Almost as good as my Swedish mother," she laughed.

Tilda tried to smile, but the disappointments of the day made it difficult. She was hot from the fast walk down the tracks in the late afternoon sun. She reached into her sleeve for her handkerchief and wiped the perspiration off her neck and the bend of her arms. She looked about for a shade tree. There was none. All she saw were scorched snags reaching up from a sea of stumps, like masts of ships that had wrecked here in the wilderness.

Tilda could feel Mrs. Nelson watching her. "Camp don't look so good at first," the lady sympathized, "but it's not all bad. In another few weeks, the vines on those stumps will be loaded with tiny, sweet blackberries. And those hills where the men have been logging will be covered with huckleberry bushes. Huckleberries like burned-over land, you know. And even though they're tiny, they're easy to pick because they grow as thick as grapes on a vine. And such wonderful pies, they make! You'll see, Mrs. Lind. Camp's not all bad."

Tilda listened.

"And in the summer, bright purple fireweed grow high as my waist on those burned-off hillsides. They're starting to bloom now..."

Tilda was grateful for this woman's friendliness, but she had stopped listening. She looked at the rusted railroad tracks in front of the houses and thought of the clean streets and sidewalks in Ballard. She looked farther down those tracks across the miles and years to her home in Finland. The camp house she'd be living in was smaller than the house she'd left ten years ago.

"Ya, I know," Mrs. Nelson said, turning to look down the tracks with Tilda. "But, Mrs. Lind, when you look at those burned-off hills, just stop and think. That's where the huckleberries grow."

Tilda heard Charlie's footsteps on the back porch and opened the door. Dusk blurred his features, but she could make out the sag of his shoulders against the late evening sky. He groaned a little as he lowered himself onto the porch stool and bent to remove his caulk shoes. Phoenix was working the men twelve hours a day, six days a week in order to harvest the trees before the dam was finished and flooded the canyon.

"Supper's ready," Tilda said. She wanted to say more, to sympathize, but she, too, had been working long hours. The people who lived in the house before them had been terrible housekeepers, and she'd had to get rid of their trash before she could even begin to clean.

They'd been in their house a week now, and she'd been cleaning steady. She washed windows and scrubbed cupboards inside and out. With lye soap and on her hands and knees she scoured the slivered wood floor from one end of the house to the other. When she finished that, she cut gunny sacks open and pasted the burlap over splintered parts of the inside walls so the children wouldn't get slivers when they ran through the house. Last night, like the other nights that week, Tilda was too tired and discouraged to talk. After supper she and Charlie dropped exhausted onto their mattresses on the floor and, without a word, fell asleep.

Night still blanketed the curtainless windows when the alarm clock went off. Charlie lit the coal oil lamp and started a fire in the wood stove. Tilda drew water from the tap and put it on the stove to heat for the oatmeal. Charlie liked his mush before he left for work in the morning.

"House is starting to look good," he said as he finished his breakfast and pushed away from the table.

Tilda looked at her hands. "It should," she said to herself as she watched him stride out the door to catch the speeder.

The kitchen was in full sun when Thelma and Leonard ate their breakfast. Leonard finished first and Thelma followed him out the door. "We're going to play with Edith," Thelma called over her shoulder. Tilda put another stick of wood in the firebox to heat more water for the breakfast dishes before sitting down at her sewing machine.

Curtain panels from their house in Ballard covered the top of her sewing machine. She had enough material from their living room alone to cover all the windows in the camp house. Maybe when she finished sewing the curtains and hung them, this company house would look better. But there were other problems, too. How would she fit a double bed, a single bed, and a crib into the ten by ten foot bedroom? The chest of drawers would have to go in the living room...

Tilda sighed. She missed having an icebox like they had in Ballard. Here, a small "screen box" was nailed to the outside wall on the back porch. Two sides were open except for a mesh screen that allowed the air to circulate and keep the milk and butter cool. Tilda wondered what happened to the milk and butter when the air was hot.

Mostly, though, she missed having a bathroom. Gabe told them they should feel lucky. Not every house in camp came with a "two-holer" like theirs. And it was just a short walk from the back porch to the outhouse—

"Yoo-hoo," Mrs. Nelson called from the back door.

"Come in," Tilda called back. "The door is open."

"Ya, we're in," she said. "Mrs. Jacobson and I just wanted to see how you were getting along. I still miss you and the children at bedtime," she smiled.

"And I miss you and the children at dinner time," Mrs. Jacobson added.

"You are wonderful neighbors," Tilda said. "Mrs. Jacobson, for feeding us for a whole week. And Mrs. Nelson, letting us sleep at your house till we could move in here. Giving Charlie and me Edit's bed so we don't have to sleep on the floor with the children."

"But now you're sleeping on the floor in your own house," Mrs. Nelson said, glancing toward the bedroom.

"Charlie brought home the boards he needs to build the beds and he'll start working on them his first day off," Tilda said.

"Well, Mrs. Lind, you done a fine job of cleaning," Mrs. Nelson said, looking around the kitchen and into the living room. "This house never looked so good. But we know you haven't had time to do any baking, so we made you some real, old-country coffee bread."

"Then I'll put on the coffee," Tilda exclaimed, jumping up from her chair, cheered at having company. "And look out the window. Here comes Mrs. West."

"Ya, she'll find us when we have rich coffee bread to eat," Mrs. Jacobson laughed.

"Mrs. Nelson," Mrs. West said, puffing as she burst into the kitchen, "I came to see you, and Edit' said you was next door. Are we having a coffee party here?"

"Ya, I guess we are," Mrs. Nelson laughed. "But a week from now, next Saturday night, we're having a real party at my house to welcome the Linds. We'll have lots of food and coffee, and maybe some music. What you say to that, Mrs. Lind?"

"I say it sounds good," Tilda said. "Do the children come, too?"

"Sure they come," Mrs. Jacobson said. "They can go in the bedroom and lie down if they get tired. By the way, where are the children this morning?"

"They're next door playing with Edit'," Tilda said. "Mrs. Nelson is so good to let them come play any time. It has been a big help to me this week."

"They're no trouble," Mrs. Nelson said. "But, Mrs. Lind, I haven't seen Leonard this morning."

"Was he playing outside?" Tilda asked, stepping to the window.

Mrs. Nelson shook her head. "I didn't see him."

"He wouldn't wander off, would he?" Mrs. West asked, sitting down to catch her breath. "He wouldn't go as far as the woods, would he? There's bears. And cougars—"

Tilda ran for the door. Leonard's toy car rested in the dirt by the porch steps, but Leonard was nowhere around. Tilda called, but he didn't answer. She ran to Nelson's back door and called Thelma. "Have you seen your brother?"

"No," Thelma answered, glancing across the clear cut.

"Maybe he fell behind a stump," Edith said, running up behind Thelma.

The women circled the stumps and windfalls, then spread out across the clear cut in widening circles. Thelma and Edith darted about, calling as they ran.

Tilda's thoughts raced. A little boy not quite three couldn't wander as far as the woods, could he? She tripped over a projecting root and then dashed toward the edge of the clearing. Thelma ran close behind her, jumping over the blackened wood debris.

Bears had been reported next to the houses, Tilda knew, and Leonard wouldn't be afraid. He'd try to pet the bear or big cat!

"Look, Mama," Thelma said, stopping suddenly and pointing to the far edge of the clearing.

Tilda stopped, her eyes searching the area where Thelma pointed. Then she saw it. A patch of blue, the blue of his overalls. Leonard was sitting high on a rock looking off into the woods.

First the hugs. Then the scoldings. Then, why did you leave the yard? It was a rabbit. A tiny, grey rabbit led him to the edge of the clearing and then vanished into the woods. He was just waiting for it to come out of the woods so he could watch it some more. Mama should have seen it, it was so cute.

The women laughed and patted him on the head. Thelma and Edith danced in a circle around the happy group. Then Tilda took him by the hand and started back to the house.

"Wait," Mrs. West said, stopping abruptly. "Do you smell smoke?"

The women froze. No one spoke, as if smoke were something they listened for, not smelled.

There was no mistake. They all smelled it. And when they turned around, they saw it boiling up the side of the mountain, spiraling, riding on a wind that suddenly gusted in their direction. Then they felt the smoke in their throats. And then they tasted it, acrid and ominous. Before they reached the track in front of their houses, they all knew. Fire was loose in the mountains.

Nightmare

"The worst forest fire was in 1902," John, the balding logger with the hoarse voice, said. "Twenty years ago come September. If you wasn't there fighting that fire, you no doubt heard about it. We'd had a terrible drought—"

"I was there," the ruddy-faced one named Vic said. "I just started logging then. I remember a hell of a heat wave that summer. No rain. Brush was brittle and all the grass was dead. Wells and water holes, dried up. September eleven was the day the fire broke out, two days before my birthday. I remember thinking, the tops of those hemlock are lighting up like candles on a cake, only this sure ain't no celebration."

"Ya, I remember the fire exploding in the brush," the first man said. "Spun up those helpless trees and raced across the tops. No stopping it then. No sir-eee!"

The young logger spoke up. "I heard a hot wind from east of the Cascades spread that fire over the western half of both Washington and Oregon, and the loggers and families had to run for their lives. Left their logging equipment and houses behind to burn up..."

"Mama," Thelma said, tugging at her mother's sleeve, "why are you standing in the dark looking out the window?"

"Sh!" Tilda said. "Go back to bed."

"I don't have a bed! Anyway, Mama, I'm hot."

"Lie still and you won't feel so hot," Tilda whispered. "Leonard's asleep. See that?" She pointed to the crib.

"Maybe if I had a bed, I'd be asleep, too," Thelma complained.

"Daddy will build our beds when he has time. Anyway, it's always cooler on the floor. And feel the breeze coming in the window now. The house will soon be cool."

Thelma kicked her sheet off and turned on her side.

Tilda hadn't intended to eavesdrop. Three boys from the bunkhouse had come by to see Charlie. He'd introduced them to her, and they and Charlie sat down on the porch steps. She'd excused herself and gone inside to put the children to bed. She knew men liked to sit outside on warm evenings, to smoke and tell stories. She heard their husky laughs, but when, unexpectedly, their voices became quiet and serious, she'd stopped to listen. When she heard "forest fire," she had hurried to the open bedroom window. The men were still talking—

"How'd that 1902 fire start?" Charlie was asking.

"They don't know for sure," John said. "But a hot wind can whip fire out of six-week-old ashes if it blows hard enough."

"I suppose it could have started from a spark from the lokey, like the one we put out on Dow Mountain two days ago," Charlie said.

"Could have," they all murmured in agreement.

"Did everyone make it out of the 1902 fire?" the young man asked.

"Not everyone," Vic said. "They know thirty-five people died, but they don't know how many more. It was a hell of a fire. The whole country this side of the Cascades was so dark from the smoke that people had to burn lights in the middle of the day, and smoke drifted forty miles out over the ocean."

"How'd they ever get it under control?" Charlie asked.

"The wind finally shifted and brought rain back from the ocean and the fire had to give up."

"I heard about a fire here in Mason County four years ago that was just as bad," Charlie said. "Maybe worse. Didn't families have to ride the train to get away from that one, too?"

The men nodded. One answered. "Ya, fire burned that whole damn camp, too. They say..."

Tilda felt sick. She couldn't listen to any more. The fire on Dow Mountain this week had been frightening enough and the men had had that under control in two days. It was mostly green brush that burned, they said, and that explained the heavy smoke. But what if that fire had started in the dry month of September?

Tilda decided she wouldn't think about the Dow Mountain fire or the Mason County fire four years ago or the 1902 fire. But that night when she finally went to sleep, she couldn't control her dreams. She dreamt that the trees surrounding the camp were flaming sticks that burned and burned and wouldn't burn out, and that she and the children had no place to run.

Buttercup

The camp house, unprotected from the summer sun, was unbearably hot, but in the afternoon Tilda found relief from the heat on the shaded front porch. She wiped the perspiration off her forehead and neck with her handkerchief and sat down on the top step. A slight breeze still carried traces of the acrid smoke, but the movement of air was cooling her—

"So there you are," Mrs. Nelson said as she walked around the corner of the house. "Where's Leonard?" she asked as she sat down next to Tilda. "Out chasing rabbits?"

"No," Tilda smiled. "He's taking his nap. He doesn't seem to mind the heat."

"Are you ready for the party Saturday night?" Mrs. Nelson asked. "You and Charlie are the special guests, you know. We always have a good time. Everyone brings plates of sandwiches and breads and cakes and cookies, a real **smörgåsbord**.

And someone fixes coffee, and sometimes Harold Swenson from the bunkhouse plays his accordion.

"It's too bad we don't have any place to dance to the music," Mrs. Nelson said. "But one time Phoenix did treat us to a dance. The company paid the lokey engineer and fireman to take us to Lower Camp One where they have a dance hall. We rode a flatcar behind the locomotive and I believe we had as good a time on the ride as we did at the dance."

"I'm surprised you're still having this party tomorrow night," Tilda said. "I thought the men would be too tired from fighting fire."

"No, that's why they put the fire out so fast," Mrs. Nelson laughed. "So it wouldn't interfere with the party."

Tilda tried to laugh, too, but she couldn't shake the gloom of last night's nightmare. "Mrs. Nelson," she said, "I have to ask you a question. Do you ever get used to living where always there is the danger of fire?"

Mrs. Nelson hesitated. Then, "No, I worry about fire, but I have to say I worry more about logging accidents."

"But Charlie told me accidents in the woods don't have to happen," Tilda protested. "He says if a logger is strong and quick and pays attention to what he is doing, he don't need to get hurt. Isn't that true?"

Mrs. Nelson shook her head. "I've been a logger's wife long enough to know better. He has to have the luck with him, too. A faller might jump clear of his springboard when he's cut through the tree, but if the tree gets tangled with other trees on its way down, the cut-off trunk can kick back and catch the faller before he can get out of the way. Or a falling tree might bump another tree on its way down and knock a limb loose on the standing tree. The limb, called a 'widow maker,' hangs there until sometime later when, because of a little wind or for no reason at all, it falls on a man. Kills him. Some of those widow makers are as big around as a man's body and might have been sitting in a tree for months.

"Last spring a young boy from Shelton on his first day's work saw his partner killed by a widow maker. That night in the bunk house he told the others, 'I'm going to be careful. It won't get me.' Next day when a small tree was being felled, he thought it was going the other way and ran right under it. He died an hour later."

A grasshopper flitted through the air and lit on the step, startling Tilda. Mrs. Nelson didn't seem to notice it and went on.

"Ya, and the men that buck up the logs have to watch for trees being felled around them. And the rigging slingers, especially the choker setters, they have the worst job. They have to see that the steel cable they hook around the log don't break loose and fly around, or that a loose branch don't fall on the whistle wire and the donkey operator think it's a signal to pull the log in. Not long ago two choker-setters were crushed when that happened. They were under the log hooking the cable—"

She must have remembered then that Charlie set chokers. "Mrs. Lind," she said, putting her hand on Tilda's arm, "I'm sure Charlie knows—"

"Mama! Mama! Mrs. Lind! Come quick!" Edith screamed, spinning around the end of the house. "Quick! Thelma dropped Buttercup down the hole in the outhouse!"

"No!" Tilda exclaimed, jumping to her feet. They caught up with Edith just in time to see the orange-striped cat shoot out the open outhouse door and disappear behind a log with Thelma scrambling after it.

"Telma!" Tilda hollered. "What are you doing?"

Thelma stopped. "I poked Buttercup down one hole and she popped out the other," she grinned.

"Why did you do that? You, a big four year old! And you love cats! What got into you?"

Thelma hesitated, her smile fading. She dropped her eyes. "I don't know," she whispered to the buttons on the front of her dress.

"Don't be too hard on her, Mrs. Lind," Mrs. Nelson said, coming to Thelma's defense. "So much has been going on— living with other people, moving into a dirty house, Leonard disappearing, a forest fire that scared us all. Maybe she was just looking for a little attention."

"I'll give her a little attention," Tilda said, grabbing Thelma by the arm and shaking her, blinking back the tears. Was this what living in a logging camp was all about, she despaired as she marched Thelma toward the house. Wild fires. Widow makers. Everything out of control. Even Thelma!

Ole's Present

"So you must be the Lind kids," the tall man said. "Welcome to Camp Cushman."

Thelma looked up at him from where she sat on the timekeeper's steps, but the sun splintered behind his head so she couldn't see his face. Leonard was lying on his stomach beside her, but his eyes were on the man's caulk shoes. He pulled his hand back in case the man stepped closer. He knew about the sharp spikes on the bottom of those boots.

"I'm Ole Johnson," the man said, squatting on his heels to talk to them. His face was friendly. "I just met your mama in the timekeeper's office. So how you like living in a logging camp?"

"We like it fine," Thelma said, answering for both herself and her brother.

"And are you going to be a logger like your Papa when you grow up?" he asked Leonard.

"No," Thelma answered, even though Leonard could talk for himself very well at almost-three. "Daddy says Leonard is going to go to school and learn to be a doctor or a lawyer."

"Well, ain't that good," Ole smiled. He reached into his pocket. "Say, do you know that 'Irish' Mullins, the timekeeper, has a shelf in his office where he sells candy and gum and cigarettes?" He pulled a handful of money out of his pocket and held it on the palm of his hand, pushing it around with a finger of the other hand, studying it like he was reading.

"Now, I don't suppose either of you smoke," he said. Leonard shook his head, but Thelma knew he was joking. "But I bet you both have a sweet tooth."

Leonard started to feel in his mouth.

"So here's a little money for candy."

Thelma reached out her hand. Leonard did the same.

"One for you and one for you. Tell your Mama it was a welcoming present from Ole." He turned and strode down the tracks, stirring up dust with his big caulk boots.

Thelma looked in her hand, not quite believing what she saw, and then back at the man striding away.

"Thank you," she called.

"Thank you," Leonard echoed.

The big man slung his mackinaw over one shoulder and waved the other hand without looking back.

Thelma stared at her coin. It was small and shiny. She didn't know the name of it because Mama and Daddy never gave them any money, but she knew it was worth a candy bar. The man said so.

"What'd he give you?" Thelma asked Leonard, still not believing what had happened. Leonard held out his coin.

Thelma looked at his coin and then at her own. "Hey, that's not fair!" she exclaimed. "Yours is bigger. I need the bigger one. I'm bigger than you!" Leonard closed his hand on the piece of money until all Thelma could see were the dirt streaks between his fingers.

"Let's trade," Thelma said, suddenly sure of what to do.

"No!" Leonard said and drew his tightly-squeezed fist behind his back.

"Yes," Thelma said. "You've got to trade with me. I'm your big sister and know best."

Leonard looked at Thelma and slowly brought his hand around. He opened his fist. The coin wasn't shiny like hers, but it was certainly bigger.

"Trade!" Thelma ordered. She picked up his big coin and replaced it with her little one. "Let's go!" she said, jumping to her feet and running for the office door. Leonard hopped up and followed her, bumping into Mama coming out of the office.

"Look, Mama," Leonard said, holding out his hand.

"A man gave us money for candy," Thelma explained. "He said to tell you it was a present from Ole for moving to camp."

"What a nice man," Mama said. "I wait for you here on the porch in the sunshine."

Thelma spotted the candy shelf the minute she opened the door. She knew what she wanted. The bar in the dark-brown wrapping that had shiny silver paper inside wrapped around squares of chocolate that melted on her tongue. Daddy sometimes brought this bar home for her and Leonard to divide, but this time she would have one all to herself.

"So who do we have here now," a voice behind her said.

Thelma looked around at the man who spoke. He was much smaller than Ole and wore glasses. She saw he wore a belt instead of suspenders like Daddy and Ole, and low shoes, the kind that were smooth on the bottom.

"We're the Lind kids," Thelma answered, remembering what Ole had called them. "I'm Thelma and this is my little brother Leonard and we're here to buy candy. Here's my money." She held out her coin but kept her eye on the candy in the brown wrapper.

Mr. Mullins took the nickel and looked at it carefully. "Well, it's a little dirty, but I think it's still good," he said. "In fact, it's exactly right for one Hershey bar."

"I want one, too," Leonard said, reaching up with his coin.

"Well, well, you must have struck it rich, young fella! I see you have a dime. That will buy you two Hershey bars anywhere in these United States. Here you are."

He handed two candy bars to Leonard and patted him on the head. People were always doing that to Leonard. Maybe he was just the right height for patting. Then Thelma realized what had happened.

"Two candy bars! How come he got two candy bars? My money was bigger!" she exclaimed, stepping between Leonard and Mr. Mullins. "That's not fair!"

"Get along, now," Mr. Mullins said with a cough that almost sounded like a chuckle. "Your Mama is waiting for you." He made that funny cough again and shooed them out the door.

"Wait," Leonard said, running to keep up with his sister as they followed Mama down the tracks toward home. "Here." He held out half of an unwrapped Hershey bar.

Thelma stopped walking. She looked at her little brother. She guessed she understood why people liked to pat him on the head. She almost did it herself just now. Instead, she decided to race him to their house, and give him a big head start.

Donkey

Thelma sat on the porch step listening for the speeder. She and Mama and Leonard were riding into the woods today with Mr. Hamilton, the "donkey doctor," to see where Daddy worked. Daddy said the donkey needed some attention, and they could ride with "Ham" to the logging "side". He explained to Mama that "side" meant the place where they were logging. Thelma hoped they'd see a bear along the way. That would be more fun than seeing a plain old donkey.

A minute later Mr. Hamilton stopped the speeder in front of the house like he promised. Thelma had watched the little rail car shuttle loggers back and forth to work, but this would be the first time she ever rode on it. The speeder reminded Thelma of the streetcars in Ballard, except the speeder was noisier and shorter and only the ends had walls.

The step to get onto the speeder was high and Thelma and Leonard used their knees to climb on. Mr. Hamilton gave Mama a hand up even though she didn't need it. For being twenty-six years old, she was very quick.

"You can sit wherever you want," Mr. Hamilton said, pointing to the benches running the length of the car on each side of the boxed-in motor. "The view's as good either way."

Mama and Leonard sat down next to Mr. Hamilton. Thelma climbed over the middle and sat on the other side. Mr. Hamilton pushed the spoon-shaped throttle forward with his hand and the speeder jerked ahead, clacking across the camp clearing and picking up speed as it moved toward the woods. Soon they were in deep shade, hustling through thick underbrush, following rails that weaved between the trunks of the huge trees. Thelma watched the trees and brush whiz by while

Leonard looked straight down past his feet where the ends of the ties blurred together. Mama mostly listened to Mr. Hamilton.

"I have to bring men out on this speeder all the time to cut back the brush," Mr. Hamilton shouted over the noise of the motor. "It would take over the rails in no time if we gave it a chance."

Still shouting, "This little gasoline speeder is mighty valuable to a logging outfit. Besides shuttling the section crews back and forth to keep the railroad line safe, it carries other small work crews to the job. Besides that, it hauls mail and supplies up to camp and carries the injured out of camp."

Thelma saw Mama give him her worried look and start to say something, but Mr. Hamilton went right on talking

He told Mama that the fattest, tallest trees were the Douglas firs and that some of them were four hundred to six hundred years old, and that the skinny, straight trees were red fir and only two to three hundred years old.

He turned to Thelma. "My boy Wayne looks about your age, Thelma," he smiled, "and I have two older boys and a girl. You and Leonard can come over and play with them anytime." Thelma smiled back politely, but right now she was more interested in looking for bears. She told Leonard to watch for bears, too, which he did, but he didn't see any either.

Before Thelma could ask when they would get there, the speeder began zig-zagging down a steep incline. Bright blades of sunshine suddenly split the overhead branches, and the speeder clickety-clacked out of the trees and into the full sun of a clearing. Freshly-cut stumps smelled of pitch. Brush lay flattened under sawed-off tops and branches of trees. Noise and dust filled the air. The speeder slowed to a stop.

"Stay on the speeder now," Mr. Hamilton said, "so you don't get hurt. You're in a good spot to see and hear what goes on at a logging side. You can hear that big steam engine working hard right now, and there'll be some whistles, and if you listen carefully, you'll hear someone holler, 'Tim-ber!' and then hear a big crash when the tree hits the ground."

"Can I see Charlie from here?" Mama wanted to know.

"Afraid not," Mr. Hamilton said. "See that big steel cable? See how it runs through a pulley way up on that spar tree and then stretches out of sight through the brush and over that hill?" Tilda nodded. "That's where Charlie's working. He and another choker setter are hooking a steel cable around the ends of the logs. When they're ready, they signal the whistle punk and he pulls the whistle wire to signal the engineer." He took a deep breath. "Now see that big engine on skids over there?" Mr. Hamilton asked.

Mama nodded.

"That's where the engineer sits. Keep watching now. When he hears the whistle, he'll open the throttle on the engine and it'll start steaming and snorting and the spool that holds the cable will start turning. Then, way out at the end of that cable, the noose around the log will cinch up and the rigging crew will jump clear, and the log will come roaring through the brush like a mad dog on a leash."

"There's the whistle, Mama!" Thelma exclaimed.

Quick, sharp blasts! Then, just like Mr. Hamilton said, it came. Crashing and snapping, head held high by the lead line, the log bumped and battered its way through the jumble of broken limbs and windfalls that covered the ground until it stopped just short of the throbbing engine. There it swung and twisted a minute before dropping onto the "cold deck," the stack of logs encircling the spar tree, in a splintering crunch of bark and dust. Thelma held her breath and heard the echo of the log's impact bounce back from the side of the mountain behind them.

"Watch now," Mr. Hamilton said. "Watch and you'll see the haul back line pull the main line cable back to the timber for another log. In early days, 'line horses' or one of the men dragged the line back out to the choker setter for the next log, but a simple improvement changed that. The haul back line was hooked to the main line in a long loop that ran over spools and pulled the main line back out to the timber. It put a lot of horses out of work," Hamilton laughed.

"But logging got easier when someone thought of 'highlead' logging," he went on. "A 'high rigger' climbs a tall, straight tree, cutting the limbs off as he goes. When he is most of the way up, he tops the tree and makes it into a "spar tree." Now he fastens heavy pulleys to the top of the spar tree, like you see over there." Ham pointed at the spar tree again. "No more pulling logs along the ground. They run lines out to the timber through those high pulleys and lift the front end of the logs high enough to clear the stumps and brush and so they move easy over the ground.

"In early times, before the spar tree and the steam engine, logging outfits laid logs crosswise of a road and horses or bull-oxen pulled strings of logs across the skids to the loading yard. Those were called 'skid roads'."

Mama said, "There's a street called Skid Road on the waterfront in Seattle—"

"Ya, they were still using skid roads when they logged around Seattle. Now loggers go there when they have time off. Lots of cheap hotels and fancy saloons. Some good entertainment, and fights, too, but it's all in fun. The men work hard, sometimes for months at a time without a break, and need to let off steam. Just like the steam engine over there," he laughed.

"But wait," Ham said as he jumped off the speeder. "Here I'm talking and I'm supposed to be looking at that engine. Stay where you are and listen for the quitting whistle. That brings Charlie and the rest of the crew out of the woods in a hurry."

The sun was cooler and the shadow of the spar tree longer when they heard the whistle and spotted the men striding through the logging slash toward them. Dirt and twigs stuck to their long-sleeved shirts and "stagged" pants, pants cut off at the boot tops to clear the worst of the brush. Their caulk shoes churned the dust as they walked.

"Well, Tilda, did you learn something about logging today?" Daddy asked as he came up to the speeder. He looked happy to see Mama.

"Ya, that we did!" Mama said.

"But, Daddy, when do we get to see the donkey?" Thelma asked.

"But you've been watching it all afternoon," Daddy laughed. "There's the donkey right over there. See it puffing and steaming from working so hard? We'll go ask Ham if you can watch him fix it."

He picked up Leonard and led Thelma by the hand down the track to where the donkey sat, its skids—or sleds—half buried in broken limbs and chunks of bark. A flat, tin roof, held up by four rough posts, covered grease-coated machines and a round firebox that stood in the middle of the slivered floor, its smokestack reaching through the roof towards the sky. Mr. Hamilton was on his knees poking around in the machinery like he'd lost something.

"Say, Ham," Daddy said, "I got two kids here who would like to ride this donkey. What you think?"

"Sure. Why not?" Ham said. "The engine's down so they can't get hurt, and I'm about finished here anyway." He straightened up and stretched his back. "Don't think this donkey will act up any more for a while, Charlie."

Thelma and Leonard climbed up onto the battered floor of the donkey and looked around. The heavy cable that had pulled in the logs was now wrapped around a drum at one end of the donkey and looked like a giant spool of thread from Mama's sewing basket.

"Daddy," Thelma said, pulling hard at his sleeve. "Is this really a donkey?"

"It's the best kind of donkey," her daddy laughed. "It's stronger than any four-legged animal and stubborn enough to keep pulling when a log gets stuck behind a stump. With these cables it can pull any log out of the woods and never even work up a sweat." He poked Mr. Hamilton who was listening and smiling. "All we have to do is feed it lots of fresh-cut wood and it will outwork ten straw-eating animals."

"But how can we ride it when it doesn't go anywhere," Thelma persisted.

"You'd be surprised how this donkey can move. A man wraps its cable around a tree up ahead and the steam from the powerful, little donkey turns the spool that rolls in the cable. The donkey pulls itself along on its sleds like a giant caterpillar.

When it reaches the tree, someone wraps the cable around the next tree, and it moves along some more."

Leonard was still looking disappointed.

"Next time we move the donkey, you two can ride along," Daddy said, patting Leonard on the head. "Now let's get back to the speeder. I'll ride home with you and Ham."

The day's crew were already sitting on the flatcar behind the locomotive waiting for the speeder to move out of their way. Scratched and dented lunch buckets rested at the men's feet. Ole Johnson smiled at them as they walked by and then asked Leonard if he had spent his nickel yet. Someone else asked Leonard if he was signing on as a whistle punk because most of those fellows weren't much older than Leonard. Daddy said he didn't think so and lifted Leonard onto the speeder. Thelma and Tilda followed and the speeder clanged ahead.

As the speeder picked up speed, Thelma looked back at the donkey. She could understand why Daddy thought it was so good if it could do all the things he said, but since she hadn't seen a bear, she wished that at least the donkey had been real, the kind you could talk to and maybe scratch behind the ears.

CHAPTER 4: FIRST YEAR

Fourth of July

"It's too hot tonight to take a bath," Charlie complained as he unbuttoned his work shirt. "And it's not Saturday night!"

Tilda picked the tea kettle up from the stove and poured more boiling water into the wooden washtub sitting in the middle of the kitchen floor. She stirred it into the cold water from the faucet with the stick she used to poke down clothes in the wash boiler.

"It's better than Saturday night," Tilda said, laughing at his grumpiness. "Tomorrow we're celebrating the Fourth of July. Good reason to take a bath."

"There should be saunas in America like in Finland. That was the way to get clean."

Still cranky. He must have had a hard day in the woods.

"When I threw cold water on the hot rocks, sweat ran off me in rivers," Charlie said. "When I beat myself with the birch switches to get the circulation going and then ran and jumped into the ice cold sea, I knew I was clean. Believe me, Tilda, when I was through, I was more than clean. I was a new man!"

He slid his suspenders off his shoulders and took off his shirt and pants. Twigs and sawdust dropped onto the floor.

"Where are Telma and Leonard?" he asked as he started to unbutton his long, summer underwear. "I don't want them running in on me when I'm undressed."

"They're outside playing with that nice Lillian Box. Lillian must be three years older than Telma, but she comes and plays anyway. Today the three of them sat on the porch and talked for an hour. You know," Tilda went on after closing the kitchen door, "people are friendly here in camp, I have to say that."

Tilda sat down. She had been on the go all day frying chicken, making bread and potato salad, packing the picnic box, and it felt good to get off her feet. She watched her husband test the bath water with his toe and then fold his big frame into the small, round tub. His knees came to rest under his chin. She was so used to seeing his brown hands and ruddy face that she sometimes forgot how white his skin was. But, she smiled to herself as she watched him bathe, she never forgot what a strong, fine-looking man he really was.

"Charlie," she said, "I can hardly wait to see Cushman's big house."

Charlie had told her about the house where they were going for their picnic. A. G. Cushman was a rich business man who chose to build this fine home between the lake and the mountains because he thought it was such a beautiful spot, or, as some say, because his name happened to be Cushman, same as the lake.

It wasn't easy building such a big house in the wilderness in 1908, Charlie had related. All the lumber and furniture had to come in by boat to Potlatch. A logging train hauled the lumber to a horse-pulled wagon that brought the supplies the rest of the way to the lake. Then Cushman and his workers had to row the supplies across the lake in small boats to the building site.

"I think it's too bad that the Cushmans had to give up their beautiful house because of the dam," Tilda said, moving to the washtub to scrub the fine dust off her husband's muscle-hardened shoulders.

"Tacoma Power had to buy them out," Charlie reminded her, "like they bought out the Antler Hotel and other properties. The power company has to tear them down or burn them before they flood the valley."

Tilda wiped the soapy water off her hands with her apron. "How far is it to Cushman's house?"

"Just three miles on the speeder, and then a short walk around the end of the lake." Water splashed onto the waxed floor as he boosted himself out of the tub.

"Tilda, where's the towel? Am I supposed to shake the water off like a dog?" he groused. Tilda didn't worry about his bad temper. She knew he'd feel better in the morning.

The sun was barely up when the little speeder clattered down the tracks, stopping at each house. Tilda could see her friends piling onto the car with their picnic boxes until, finally, it stopped at her own door.

"Here, let me give you and Leonard a hand up the high step, Mrs. Lind," Mr. Hamilton said, leaning down from his driving position. "Isn't this a fine day for a picnic?"

"Ya, that it is," Tilda said, accepting his help and returning his smile. It still startled her when someone in camp didn't talk in broken English. She'd have to get used to the Hamiltons and Boxes and a few other American-born people talking so different.

Tilda nodded to her new friends lined up on the two benches. Almost everyone was there. The Wests and their boy, another "Leonard." Mr. and Mrs. Nelson and Edith. Mr. and Mrs. Box and their girls, Louise and Lillian. The Warners and the Jacobsons and their children were sitting on the bench on the other side of the speeder. Someone said Mr. Hamilton would have to make a second trip to pick up the other two families and a few of the single loggers who wanted to come along.

"Telma, we're leaving," Tilda called. Where did she get to? She was right beside her when they came out of the house.

Leonard moved closer to Tilda. "We don't want to go," he said, pressing his face into her shoulder.

"You don't want to go? What's going on here?" Charlie exclaimed. "Telma," he hollered, "get over here right now."

Thelma moved out from behind the house, dragging her toes in the dust. Charlie met her half way and pulled her by her arm so her feet flew. He lifted her up and plopped her onto the speeder next to Leonard.

"What's the matter with them anyway?" he asked Tilda over the top of Leonard's head.

Tilda patted Thelma's knee. "Look," she said, as the speeder lurched ahead, "here's your friend Lillian. And the other children. We're going to have a good time!"

Mr. Hamilton turned to Tilda. "Last time you rode with me, we only went as far as the logging operation. This time you'll see some real sights."

He was right. As they topped a rise a short mile past the logging side, Mr. Hamilton slowed the speeder, and Tilda looked down. There it was. Lake Cushman, a blue jewel resting in the palm of the Olympic range. An early mist was gathering itself up from the lake's surface and slipping away as the sun warmed the air.

"That's Mt. Elinor above the lake," Mr. Hamilton shouted over the clang of the speeder. "Sits up there so proud, like she was the queen of Sweden.

"And look over there, Mrs. Lind, and you'll see something interesting." He pointed at the far hillside. "Two young girls, Marion Hoffman and Harriet Saters from the University of Washington, went to bee-keeping school in Shelton. They knew that berry vines and fireweed grow well on logged-over hillsides, so they set up their business here where the blooms would attract the bees. Mountain Flower Honey Farm, they call it. Doing all right, too, even though they were nearly burned out last summer when a spark from a donkey set the hillside on fire." He pushed the throttle ahead again. "Good workers, those girls."

"Heard they set out eighty beehives yearly," Mr. Nelson said.

"That's right," Mr. Hamilton said. "They supply honey to folks all up and down the canal and as far away as Olympia."

"Now all the girls have to do is keep the bears from putting them out of business," Mrs. Box laughed. "Those big black bears really like honey!"

Lillian smiled at her mother. Leonard climbed into Tilda's lap, and Thelma gripped her mother's arm.

The speeder slowed to a stop at the edge of the lake. A trail led around the lake, but Tilda could see Cushman's house from where she sat. It was two stories high with windows all along the front. A covered porch ran the full length of the house and wide steps led up to the front door. This house was almost as fine as the wealthy home in Portland where she'd worked as a maid before she was married. And now the Cushman's house stood empty, waiting to be torn down before the valley was flooded.

Charlie poked her. She and the children needed to get off the speeder with the others so the men could unload the picnic boxes.

Tilda sat down at the partly-cleared picnic table and wondered where the day had gone. It went too fast, she knew that, with all the walking and swimming and visiting and eating.

"Didn't we have a good time today!" Mrs. Nelson said.

"Ya," Tilda answered. "I've been drinking coffee till I don't want to see another cup."

"Did you ever taste so much good food?" Mrs. West asked, eating what was left of the potato salad out of the serving dish.

"Ya, and didn't the children have fun," Mrs. Nelson said. "But, Mrs. Lind, I don't see Thelma and Leonard joining in very much."

Tilda had wondered if others were noticing that, too. Even in the afternoon when the grownups sat on the front steps of the big house and took pictures, Thelma and Leonard stayed with them instead of playing with the other children.

"Here comes my Leonard," Mrs. West said. "I have to remember to call him 'Big Leonard' now that we have two Leonards in camp. He's a lot bigger than your Leonard, you know," she said to Tilda.

"He's three years older," Tilda said, a little rankled.

"Hey Mom," Big Leonard hollered as he approached the ladies. "Hundred times I asked Thelma to wrestle and she won't. She just hangs around you guys."

"Want to know why?" Lillian Box whispered, walking up behind Big Leonard and smiling at Thelma.

"Never mind, now," Mrs. Jacobson said. "It will soon be dark and time for the firecrackers."

The women packed their dishes and leftover food into their picnic boxes and walked out to the front steps to join their men and wait for the fireworks. Twilight was long in midsummer here like in Finland, but Jacobsons and others had brought home-brew, so no one minded waiting for dark.

At the "pop" of the first firecracker, the women jumped, and when someone threw one too close, they screamed and laughed. Then they listened to it "bang" a second time when it bounced back at them from the hills across the lake. When the children lit sparklers and ran and twirled them in the air, the women cheered, and when the fireworks were used up, the men and women moved closer together on the porch steps and sang *"Yankee Doodle"* and *"My country 'tis of thee, sweet land of liberty..."* Some of the men blew their noses.

Then one of the single boys sat down on the porch and started playing his accordion. He played a schottish and a polka and then another schottish. The whole porch shook from the hopping and the stomping. They danced under the stars, trading partners, and then trading back. Some of the children joined in until they tired and one by one fell asleep in a chair or on a sweater tossed aside by one of the dancers. Then, when it seemed like they could dance no more, the boy played another waltz and everyone danced one more time before they picked up their flashlights and picnic boxes and woke their children for the walk back to the speeder.

Lillian and her mother sat down next to Thelma for the ride home. Thelma jumped up and moved to the other side of Tilda. "What's going on here?" Tilda asked, turning first to Thelma and then to Lillian.

"Nothing," Lillian smiled.

"There is too," Thelma exclaimed, shouting over the noise of the speeder. "Lillian says bears come after the honey in the beehives."

"That's right, Telma," Tilda said. "We all know bears like honey."

"That's not all," Thelma went on. "She said not to tell, but I'm going to tell." Mrs. Box and Charlie turned to listen.

"What else?" Tilda asked, looking at Lillian.

"I just told them," Lillian said, smiling at Thelma, "that what bears like even better than the taste of honey is the taste of new camp kids."

"Oh, my!" Mrs. Box laughed. "Isn't that just like my Lillian! She always likes her little jokes."

"Mama," Thelma said, suddenly brightening up. "You know what? I'm going to let Big Leonard teach me to wrestle."

"You want to learn to wrestle?" Charlie asked. "You planning on wrestling the bears?"

"No," Thelma said. "Not the bears. Lillian!"

An Ultimatum - September

"We're in for it this time," Charlie announced as he came through the door. "The whole damn mountain's on fire."

Charlie had left for his shift on the fire line at midnight, and now it was noon, but the smoky haze that covered the sun belied the fact. Tilda helped him out of his stiff jacket and stood it up in the corner. No wonder they called these work clothes "tin," she thought. The canvas cloth was dipped into some kind of paraffin oil until it was as hard as metal and would shed the worst weather. Even the rain of cinders.

Tilda watched Charlie as he dropped into his chair at the kitchen table. He had only a half hour to eat and rest while the lokey took on more water, he told her. No time to change out of his tin pants and caulk shoes. Tilda noticed he'd forgotten to strap onto his boots the shoe-length boards he'd designed for the floor's protection when he wore his caulked shoes into the kitchen.

A spark from the lokey had started this fire, he said. It didn't take much when the dead grass next to the railroad tracks was dry as bone. Logging operations had already been down for two weeks, and every man in camp had been placed on the fire line as well as any available man out of Hoodsport and Potlatch.

The men were fighting the fire night and day. Where no roads led to the fire, they built fire trails by cutting and sawing through thick underbrush. When they had worked until they could no longer stand, they stretched out on the ground to rest and maybe doze a little until they regained the strength to again wield their shovels and picks and axes. Where the fire could be reached by rail, the locomotive with filled water tanks shuttled a crew to the scene. Before the lokey would come to a full stop, the men would jump off the flatcar and begin dragging the heavy canvas hoses to the fire's edge.

Charlie, bigger and stronger than most of the men in his crew, was usually assigned one of the hoses. Whenever Tilda heard him limp up the porch steps at the end of a shift, she knew this had been his job that day. Holding the cold water hose while standing next to the hot fire caused his legs to cramp until he could hardly walk. Tilda would rush to pour hot water in the washtub so he could sit and soak his legs until the muscles finally relaxed and he could return to the fire line.

"Is this fire worse than the one at the beginning of the summer?" Tilda asked, massaging his shoulders as he sat at the table. She already knew the answer but wanted to learn more.

"Ya, that one burned slow and was easy to put out because the woods was wet, but now even the evergreens are dry as sticks." He flexed his shoulders as she kneaded the muscles with the heels of her hands. "It's been too hot and dry a summer."

"Do you think we're safe here in camp?" Tilda asked, not knowing the answer this time.

Charlie hesitated. "The fire's close," he finally answered, "but if the wind don't change, the camp will be all right."

He wiped the sweat off his forehead and from around his neck. His red handkerchief turned black from the soot. His eyes were red-lined and black-rimmed. Tilda set a basin of water and a towel in front of him on the table so he wouldn't need to get up and go to the sink to wash. She rinsed out his thermos, refilled it with fresh coffee, and then sliced the rye bread for sandwiches.

"What happens if the wind changes?" Tilda asked, this time afraid of the answer.

Charlie didn't hesitate. "You get the hose like I showed you, and water the roof and sides of the house. Pack our clothes and anything else we can carry. Keep Telma and Leonard close and be ready to move fast when the train comes to pick you up."

Tilda remembered the stories the boys from the bunk house had told that night shortly after the June fire. How in another September, four years ago, the loggers and their families had raced out of camp, barely ahead of the fire, leaving everything behind. Her hands shook as she pulled the simmering stew to the side of the stove and dipped the meat and vegetables onto Charlie's plate.

Charlie ate silently and quickly. Tilda started to refill his plate when she heard the chug of the lokey. Charlie jumped up from the table, grabbed his tin coat and hat, and raced out the door. She watched him leap aboard the crew car as it slowed in front of their house, and then she followed it with her eyes and her heart as it picked up speed and headed for the burning woods. That afternoon what they most dreaded, happened. The wind changed and blew towards camp.

Tilda, like every other woman in camp, found herself alone with her children, choking with smoke and fear, praying for the safety of her husband, and for their own safety. For two days the women hosed down their houses and watched the sky. The smoke swirled out of the hills and across the clearing until it erased the roundhouse and bunkhouses at the far end of camp. Then the grey-black billows rolled through the row of family houses until the women could no longer see each other. They saw only flakes of ash floating around them like frightened birds looking for a place to land.

"Telma, hold the hose and keep sprinkling. I'm going in to pack," Tilda shouted even though both children were standing next to her. She ran into the house with Leonard at her heels. She threw clothes into their grips and looked around to see what else to take. She'd leave the copper coffee pot from Finland on the stove until the last minute. Leonard followed her out again and stood close to her when she took the hose back from Thelma.

The smoke intensified. Tilda sent the children inside and held a handkerchief over her nose and mouth as she watered. "They've built a backfire on the edge of camp," someone shouted from the speeder as it rattled by with a fresh crew.

Then, slowly, at the end of the day, the smoke began to thin. Thelma and Leonard ventured out of the house to look. The voracious flames had reached the burned-out area of the backfire and run out of fuel. The women dropped to their knees, thanked God, and hugged their children.

"It's over now, isn't it?" Tilda asked Charlie one morning a week later. "We even had a little rain yesterday."

Charlie had just come home from his night shift on fire watch and was sitting on the back porch step unlacing his caulk shoes. "Everyone says the fire is under control," Tilda said.

"Ya, the worst is over," Charlie said. "But we still have work to do." He pulled off his boots, brushed the dirt from his heavy socks with his hands, and followed Tilda into the kitchen.

He told her how smoldering coals that hide around stumps or under logs can, with a little breeze, start a new fire. When the men go back to logging, they'll carry picks and shovels to bury these spot fires. For months around the clock, men will stand fire watch, as he had been doing all week.

Tilda set a cup of coffee and the bowl of sugar lumps on the table in front of him. "Well, at least the danger is over," she said, more to herself than Charlie. Charlie sipped his coffee and said nothing. He wondered if he should tell her about last night's fire watch.

The moon had been covered by a cloud, but the stars were out, silhouetting the skeletal remains of a once verdant growth of firs. Ashes, dampened by the first rainfall, gave off a sharp stench. He had been reaching into his pocket for a handkerchief when he heard a rock roll down the sidehill toward him. As he poked his handkerchief back into his pocket, he heard another rock, and another. Then, a growing rumble.

He had stepped behind a charred snag and squinted up the hill into the dark. When the moon came out from behind a cloud, he could see what was happening. Rocks and boulders, loosened when the fire burned away the hillside vegetation and further loosened by the rain, were tumbling down the hill on all sides of him. He'd crouched behind the scorched tree for protection until daylight when he could see well enough to pick his way across the sliding landscape.

Charlie knew he shouldn't tell Tilda about this, but he did. That's when he discovered that fire in the woods wasn't the worst danger. It was the fire in Tilda's eyes.

"So this is what we have to look forward to," Tilda began, drying each plate like she was trying to rub off the painted flowers. "A lifetime of hardship and danger when we had it so good in Seattle. This is what we came to America for? Well, this wasn't my dream of America. We don't find streets paved with gold here." She took a deep breath. "We don't even find streets!"

Charlie sat with his hands resting next to his coffee cup. What could he say? She was right.

"And danger. Always I worry about fire, and accidents. And we were moving closer to my sister? And when do we see her? Not during fire season. You don't get any time off. Now winter is coming and I hear the camps can be snowed in for months. And when the snow melts, the creeks flood and damage the trestles so we still can't get out!"

She was blinking hard, trying not to cry, but the last weeks had worn her down. She had never talked to Charlie like this, but she couldn't bring herself to stop.

"Ya, and you know what Mrs. Nelson will say? She'll say, 'Huckleberry bushes will grow good on that burned-off hill. Think of all the huckleberry pies!' Well, we're so busy fighting fire, we don't have time to think, or pick berries, or bake pies."

Charlie put a sugar lump in his mouth and sipped the coffee through it. He set down his cup and studied the backs of his hands. With all the hair burned off, they looked like someone else's hands. Tilda wasn't like herself either. He'd never seen her like this. He could feel heat coming up into his own face. It wasn't the coffee. It was his working so hard without rest for so many weeks, for this. No understanding! Did she think he'd set the fire?

He pulled himself to his feet, a giant of a man beside his five-foot-four wife, and looked down at her. "What's the matter with you? You should be happy the worst is over."

"The worst is over? Winter's coming and—"

"I never said living in a logging camp would be easy! Tilda, you're forgetting the good times. The Fourth of July picnic, the parties on Saturday nights—"

"Charlie," she said, putting down the dishtowel and looking up into his face, "Charlie, if we stay here this winter and next summer, then we should move in the fall!"

Charlie looked down at her soft, brown hair and into her deep-blue eyes. Her cheeks were flushed pink. His anger left him and he felt a flush of another kind. "I'll tell you what, Tilda," he said, placing his rough hands on her shoulders. "If you'll stay here this whole first year like you say, then we'll go, if that's still what you want to do."

Holiday Train

It was Christmas morning and still dark when her Daddy picked up their suitcase and led her and her little brother out the door. "Hurry up, now," he said. "We can't miss the train on our first vacation since we moved to camp."

He helped Mama down the slick steps and then stamped a path through the fresh snow toward the railroad track. Thelma and Leonard, crunching along behind, holding their Christmas dolls close against the sharp air, heard the distant train whistle and the huff-puff of the locomotive.

When they reached the track, others were already waiting there. Thelma leaned around her mother to watch the big, round moon of a light tunneling its way through the blackness in their direction. Mama and Daddy pulled her and Leonard back from the tracks as the giant engine spit steam and hissed to a stop in front of them, announcing with another scream of its whistle that it had arrived.

This was almost as exciting to Thelma as last night, Christmas Eve, when Santa himself came to their house and left them two presents each—Leonard, a set of Lincoln logs and a Jackie Coogan doll "made especially for little boys," and Thelma, a box of sewing cards and a Mama Doll just like the one she'd seen in the Sears Roebuck catalog. Thelma cried to stay home and play with her doll instead of going to Shelton, but then Mama said she and Leonard could take their dolls with them, so it was all right.

Their teeth chattered with cold and excitement as they watched snowflakes fall out of the dark and feather their way through the beam of light from the locomotive. The logging camp had shut down for two weeks and the train would take them to Potlatch where they could catch a bus to any city they wanted. Almost everyone in camp was going somewhere for Christmas vacation.

Mama with her pink cheeks was exited, too. She was smiling at everyone as she pulled her coat tight around her and tugged her cap down over her ears. But Daddy looked like he was having the most fun, talking and laughing with the others who were waiting.

"We're going to Shelton to visit Tilda's sister and family," Daddy said to someone from the bunkhouse. "We haven't been together since we moved to camp and we used to see them all the time when we all lived in Seattle."

"Well, be glad you don't live in Seattle any more," the man said, shaking his head. "Lots of mill workers are out on strike, and Prohibition means bootlegging and that means gangsters flooding the city."

"Hey, maybe that's what's bringing in all them earwigs, too," someone else from the bunkhouse said. "I read in the paper that they're about to eat Seattle up," he laughed. "They crawl into your hair or your ears and make you crazy, they say. Parents worry about their kids..."

Thelma reached for her daddy's hand.

"Guess it's not really funny," the man said, noticing Thelma. "The mayor is paying big money to anyone who can get rid of them."

"Ya, it sounds like they're even worse than the bears we have around here," Daddy laughed and gave Thelma's hand a squeeze.

The locomotive puffed patiently while it waited for people to pick up their bags and climb into the two long, box-like cars. Mama took Thelma's hand and helped her up the high step into the car hooked to the engine. Daddy picked up Leonard and swung in behind Mama. They found a place to stand as the train started inching its way toward the trestle that led out of camp.

Soon everyone was sitting on their grips and talking all at the same time. The ladies took out thermos bottles and uncapped them. Smoke puffed from the top of each bottle, the kind of smoke she and Leonard liked to make with their breath on a cold morning. Mama handed Daddy a sugar lump and he put it in his mouth and took a big sip of his coffee. Then she gave Thelma and Leonard each a sugar lump even if they didn't have any coffee. Probably because this was a holiday.

All at once the clickity-clacking wheels sounded louder and everyone quieted a little and looked out the window. They were crossing the trestle. The sun had pushed away a little of the dark and they could see the river far below, tossing pieces of ice at the rocks and the rocks tossing them back again.

Thelma remembered another time when a friend of Daddy's drove them from Hoodsport to the end of the road and they walked across the trestle to get home. She'd crossed the trestle holding Mama's hand many times in the daylight, but this time it was dark and snowing. They could hear the river, and she knew if she slipped and fell between the ties, she would fall forever.

Daddy went first with a flashlight and kicked the snow off the ties so she and Mama would have a place to step. He carried Leonard, and Mama held Thelma's hand as they inched along, listening to the wild river below. Mama and Daddy laughed later because Thelma had cried all the way across the trestle because she wanted to be carried, and Leonard had cried because he wanted to walk

The train was moving faster now. Someone in the back of the car was telling a story in a loud voice over the clacking of the wheels. When he finished, everyone laughed and then Thelma guessed it was her daddy's turn because he started talking loud for everyone to hear.

"Well, I was riding on a log-train out of Portland on my way to my first job," Daddy was saying. "Sven Svenson, who just came to this country, too, was riding beside me. 'Listen,' I said, 'listen to the crew talking. If we pay close attention, we can learn some English before we get to camp.' So Sven listened," Daddy said, "and we both listened, and when we got to camp, we found out we was riding with a crew of boys who'd just come over from Italy and were talking Italian."

Everyone laughed and then Mr. West must have wanted a turn. He told how years ago word got back to Finland that a camp foreman named Jack Cole liked hiring Finn boys and always treated them good because they were such hard workers. So they came to Ellis Island, hundreds of them, asking how far it was to Jack Cole's camp. 3000 miles, they were told, but that didn't stop them. They couldn't speak English, so when they reached Shelton, they just said, "Yack Cole." Cole had told the conductor of the log train, The Blakely, where he wanted the new men to work, and the conductor had made up a system. With a piece of chalk he marked the number of a camp on the back of each Finn, and then when the train reached that camp, he pushed him off the flatcar.

Everyone laughed.

"Did that happen to you?" Mrs. Nelson asked.

"No, but I heard it really happened," Mr. West grinned. "I heard, too, that that's why our camps have numbers instead of names, just so it would be easy to set up the logging crews." Thelma looked at her daddy and he was smiling and shaking his head.

"Well, were those boys Finn-Finns or Swede-Finns?" Mrs. Box giggled. "I always get mixed up."

"Either one," Daddy answered. "Swede-Finns, like Tilda and me and some others on this train, are from Finland, but we have grown up with Swedish customs and we talk Swedish instead of Finnish. That's the difference."

"Well, I never know if a man's from Sweden or Finland," Mr. Box put in. "All I know is I hear more broken English around camp than American English. Nothing wrong with that, you know," he said, looking around the car like he might be in trouble. "Swede or Finn, they're damn good workers, even if they don't talk good American!"

Mrs. Box giggled again.

"Well, me and Mrs. Jacobson talk broken English, too, just like the Swedes, but, as you know, we come from Norway," Mr. Jacobson said.

"And we're from Denmark. Me and Karen," Knud Jensen said, nodding at his pretty, young wife.

"Ya, most of us in camp come from the old country, all right," Mr. Nelson said.

"We aren't all immigrants here," Mr. Warner said. "I was born in this country. It was my grandparents who came over on the boat. And yours did, too, didn't they, Box?"

Mr. Box nodded. "From Germany."

"Well, we've been here longer than anybody," Mr. Woodworth said. "It was my people that met the boat, remember!" and everyone laughed again. Thelma guessed that that had something to do with his being Indian. Daddy said there were quite a few loggers in camp from the Indian reservation next to Potlatch.

"Well, so far us immigrants here have stuck it out in the logging business," Mr. Jacobson said, "but I know a few that didn't last. They rode to camp on the flatcar one year, like we did, and out through a trap door the next. Just like that, they were gone," Mr. Jacobson said, snapping his fingers.

Thelma stood up to find Mr. Jacobson and noticed that Mrs. Jacobson was pouring Irene and Harold a small cup of coffee each. But then they were a little older. Irene waved to Thelma. She was nice. Not like Lillian Box.

"That was just in the early days," Daddy said, patting Mama on the knee.

"Ya, and they could only put you on the trap door if you was dead drunk or been slipped a Mickey Finn," someone else said.

"What's he talking about?" Mama whispered to Daddy. "What about a trap door?"

"Oh, that's nothing. It wouldn't happen to me, don't worry. Usually it happens to one of the single boys who goes to Skid Road in Portland or Seattle and spends too much time in a waterfront saloon."

Thelma could see Mama wasn't satisfied and Daddy would need to explain.

"Some of the sailors that came into port from the China run were miserable. They hadn't had a foot on dry land in two, maybe three years. They were tired of poor pay and bad food. They heard about the logging camps with all the meat and potatoes they could eat and a good pay check and a trip to town on days off. It sounded mighty good to them. So they'd jump ship the first chance they got."

Daddy had switched to Swedish to explain this to Mama. Thelma was glad she could understand Swedish, so she could hear about the trap door.

"So then," Daddy went on, "when the captain of a ship was short-handed, he'd Shanghai a logger to take the sailor's place. He'd hire one of the fancy-dressed girls who entertained in the waterfront saloons to get a young logger drunk, or maybe give him a drug, a Mickey Finn, and then lead him to a little room in the saloon that was built over the water. She'd set him in a chair over a trap door and talk to him while she tapped out a signal with her shiny, high-heeled shoe. Someone from the ship would be waiting below for the signal and he'd un-hook the trap door and the logger would fall into a little boat and be rowed out to the ship. When he woke up he'd be far out to sea."

"Starting a new career," Mr. West laughed. He had been listening, too.

Thelma noticed everything was funny to everyone today. Even the scary story about the trap door made people laugh. Maybe they all felt good because it was Christmas Day.

Now everyone was telling stories to each other and passing coffee bread and dipping it in their coffee. Thelma watched Leonard draw pictures with his finger on the fogged-over window next to where they were perched on their bags. She cleared the steam off the window with her hand so she could peek out at the snow-dressed trees rushing past the train window.

Everything was white outside, as white as Mama's company tablecloth, only instead of lying flat, it was all bumps and hills and shapes. Some of the trees stood like snow-giants guarding the railroad tracks from bees. Or earwigs and bears. Some of the snow people looked like they were shaking hands with each other, like Daddy always did when he met someone new or someone he hadn't seen for a while. All of the snow creatures wore coats covered with diamonds like in fairy tales and were showing them off in the sun. She wished the train would slow down a little so she could wave at them and wish them all a Merry Christmas and let them know how happy she was.

When they reached Potlatch, a big bus with "Seattle" written across the front was waiting for them. Most of the people got off in Shelton, but a few stayed on and kept going. Uncle was in his car at the bus depot waiting for them.

Thelma pressed her nose against the window in the back seat of the car as they drove through downtown Shelton and started up Hillcrest where **Moster** and Uncle lived. She had forgotten about sidewalks and streets and hills covered with houses. Finally they stopped in front of a small house near the top of the hill and Thelma saw a grinning face framed by the curtains in the front room window. Arthur was watching for them.

Moster hugged Mama and then Daddy. Arthur punched Leonard and Leonard ran after him. Then everyone talked at once.

A few days here...show you round Shelton...Charlie will take you through the mill...turkey is in the oven...a day or two in Seattle...We'll stay in a nice hotel and eat in restaurants...see some of the boys on Skid Road...

"Charlie," Mama interrupted. "I don't want to go to Skid Road."

"Why not?" Daddy asked, and winked at Uncle.

"You know why," Mama said, wearing her worry frown.

"Sure there's drinking and gambling. And girly shows," Daddy said. "But it's where loggers go to see each other after months in the woods. They spend their money and get into fights and have a good time, but they don't get into any real trouble."

"Well, what about the trap door?" Mama asked.

"Oh, that!" Daddy laughed. "Those trap doors are all nailed shut now. Jacobson was talking about olden days. You didn't really think I'd be Shanghaied, did you?"

Mama smiled then, a quivery smile, and everyone laughed like someone had told another joke. Now Thelma felt better, too, and ran to see Arthur's new Christmas toys. This was going to be a happy vacation after all.

The Stranger - July 1923

How quickly time passes, Tilda reflected. One day it's Christmas and the next, July! She beat the sugar into the butter with a big wooden spoon until the mixture was light and fluffy. She added the eggs and sifted flour and beat some more.

Someone knocked at the door. Who would be knocking? In Seattle people knock, but not here. Friends in camp open the door, holler "yoo-hoo," and walk in, just like in the old country. It would be impolite to knock and expect people to drop whatever they were doing to come to you. She put down the mixing bowl and hurried into the front room to answer the door.

"Good afternoon, Madam," the stranger said. "You are so lucky I happened to come by because I have a present for you."

Tilda stepped back to get a better look at the man. She'd never seen him around camp, and he certainly didn't look like he belonged there. Shiny black shoes, bow tie, slicked-back hair. He was wearing a vest under his suit coat as if he didn't know it was a hot, summer day. Tilda waited for him to go on.

"See this book?" he asked.

How could she miss it. He was holding it up to her face.

"Well, Ma'am, this book is for you. You can have it! Absolutely free!"

Tilda studied the smiling little man. So generous, some of these Americans. "Thank you," she said as she took the book from his hand and closed the door. She started paging through it when the knock came again. When she opened the door, the man was still standing there, but this time he wasn't smiling.

"Missus, I have to tell you, I didn't mean absolutely free. But if you subscribe to one of these top-selling magazines, the book is free. That's all you have to do and you'll own this book—"

Tilda handed him the book and closed the door, firmly this time. It would have served him right if she had kept the book. But then she felt sorry for him. Him and the other peddlers who came all the way to camp to try to sell something to the housewives. Rugs, patent medicines, brushes, clothes, anything they could carry. Once she bought a housedress from a peddler. Mrs. West saw her dress and the next time the man came by, she bought the exact same one. Tilda didn't mind too much. Times were getting hard in the cities, and she was glad the peddler made another sale.

Tilda threw another handful of flour into the bowl, and hummed as she stirred. She had come to appreciate Charlie's job. It was steady and even when the camp shut down for fire season or snow, they got along. Charlie hunted and fished and she canned or salted away the meat and fish. They had a vegetable garden, so she put up string beans and corn to last all winter. Carrots and potatoes they kept buried against heat and cold, so they lasted most of the winter. All they really needed to buy was yeast and flour for making bread. And sugar and coffee, of course.

Milk and butter, too, she remembered as she added milk to the batter. She liked making cake—creaming the butter and sugar, sifting the flour, stirring, tasting. She didn't make cake very often. Just on special occasions like today, July eighteenth, Leonard's fourth birthday. Leonard would have been satisfied with a candle on a ginger snap, she mused, smiling to herself. He always seemed to know when it was Friday and the train was due to bring their week's order of groceries. He'd ask to make sure, and then he'd skip around the house sing-songing, "The ginger snaps are com-ing, the ginger snaps are com-ing..."

Tilda reached her hand into the oven to see if the temperature was right for the cake. Not quite. She poked another stick into the firebox and sat down again, spreading her lap for the mixing bowl, stirring the batter idly.

Ya, in spite of her worries about living in camp, she and Charlie had had a good year. In the fall when the fire danger was over, camp life returned to its usual order. The men went to work, the older children went to school, and the women met for coffee and sewing or card playing—after their house work was done, of course. The children not yet in school went with their mothers and ate cookies with them in the middle of the afternoon. When winter came and camp had to shut down for snow, the grownups joined the children in sledding and snowball fights, like they were kids again.

The snowfall had been heavier than usual this year, people said. Just before the snow started, Charlie had leaned a five-foot saw that needed fixing against a tree. Later when the camp shut down and he had time to work on the saw, he had to dig down in the snow to reach it.

One day the locomotive plowed the track in front of the houses, covering them with snow. The men dug tunnels through the snow so they could go in and out of their front doors. The camp kids ran up and down the fresh mountains of snow and into the tunnels, hollering and laughing. Even the grown-ups saw the fun in it.

But when the snow melted, and the floods washed out the road and damaged the trestles, Tilda felt uneasy. What if they needed a doctor quick? Ya, that would have been bad, Tilda thought, resting the wooden spoon on the edge of the bowl. But when the flooding ended and spring came, rhododendrons

and dogwood budded and bloomed at the edge of the clearing, peeking out at them from between the evergreens.

My, how her thoughts had wandered today! She'd better
get busy. She set the bowl on the table and reached her hand
into the oven again to test the heat. It was ready. Humming as
she worked, she poured the thick, creamy batter into two round
tin pans, set them in the oven, and closed the door carefully.
The bowl and mixing spoon she set on the sinkboard for Thelma
and Leonard to lick when they came in from play. The coffee
pot had been pushed to the back of the stove, but the coffee
was still warm. Tilda poured herself a **på tår** and sat down
next to the kitchen window.

The day was quiet, but her mind wouldn't rest. She was
remembering the day at the end of last summer when she'd
told Charlie she wanted to leave camp, move back to Seattle,
live anywhere but in the logging camp, and Charlie had told
her to give it a year and then he'd do whatever she decided.
The year had gone fast...

She hadn't missed Ballard as much as she thought she
would, and she had grown closer to her camp friends in one
year than she had to the people in Ballard in four years. Life in
camp wasn't always easy, but there was so much that was good.
Maybe Charlie wouldn't bring it up, and she'd have more time
to think about whether or not she wanted to move back to the
city.

CHAPTER 5: THE CHRISTMAS BELL

Christmas Eve - 1923

"Beat faster, Charlie," Mama ordered.

"I'm beating fast as this beater will go," Daddy answered, a little cross. His face was red like the hot firebox of the cookstove and his forehead sweaty. One big hand gripped the handle of the eggbeater, and the other spun the wheel that turned the beaters in the bowl. His elbows stuck out as he leaned over the table and the arms of his long underwear showed where he'd rolled up the sleeves of his bright red shirt.

Leonard stepped back, as if something in the bowl might explode, but Mama was smiling while she poured the boiling hot syrup over the swelling egg whites. Thelma wasn't scared because she was five-and-a-half now and in the first grade. She remembered last Christmas when Mama made divinity and Daddy helped. It was the only thing Daddy ever did in the kitchen, but he loved divinity.

The kitchen had been smelling good for days. First, Mama made **fattigmand**. She rolled out cookie dough real thin and cut it into short strips. She slit each strip down the middle and pulled the end through the slit. She dropped the strips into a kettle of hot oil where they curled and twisted, and when they started to turn brown on the edges, she turned them over for a second and then picked them up with a long fork and laid them on a newspaper to cool. Then she let Thelma and Leonard roll them in powdered sugar and put them in a shiny can with a lid until Christmas Eve. Mama explained to them that "**fattigmand**" meant "poor man" because even though it was a rich cookie made mostly of eggs and cream, poor people could make them. Even poor people in the old country had a few chickens and a cow.

Next Mama made the **Julgubben**. She rolled out bread dough and Thelma cut circles for the heads and bodies of the "Christmas men." Leonard shaped the arms and legs and then they pinched the pieces together and pressed raisins into the dough for eyes and buttons. When Mama took the **Julgubben** out of the oven, she poked string through their heads so they could hang on the Christmas tree. When Father Christmas came on Christmas Eve, Thelma and Leonard would each give him a **Julgubbe**, and, if it was all right with Mama, they would eat the rest themselves.

Mama made other cookies and breads, too, with names that were hard to say, but finally the cooking and baking were done, and Christmas Eve day arrived.

Mama warmed Thelma's coat by the cookstove while Thelma pulled on her boots and mittens. The teacher had said that today, Christmas Eve day and the last day of school before vacation, they would be talking about Christmas customs in other lands. Thelma wished Leonard were old enough to go to school with her just this one special day.

"Hurry up now, Telma, or you be late," Mama said. "And come right home after school. Remember Nelsons are coming for **lutfisk** tonight."

Thelma hurried into her warm coat, pulled the new cap Mama had knitted for her down over her ears, and dashed out the door. She ran down the shoveled railroad track, slipping and sliding for fun, finally stopping to catch her breath. The snow-covered firs on the far edges of the camp clearing looked to her like sparkling Christmas trees. The mountain peaks in the distance were pink in the first light of morning, like strawberry ice cream cones—and then she heard the school bell telling her to hurry. But even the bell was different today. It sounded like a Christmas bell, tolling out to her its Christmas joy.

"I'm here," Thelma announced, unbuttoning her coat and dancing the snow from her boots. The kids, already in their seats, turned to look at her.

"I know a Christmas custom," Lillian Box announced, waving her hand in the air to get the teacher's attention. "Swedes eat rotten fish on Christmas Eve."

Thelma dropped her coat. "They do not!" she gasped. The Christmas bell had stopped ringing.

"Yes, they do," Lillian went on, smiling widely. "My mother said so."

The room had become very quiet.

"And two weeks before Christmas, Swede girls set their hair on fire," Lillian added. Someone snickered.

"That's a lie!" Thelma shouted and started towards Lillian's desk. "You take that back or..."

"Just a minute here," Miss Kenny interrupted coming out from behind her desk. "Thelma, hang up your coat and take your seat."

The hook blurred when Thelma reached up with her coat, but she found it and then hurried to her desk.

"Now," Miss Kenny said, "we're going to start over. Why don't we begin with the meaning of the word 'custom.' A custom is a way of doing something. Different countries and nationalities have different—"

"Miss Kenny! Miss Kenny!" This time Laurence Lathom was waving his hand in the air. He didn't wait to be called on. "Ain't it true that Swedes open their presents on Christmas Eve instead of Christmas morning like they're s'posed to?"

Thelma caught her breath. She knew that was true so maybe the other things were true, too. Maybe Mama and Daddy were doing Christmas all wrong.

Thelma thought of the whole Christmas week at school and how much fun it had been. One of the bunkhouse loggers chopped down a tree for their schoolroom. It was still dripping snow when he carried it in and stood it up in a bucket by Miss Kenny's desk. The top almost touched the ceiling, it was so tall.

All the kids cut strips of red and green paper and pasted them into circles, hooking one into the other until they had long chains to hang on the tree. They strung bright red cranberries, too. Then they popped popcorn in a pan on the wood stove and threaded it together. When Miss Kenny wasn't looking, Laurence showed Thelma how he could swallow the strung popcorn and then bring it all up again by pulling the string. She tried it, and it worked. It tickled, too. She planned to show Leonard that trick when they strung popcorn at home for their own tree.

After they draped their handmade decorations on the tree, Miss Kenny let them hang some of her own shiny, store-bought Christmas balls while she fastened a candle to the end of each branch. Laurence, the tallest boy in school, put a star on the very top. They all stood back and admired their tree and then worked on memorizing poems for the Christmas program.

Mama and Daddy had been the first parents in the schoolhouse door the night of the program, but all the parents came, and even some of the men from the bunkhouses. Thelma and the other boys and girls recited their poems and then play-acted the manger scene. Everyone in school, all eight of them, had a part. Thelma was a shepherd boy with one of Mama's tablecloths tied to her head and a stick in her hand for the staff. Margaret Warner read the Christmas story from the Bible and Miss Kenny lit the candles on the tree while everyone, kids and grownups, sang Christmas carols. Then they drank hot chocolate and coffee and ate cookies and—

"Thelma!" Miss Kenny had been calling her name. "Thelma, do you know how **lutfisk** gets to your table on Christmas Eve?"

Last night's program was forgotten. "Mama puts it there," Thelma answered under her breath as she studied the deep grooves carved into her desk top. She felt ashamed and didn't know why.

"No, Thelma. I mean do you know what your mother does to prepare a **lutfisk** dinner?"

Thelma shook her head and traced the grooves with her finger.

"The Scandinavian countries are so far north," Miss Kenny began, "that the entire land and sea is covered with ice and snow in the winter. So to make a **lutfisk** dish for Christmas Eve, they have to catch the white fish, usually codfish, in the summer and preserve them. They do this by salting the fish and hanging them from wooden racks in the cold air. In December when you buy the fish, it looks like a piece of stove wood."

Thelma knew that.

"The Swedish family has to plan ahead for their Christmas Eve dinner," Miss Kenny went on. "They soak the fish for a week or more in a lye solution to soften it, and then they soak and rinse it over and over again in plain water for about three days to get rid of the lye. Finally, they put the fish in a kettle of water and boil it. Any lye that remains in the fish will cause it to smell bad as it cooks, but, Lillian, **lutfisk** is not rotten fish. When it is cooked, it is as moist and delicious as any fresh fish." Miss Kenny stopped to take a breath. "Students, how many of you eat **lutfisk** on Christmas Eve?"

Leonard West raised his hand first. Then Irene Jacobson, Thelma's best friend. Then two other hands went up.

"I eat it and so does my little brother," Thelma said, raising her hand high. She turned in her seat and stuck her tongue out at Lillian. Thelma was feeling better.

Lillian's hand went up. Miss Kenny called on her.

"Well, what about the Swede girls setting their hair on fire," Lillian said. "Now that's a weird custom, isn't it?"

"I was just getting to that, Lillian," Miss Kenny smiled. "I think you have some wrong information." Thelma didn't know why anyone would smile at Lillian.

"You are thinking of the Festival of Light," Miss Kenny said. "December the thirteenth is a Swedish holiday called Saint Lucia Day in honor of a young girl who was put to death during Roman times for her Christian beliefs. On this day the children of a household get up very early. The girls put on long white dresses and the boys wear long white shirts and pointed hats. Then they place a crown of lingonberry greens and seven lighted candles on the head of the oldest girl, the one chosen to be Lucia, and all the children parade into their parents' bedroom with coffee and special rolls. This in the Swedish home and the Swedish-speaking part of Finland is the beginning of the Christmas festivities. Isn't that a nice way to begin?"

This time she smiled at Thelma, but Thelma hadn't heard about Saint Lucia Day. She'd ask Mama about it when she got home from school. And she'd ask her why they opened their presents on Christmas Eve instead of Christmas morning like they were supposed to.

Now Miss Kenny was talking about German customs. "...and instead of hanging up their stockings, the children put a boot or a stocking outside their door. In the night Kris Kringle comes and fills it with candy or a switch, depending on whether they have been good or bad..."

Thelma couldn't concentrate on what Miss Kenny was saying. She could think only of getting home and talking to Mama. Even though Mama would be busy, she would always take time to listen.

"Sure, we know about Saint Lucia Day," Mama said, drying her hands. "Many people in my village celebrated it every year."

Mama dropped the peeled potatoes into a kettle of water and set it on the stove next to the **lutfisk** kettle. "So, Telma, why the long face on Christmas Eve?" Mama asked, leaning over to look at her better. It was already getting dark outside and the kitchen was filled with shadows.

"Laurence says we're supposed to open presents Christmas morning, not Christmas Eve," Thelma blurted out. "Santa brings presents in the night so how can we—"

Mama looked surprised. "Well, Telma, it's just our custom to have Father Christmas—Santa Claus in America—or one of his elves bring presents for us to open in the evening. He comes when we aren't looking or maybe when we are sitting by the Christmas tree. And I think there is a good reason for this custom," she went on as she climbed on a chair with a match to light the lamp.

"You see, in the old country everyone in the family gets up very early on Christmas morning, like five or six o'clock. They bundle up in their warmest clothes and light a lantern or a torch and walk or ride horses through the dark and the snow all the way to church. The neighbors do the same so it is a long, bright parade of lights. The horses wear little bells around their necks, and everyone sings carols. When we get to the church, we go in to celebrate the birthday of the baby Jesus. This is what Christmas is all about anyway, isn't it? And we couldn't do this in the morning and open presents, too, could we?" Mama smiled.

Thelma watched her shake the fire off the match and turn up the wick in the lamp. Mama always knew how to make the shadows disappear.

"Now we have to get busy," she said. "Daddy will be through shoveling snow off the steps any minute." Mama turned to the stove to check the potatoes and **lutfisk**. Then she stirred the big open kettle on the front of the stove, tasting a little from the spoon. "Daddy will like this," she said, fanning her mouth with her hand.

"I want a taste," Leonard said, pulling at her skirt.

"No, Leonard, this is **glögg** and it's just for the grownups. I'll fix you some hot chocolate."

"But I saw you put raisins in it."

"Ya, but it's made with wine so it's not for kids," she was explaining as the door opened and Daddy came in with his arms full of firewood. Mr. and Mrs. Nelson and Edith walked in behind him, closing the door quick against the cold air.

"**God Jul**," Mrs. Nelson said. She set a plate of butter-yellow cookies on the sinkboard. "Some Swedish **spritsar** to go with your **fattigmand**.

"Ya, **tack**," Daddy said. "And here is some **glögg** to go with the holiday." He poured the hot, red punch into four cups. "**Skål!**" they all said as they raised their cups and then brought them down for a sip.

Daddy set his cup on the sinkboard and started to lift the lid on the **lutfisk** kettle, but then he looked at Mama and the Nelsons and laughed. "I better not put my nose in the kettle," he said. "I know what it smells like when it's cooking. I wait for Mama to dish it up." Thelma wished she could put Lillian's nose in the kettle.

"And now we sit down," Mama said, and everyone pulled up a chair. Mrs. Nelson helped Leonard and Thelma even though they didn't need help.

"Have you been good children?" she asked. "Santa Claus only brings presents to the good little girls and boys, you know." Leonard looked worried, but Thelma knew she was only teasing. Still, maybe she shouldn't have wished to put Lillian's nose in the kettle.

Thelma watched her daddy. First, he covered his plate with potatoes and then covered his potatoes with the snow-white fish. He poured Mama's white gravy over the top and peppered it all until it was nearly black. Leonard did everything their daddy did except for the pepper.

"**Lutfisk** is extra good this year, Mrs. Lind," Mrs. Nelson said. Mama sliced and passed the warm loaf of rye bread and a plate of yellow butter.

"Thank you," Mama said. "Ya, it's been a good year in every way. We count our blessings."

Daddy finished eating first. "I think I get more wood for the woodbox," he said. Thelma wondered why because the box was still full, but she knew better than to question him. She and Leonard and Edith finished their supper while Mama poured the Nelsons some coffee.

"What was that?" Mr. Nelson asked, looking toward the front room. Thelma heard it, too.

"I think someone was knocking," Mama said. "Who could that be out on such a cold, winter night?" She looked around the table. "Maybe you better go see, Leonard."

Leonard, wide-eyed, jumped from his chair, ran into the front room, and threw open the door. He looked up. He stepped back and looked way up.

"Ho, Ho, Ho," from a deep voice on the porch. In he came. He was big like in the story book pictures, and he had a bright-red shirt and red suspenders holding up his black pants, and a red cap and a white beard. He walked straight to the Christmas tree and set down a fat gunny sack tied shut with red ribbon.

"It's Santa Claus!" Mama exclaimed. "Everyone come into the front room. Quick!"

Thelma stood back with the Nelsons, not sure what to do.

"We light the candles on the tree and see what Santa has in his bag," Mama said. She pulled a kitchen chair into the front room for Santa.

"So, have you been a good little boy this year?" Santa asked Leonard, taking him by the hand and lifting him onto his lap. Leonard nodded. Thelma hoped he wouldn't ask her that question because even on Christmas Eve day she'd wanted to beat up on Lillian Box.

"Come here, girls," he said, beckoning to Thelma and Edith. "Look in the sack and see if there is any presents with your names on them."

Thelma pulled each package out of the bag and read the tags. She found her name on one package and Leonard's name on another and then two more with their names, and two for Edith. And then candy and oranges and nuts spilled out of the bag.

Thelma remembered her manners. "Here, Santa, a **Julgubb** for you." The candles bounced and blinked as she pulled two cookies off the tree, handing one to her brother.

"Here's a **Julgubb** from me, too," Leonard said, finally finding his voice.

"Well, thank you very much," Santa said. "Now I have to go. I have lots of boys and girls to see this evening. Good night, 'til next year." His black rubber boots reflected the dancing candle lights as he walked out the door, taking big steps like Daddy.

"Well," Mr. Nelson said. "I wonder what's in the packages."

"I wonder, too," Mama said and picked one up and shook it and then studied another one carefully, like she was trying to see inside. Then Thelma heard the back door open and wood drop into the woodbox.

"Daddy, Daddy, you just missed him," Leonard shouted, running into the kitchen. "Santa was here and left us some presents."

"Well, I got here in time to watch you open them anyway," Thelma heard him say as he followed Leonard back into the front room.

"We'll have coffee while we sit and watch," Mama said, hurrying to the kitchen.

"And cookies. I'll get the cookies," Mrs. Nelson said and followed Mama out.

"Don't forget the divinity," Daddy called after them.

Leonard held his presents close on his lap, remembering to wait until everyone came back and sat down before opening them. Thelma waited, too, remembering how Miss Kenny had smiled at her when she talked about Swedish customs. Maybe Mama and Daddy weren't doing Christmas wrong...

And the Christmas tree waited, blinking its candlelight eyes at them, popcorn chains hanging like necklaces from its branches. It stood tall, tall as Daddy, smelling of the woods, like Daddy always did when he came home from work. Now even Daddy and Mr. Nelson had stopped talking in the magic light of the candles.

Then Thelma heard it. It seemed far away, but she could hear it clearly.

"Edith, listen!" Thelma whispered. "Leonard, do you hear it?" Thelma ran to the window. "Is it the school bell?"

Edith and Leonard listened and then shook their heads.

Then Thelma knew. It wasn't the school bell she was hearing. It was the Christmas bell inside her that had begun to ring again.

CHAPTER 6: ACTS OF NATURE

Snowed In

January 20, 1924

Dear Ida and Charlie,

Well, we're really snowed in this year, but you don't need to worry about us. The camp is down so the men are off work and we are having a good time.

Tilda licked the point of her pencil so her writing would show up better. She had a good chance to write a letter now with Charlie out shoveling snow and Thelma and Leonard busy building another snowman. They had already built so many snowmen around the house, she felt like she was surrounded by the Russian army.

She and Charlie had been enjoying themselves since shutdown—sleeping a little longer in the mornings, walking down the track to have coffee with the neighbors and then inviting them back. Sometimes they played whist or pinochle with their friends until late at night. Tilda hadn't seen Charlie so relaxed in a long time.

Thelma and Leonard were having fun, too. The older kids showed them how to build snow forts and how to hard-pack snowballs to defend the fort. When the big kids tired of snowball fights, they put on their skis and skied over the snowbanks. Tilda smiled to herself when she thought of Charlie's making skis for Thelma and Leonard.

Charlie started with four thin boards. He cut strips of leather from his old boots and nailed the strips onto the boards to hold the feet in place. Then he soaked one end of each board and bent the ends up like on regular skis. But as the boards dried, they straightened out. Charlie soaked the boards and bent the ends up again, but again they dried straight. He was ready to turn the skis into firewood, but Thelma said they were fine, and she and Leonard skied happily on their straight boards.

So much to write about...

Because the railroad tracks were buried under the snow, the men took turns hiking to Hoodsport for supplies. Charlie didn't mind the five-mile walk down, but hauling the loaded sled back up the trail was tough. Thelma coaxed to go with him until Charlie finally said she could if she helped push the sled up the steep parts of the trail. But the day Thelma went along, the sled felt heavier than ever to Charlie. When he looked back, he found Thelma riding comfortably between the grocery boxes. He was mad at first, he told Tilda, but when the men laughed, he had to laugh, too.

Tilda studied her pencil. She needed to remind Charlie to get out his pocket knife and whittle a new point because there was so much she wanted to say. She licked the dull lead point again and continued her letter.

Lake Cushman is completely frozen over now, and everyone is ice skating, but Charlie is the best. I like to watch him speed across the ice like a fine sail in a high wind. He said that when he was growing up, he skated on the Bothnia Sea near his home almost every day.

Sometimes I stay home and keep the fire going, but Thelma and Leonard always go with him and slide around on the ice in their overshoes. They play so hard they don't even get cold, but when they come into the house, I have to rub their hands to get their circulation going—

Tilda jumped to her feet. Charlie and the children were on the porch stamping the snow off their boots, and she hadn't started supper!

"Charlie," she said as the three tumbled into the warm kitchen and crowded around the stove, "when I finish this letter to Ida, will you see that it gets to the post office in Hoodsport? Someone will be hiking out for groceries in the next day or two, won't they? I haven't written my sister since before Christmas and she must think we are buried in a snow drift."

Flooded Out - March

Tilda sat at the kitchen table with her tablet and pencil. Last time she wrote to Ida and Charlie, the snow was fresh and they were enjoying themselves, but now everything around camp had turned ugly. The melting snow and the rain had filled the rivers and washed out the road and the railroad tracks in two or three places, so they still couldn't get out of camp.

Rain sheeted across the windows, darkening the room. She needed more light for letter writing, but she wouldn't light the lamp in the middle of the day when they were low on oil and needed to make it last. She couldn't ask Charlie or anyone else to carry a heavy can of coal oil up the trail in his packsack with the groceries. Now that the snow was gone and they couldn't use sleds to haul supplies, everyone ordered as little as possible.

Tilda started to lick the pencil point, but saw she didn't need to. Charlie had sharpened it good. Well, he'd had plenty of time to do little jobs around the house this winter with all the shut-downs.

Tilda looked out the window at the pools of standing water next to the tracks. Things still looked flooded, but the section crew had finished fixing the rail bed and camp would be starting up again in a day or two, Charlie told her. But he wasn't looking forward to it, he said. He'd logged in spring thaws before and it was terribly dangerous. Logs were slick, even when you wore caulk shoes. One man he knew slid off a big log and was cut so bad by the saw he was carrying that he almost bled to death. Hillsides were slippery, too, and a person couldn't get his footing when he needed to jump out of the way of a log. By the end of the day, the men were covered with mud and full of stories about close calls.

Tilda looked at the blank sheet of paper in front of her. She wouldn't tell Ida about all that. She'd just write the good news. She pulled the curtain back for a little more light, tucked it behind the back of her chair, and began her letter.

March 1, 1924

Dear Ida and Charlie,

Camp superintendent Carlson told Charlie yesterday that the company is moving the families from Camp Cushman to Lower Camp One this spring. He said it is a bigger camp with quite a few families living there now, and that they have a good school and even a dance hall. The men will still be logging around Lake Cushman, and will ride the train to work from the new camp like they do from here.

Lower Camp One sits between two high railroad trestles. There's no road, but the company plans to build one and, like Charlie says, we don't have a car anyway. To get in and out of camp, we ride the speeder or the logging train.

The move will be easy. I've told you how the locomotive hooks a cable onto the skids under the house and pulls the house onto the flat-car. All I have to do is pack the dishes in a box so they don't break, while Charlie ties the furniture down. The company unloads the house on a cleared spot next to the tracks in the new camp and that's that.

Tilda sat back and read over what she'd written. She was excited about moving to a newer, bigger camp... What? A shadow had crossed the page, startling her! The curtain had slipped back across the window... That's all. It was just the curtain. This time Tilda tied the curtain to the back of her chair before she turned to finish her letter.

The Logging Camp

Sunbaked, set in a hollow of the logged-off hills,
Guarded by grim, dead sentinels of unwanted trees;
Fireweed, spreading its purple bloom
Over the black scars of an ancient burn,
Floods it with waves of changing color.

The bunkhouse rows, burned brown by scorching sun
And streaked by driving, bitter rains,
Face each upon a narrow splintered walk,
And centering all, the cookhouse with its swinging steel
Whose welcome call to hungry men
Is sweetest music to their waiting ears.

This is the camp, home to this man's-world,
Where life is crude and hard,
Threaded with danger, dark with sweat and dust;
No alien luxury strikes a root herein,
But only fundamental needs
Are catered to,
And bed and food and shelter from the whole.

Rona Morris Workman
JUST LOGGIN', 1936

Portland 1912
Ida, Ivar, Tilda

Lind Family in Seattle
Tilda, Charlie, Thelma & Leonard

Lower Camp One

Little Leonard, age 5
Arthur, age 3

Little Leonard

Speeder shuttling work crew

Big Leonard, Irene Jacobson, Thelma

HIGH LEAD LOGGING

The hard-working little steam donkey is "yarding" (pulling in) the huge log attached to the cable. The steel cable holds one end of the log up so it will slide more easily through the logging debris that covers the ground. The cable runs through pulleys which are attached to the top of the spar tree (left of the donkey). Next, the logs are loaded onto the rail cars for their journey to the mills.

TRESTLES

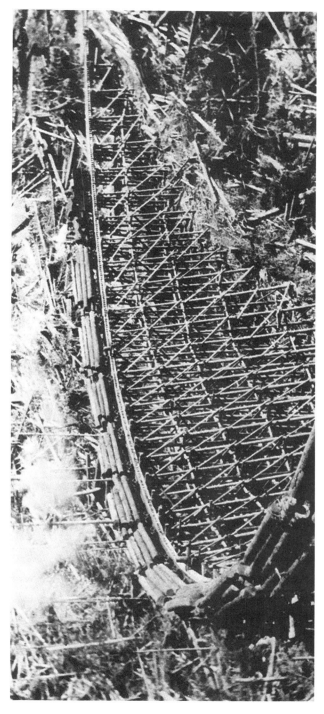

The locomotive pulls its load of logs out ot the mountains across high trestles, and through the hills on its way to the waiting lumber mills. Some of the mills can't be reached by rail, so the logs are dumped into a water storage area like Potlatch on Hood Canal. There they are tied together into a huge raft and floated to the mills. Parents in camp warned their children not to climb around on the trestles because it was so dangerous, but some kids did it anyway.

MOVING DAY

When a logging company has "logged out" one area, it moves its equipment to a new location. Sometimes the company loads their family houses, bunk houses, and schoolhouse on flat cars and brings them along. Tilda liked moving this way. She didn't have to pack and unpack because everything in the house stayed where it was.

PART IV - LOWER CAMP ONE
1924-1928

CHAPTER 7: MURDER ON THE TRACKS

The kitchen was hot. It was hot outside in July in this new camp like it was in Camp Cushman, like it was anywhere if it was Tuesday because Tuesday was ironing day.

Tilda folded a bed sheet in half three times and laid it on the kitchen table, running her hands across the top to be sure there were no hidden bumps. She added a stick of wood to the stove and set the flatiron on to heat. When the surface of the firebox glowed red, she clamped the wooden handle onto the iron and lifted it off the stove. She reached into the ironing basket for Charlie's shirt and laid it on the table.

"Stop crying now, Leonard, and move your milk glass so it don't tip over on my ironing," she said.

Leonard smudged the tears across his cheeks with the heels of his hands and then slid his glass along the edge of the table toward the window.

"What's the matter with Leonard?" Charlie asked, walking barefoot out of the bedroom with a clean pair of socks in his hand.

"He went into the wrong house when he came in from play," Tilda said.

"That's easy to do. In a new camp all the houses look alike at first. Why the crying? Did someone bawl him out?"

"No, they gave him a glass of water."

"What's wrong with that?"

"He says he drank it."

"Why did that make him cry?"

"Maybe he was embarrassed," Tilda said. "I don't know. Maybe he figured it didn't belong to him. He always likes to do what's right, you know."

Charlie started to say something, but instead reached across the table and ruffled Leonard's hair. Leonard's eyes smiled back at him over the rim of his milk glass.

Tilda licked a finger and touched the face of the iron with a quick stroke. Leonard, his troubles forgotten, listened for the sizzle sound that meant the iron was ready. The iron sizzled again when it touched the dampened shirt laid out on the ironing table. Steam rose from the surface and Tilda moved the iron back and forth quickly so it wouldn't scorch Charlie's good shirt. She hummed as she slid the iron deftly around the buttons.

"Leonard, where is your sister?" she asked.

"Outside," he said, sipping his milk.

"Tilda," Charlie said as he sat down and began pulling on his socks, "I think I like working hoot-owl shift. It's not so bad going to work at two in the morning when I can be home by noon. It's cool when we work, and we don't have to worry about starting any fire—"

The door flew open, banging against the cupboard behind it, and Thelma stood wide-legged in the doorway, drawn up to her full, gangly, six-year-old height. "I just killed Lillian Box," she announced.

Tilda dropped the iron. Charlie jumped to his feet. "What did you say?" he exclaimed.

"I said," Thelma stated, placing her hands akimbo on her hips, "that I killed Lillian Box!"

Camp kids, like kids throughout the state, weren't supposed to start school until they were six, but Thelma had known when she turned five, that she was ready. She'd wheedled and coaxed until finally Tilda asked Miss Kenny, the camp teacher, and the Hoodsport School Board if Thelma could be tested. When they found out Thelma could already read, they made an agreement with her. She could start school in the fall if she would take a nap every day after lunch in Miss Kenny's bedroom adjoining the classroom. Strong-willed and determined, Thelma had gotten her way and was not to be ignored now when she announced she'd killed Lillian Box.

"What are you talking about?" Charlie demanded. "Why would you kill Lillian Box?" Leonard could smell his dad's shirt scorching but couldn't take his eyes off Thelma.

"I killed her because she called me a dirty Swede," Thelma answered, unabashed.

She didn't look like a killer. Perhaps a little taller than some six-year-olds, more sun-browned, a scab on an elbow and a knee. Her dress was a little dirty, but there was no real sign of a struggle.

Tilda peeled the scorched shirt loose from the iron and set the iron back on the stove. Leonard pushed away from the table and waited for what would happen next. Thelma's disheveled hair kinked around her face where it was damp with perspiration.

"Where is she now?" Tilda whispered.

"I'll show you," Thelma said, leading the way out the door, down the porch steps, and onto the track.

"Wait for me," Leonard called, racing to keep up with his big sister.

Neither Tilda nor Charlie spoke as they walked down the track, but their minds whirled. They'd never known Thelma to lie. Or make up stories. She got into fights sometimes, like other camp kids, but she wasn't mean.

Thelma strode on ahead. Tilda grabbed Charlie's arm to slow him a bit. She had to watch the ties to be sure she didn't trip. Every-other tie fit Charlie's stride but not hers. Thelma got her long legs from her dad, it was easy to see.

"Charlie," Tilda said, trying to catch her breath, "we know that Lillian can be awful mean..." already planning Thelma's defense.

"Like how?"

"Well, remember how she scared Telma and Leonard with her talk about bears at the Fourth of July picnic?"

Charlie nodded.

"And once Lillian asked Telma to her house for lunch. Telma was all excited to be asked home by an older girl. When she got there, Lillian's mother wasn't home, and you know what Lillian gave her for lunch?"

Charlie didn't answer. Just kept his eyes on Thelma walking ahead and Leonard running to keep up.

"She gave her a sandwich filled with soap!"

Charlie looked at Tilda. "No reason to kill her," he said through his teeth.

Thelma stopped. "She was laying right here," she said. "I left her right here."

"Well, where is she now?" Charlie asked.

"Maybe her daddy came and got the body," Leonard said.

Thelma looked from her mother to her father and back again. "I kicked her hard in the stomach and she fell right here and didn't move. That's when I ran home."

Charlie was relieved. Many times he'd seen one logger punch another in the stomach with a hard fist, knocking the wind out of him. The downed logger would get up and stagger back to his bunkhouse holding his stomach but otherwise all right.

Now it was Thelma's turn to ask, "But where is she?"

"There she is!" Leonard pointed. They all looked down the track and saw the bent-over figure of Lillian limping toward home.

"Guess she got her wind back," Charlie said.

"She's okay then?" Thelma asked, sounding disappointed. Tilda sighed in relief as Lillian disappeared into her house.

"Daddy," Thelma said, pulling at his arm, "am I going to get a lickin'?"

"You damn right you are!" he said.

"With the strop?" she asked, knowing well the sting of the leather razor strop.

Charlie was still looking at Box's house. "You say she called you a dirty Swede?"

"Yes, she did," Thelma said. "And I didn't mind being called a Swede, but when she said 'dirty Swede,' it sounded like something bad. So I kicked her in the stomach."

Charlie was quiet for a minute. Then he turned and looked down at Thelma. "Well, I don't think we'll use the strop this time," he said, taking her by the hand and leading the way back to their house.

CHAPTER 8: LITTLE LEONARD

Just Turned Five

"Curl my hair, Mama," Leonard coaxed, standing next to her chair. "Make it pretty like yours." He leaned his elbows on her lap to watch her more closely as she clamped and rolled one section of her hair after another.

"Your hair is already pretty," she told him.

"But make it curly like yours," Leonard pleaded.

Tilda set the curling iron down and looked into those clear, blue eyes that were so much like his daddy's. She pushed back his bangs, yellow as the buttercups that bloomed at the edge of the woods, and studied his upturned face. Was there ever a more beautiful little boy?

"Well, we can try," she said, lifting him onto the edge of the kitchen table.

She reheated the curling iron over the lamp flame and rolled his hair as she had done to her own. She watched his face break into a smile when he looked into the mirror, and then he was off the table and out the back door.

"I want to show Thelma, and Mrs. Nelson, and Mrs. Jacobson..." his voice trailed off as he jumped off the porch and headed for the neighbors. The ladies said they had all told him how "pretty" he looked that August morning, the morning of the accident.

Once during the short daylight hours of winter when Big Leonard had come to play, Tilda neglected to send him home while it was still light outside. "Mrs. Lind," Big Leonard said,

"I don't want to walk home alone in the dark."

"You scared of the bogy man?" Charlie had laughed.

Big Leonard had stood immobile by the open back door. Little Leonard got up from the floor where they had been playing with Lincoln logs and said, "I'll walk home with you." He then put on his coat, took Big Leonard by the hand, and walked him out the door.

Charlie decided to have some fun. After the boys left, he hid behind a stump in the dark and waited. As Leonard came skipping by the stump on his way home, Charlie hollered and jumped out at him. Leonard had laughed and said, "Aw, I knew it was you, Daddy." Charlie liked telling that story.

When the company had first logged off the camp site for Lower Camp One, the ground was wet, and the donkey left ditches where its skids sank into the soft soil. Each year the rain filled the ditches, and frogs, toads, and snakes moved in. When the summer sun dried up most of the water, the camp kids played with the little creatures.

"Big Boy is the champion jumper in camp," Thelma told Leonard. "All the kids say so." She poked the big toad with a stick. "See how far he can jump."

Leonard had watched for two jumps and then grabbed the toad and held him close.

"Put him down," Thelma said. "I have to keep training him!"

Leonard shook his head and petted the toad. "He doesn't like being poked. I'm putting him back in the ditch." Mrs. Nelson had been watching and liked telling that story.

Irish, the timekeeper, always told how Thelma and Leonard came into the company store to buy candy, and how surprised both children were when he gave Leonard two Hershey bars for his smaller piece of money. He'd heard later that Leonard shared his second bar with his sister.

Everyone in camp had a favorite story to tell, but they could only bear to tell them a long time after the accident.

Sometimes there is no whistle...

Thelma sat alone on the top step of the back porch wishing there were more shade. Wishing everything weren't so quiet. Doctor had given Mama something from a little bottle so she could sleep. Daddy had gone walking alone again. He didn't say when he'd be back. **Moster** and Uncle were sipping coffee at the kitchen table. Not talking. Just sitting and looking off at nothing. Leonard's Jackie Coogan doll lay on the ground next to the bottom step.

Thelma bumped her way down the steps and picked up the doll, shaking the September dust from its clothes. She adjusted Jackie Coogan's tam and tried to button his overalls. The button was missing. Leonard would have to tell Mama so she could sew it back on...

Camp was so quiet today. The only sound had been the whistle of the train this morning when it left to pick up its load of logs. That was a good whistle. She and Leonard used to run out of the house and wave at the engineer, and he would smile and wave back.

There were other good whistles, too, Thelma mused, drawing circles in the dust with a stick. On quiet days they could hear the whistle of the busy steam donkey yarding in logs where Daddy was working. And then there was the quitting whistle that everyone liked to hear. It meant that soon the speeder would be coming down the track in front of their house with Daddy and the other men just in time for supper.

But then there was that other whistle that no one wanted to hear. When the donkey whistled six times real quick and then did it again and again, it meant there had been an accident. Then all the moms and kids in camp rushed out of their houses and to the track to wait for the speeder to bring out whoever was hurt, or maybe dead. Always they heard this whistle when there was an accident.

"It happens too often," Mama used to say to her friends. "We never know when we kiss our husbands good-bye in the morning if..." she would start to say but never finish.

But the six sharp whistles weren't meant for the ladies who ran to the tracks holding their children. They were to call the timekeeper. Whenever he heard the signal, he ran with his bag of iodine bottles and bandages to meet the speeder, to get aboard and help. That's the way it always was. Always there was a whistle to let the timekeeper know there'd been an accident. So how could there have been an accident this time when there was no whistle?

Thelma threw Jackie Coogan off her lap and back into the dirt. It never happened! There couldn't have been an accident when there was no whistle!

But there had been an accident, and she knew it.

All the kids liked to go to the camp store on a summer day when they ran out of things to do. There wasn't much to buy, but the timekeeper was always friendly and he had candy bars and gum on a shelf by his desk. Thelma found that if she and the others stood and looked at the candy shelf long enough, someone who came in on business would buy them a Hershey bar to share.

That's what she was doing that morning when Mr. Hamilton, the driver of the speeder, burst through the door and shouted at "Irish" Mullens, the timekeeper, to come quick.

Mr. Mullens had grabbed his bag and run after Mr. Hamilton. Thelma and the other kids followed, racing to keep up.

They could see the speeder down the track. It was sitting in front of Thelma's house. When they came closer, Mr. Hamilton stopped them and held them back. The timekeeper ran on with his bag.

It had been hard to see from where they were standing, Thelma remembered, but she could tell that the speeder was off its track and Mr. Mullens was on his knees reaching under the speeder. Then the stretcher came out. There was a white sheet over it with patches of red. Now someone was pushing the ladies back and they were running into Mama and Daddy's house. Thelma ducked under Mr. Hamilton's long arm and ran for home.

Mama was lying on the couch, but Thelma wasn't able to get to her with the ladies all standing and kneeling around her. They were all talking and crying at the same time.

"He never knew what happened," one lady whispered.

Another said, "Such a beautiful child he was."

Other whispers.

"They say God takes the good ones first."

"But what will we do without little Leonard?"

Thelma reached for the door frame and leaned against it. She heard people talking on the porch behind her.

"How did it happen?" a woman asked.

"You know how Ham gives the kids rides to the round-house after he takes the men to work," a man explained.

"I know. They stand by the tracks and wait for him."

"Well, I guess Leonard tripped a little when he tried to climb up on the speeder. Ham reached over to give him a hand, but his mackinaw caught on the throttle." He paused.

"And the speeder jumped ahead!"

"Ya, Tilda heard the commotion and looked out her kitchen window. She saw his blue overalls under the speeder—"

"God in heaven!" someone exclaimed.

Thelma didn't remember much about what happened next. Daddy had come home from the woods that day and didn't go back to work. **Moster** and Uncle came to camp and, a few days later, she and Mama and Daddy rode with them to Shelton. There were lots of people at the funeral parlor and a lady sang "Beautiful Isle of Somewhere," and Thelma touched Leonard's cheek but it was cold. And then **Moster** and Uncle drove them back to camp.

Thelma poked the dirt with her foot. Little whorls of dust spun up between her toes. A yellow jacket buzzed around her head and then flew off. Would she ever see Leonard again, she wondered. Someone said God takes the good ones first. Could she ever be good enough to see her little brother again?

The yellow jacket was back. She didn't care if it stung her.

She looked at the doll lying face down in the dust where she had thrown it. Leonard would never ever have let his doll lie in the dirt like that.

She picked up the doll. Its soft body was warm from the sun. She brushed it off carefully and studied the loose strap on its overalls. If there hadn't been an accident, Leonard would have been here to pick up his Jackie Coogan doll himself, Thelma admitted, blinking hard. The accident really had happened. Her little brother really had been killed. She guessed maybe there wasn't always a whistle.

She held the warm doll close and rocked it gently. Tomorrow she'd look in Mama's sewing basket for a button to sew on Jackie Coogan's overalls....

THE MASON COUNTY JOURNAL, SHELTON,

FIVE YEAR OLD BOY LOSES LIFE IN FALL FROM HANDCAR

SAD ACCIDENT SATURDAY AT PHOENIX CAMP ONE NEAR LAKE CUSH-MAN

One of the saddest of the year's casualties was the accidental death of Carl Edward Lind, the five-year-old son of Mr. and Mrs. Chas. Lind at the Phoenix Company's Camp 1 near Lake Cushman last Saturday. Death was due to falling from a handcar and being dragged some distance before the situation was discovered, and the little body was so badly bruised that death soon followed. One of the camp employes had occasion to use the car and the two small children playing about the camp asked for a ride. While the man's attention was attracted to one of the children's questions the Lind boy lost his hold to the opposite side of the car and fell to the track, his cries, if he made any, being lost in the noise of the moving car. He was beyond help when taken to his mother's arms and the remains were later brought to Shelton where the funeral was held from the Chapel Tuesday afternoon, attended by many friends and sympathizers of the stricken parents, who have only the little sister left to console them.

"Don't know if you seen the Shelton paper, Charlie," Jacobson said. "They have a long article about the accident on the front page. I brought you a copy in case you want it."

Charlie took the paper out of his friend's hand and thanked him. He hadn't noticed Jacobson and Nelson walk up to the porch where he was sitting.

"They got some of the facts wrong," Nelson said. "You know newspapers."

Charlie nodded and looked at the paper. "'Carl Edward'? It's 'Carl Leonard'! How can they make a mistake like that?"

"Ya, and they said it was a handcar instead of a speeder," Jacobson said.

"Probably written by some reporter that don't know the difference," Nelson said. "They don't have the straight of how it happened either. The driver's mackinaw caught on the throttle..."

"It don't matter," Charlie interrupted.

The men were silent. A rabbit hopped out from behind a stump and then scurried back out of sight.

"Well, the paper had it right when it said it was the saddest accident of the year," Jacobson said, clearing his throat. "How's Mrs. Lind?"

"She rests most of the time."

"And Telma?"

"Telma doesn't know what to do with herself."

Mr. Nelson said, "The Missus is bringing over some dinner after a while. If there's anything we can do..."

"*Tack*, there's nothing you can do," Charlie said. The paper slid off his lap unnoticed when he stood up to go into the house. He turned at the door. "I have to write a letter," he said.

September 5, 1924

Kära Mor,

*I have bad news. Our little Leonard was killed a week ago, on the railroad track in front of our house. He had just turned five. I want to tell you he was a **duktig pojke**. It is hard to think of going on without him.*

We planned to take a trip home sometime soon, but I don't look ahead much now...

Charlie leaned back in his chair and stretched his fingers. A logger's hand wasn't fine enough for writing. Leonard would have had no trouble writing. As a man he would have found better use for his hands than wrapping steel cables around logs. With schooling, smart as he was, he could have been a professional man, a doctor or lawyer or teacher.

A shuddering sigh escaped him. Maybe he'd planned too much for Leonard. But why wasn't the boy given a chance? Charlie wanted to understand, but he couldn't...

Tilda came out of the bedroom, and joined Charlie at the table. She hated to write home, but she knew she had to sooner or later, so she began.

Dear Ivar and Ester,

Ida said she wrote and told you that we lost our sweet Leonard. There are lots of bad accidents in a logging camp, but everyone says this is the worst. I know the sun comes up and goes down like always, but right now I feel like the world has stopped turning. Thelma runs in and out of the house like she is looking for him. Camp friends bring us food and try to get us to eat.

Tilda found her handkerchief in the pocket of her apron and blew her nose. She put down her pencil and walked to the window. Maples on the far edge of the camp clearing were turning yellow. Leonard liked the fall, watching bright, crisp leaves swirl to the ground and then hearing them crunch under his feet. He never tired of seeing chipmunks hurry back and forth with puffed-up cheeks, storing food for winter. Leonard, like his Daddy, loved living in the woods.

Tilda sat down again at the kitchen table. She remembered her first view of camp, its ugly, barren greyness. She remembered the drought and the heat of that first summer and fall. She had wanted to leave, and Charlie talked her into staying. He said if after a year she still wanted to go, they would move. They had lived in camp a little over two years now and neither she nor Charlie had brought up the subject again, but if he did, she knew what she would say.

She would tell him that camp was her home now. Leonard was most real to her here. Camp was where she had found so many friends and so much help when she needed it. And Thelma loved camp as much as Leonard did. She would want to live here. Thelma didn't know what to do with herself now with her brother gone, but she would be lost without him no matter where they lived.

They were all lost without Leonard. Why did the accident have to happen? Why did God take him from his mother and father who loved him so much? Was God punishing them for something they had done? For too much dancing and card playing?

Tilda picked up her pencil and reread the start of her letter. She wanted to tell Ivar and Ester not to worry, that she and Charlie and Thelma would be all right. But she wasn't sure this was true. Tilda wondered if life would ever be good again, for any of them. What she could tell her brother and wife was to love their little boys every day. Little boys are so precious.

...Stole a pig and away she run ...

Thelma tracked the raindrops with her finger as they streamed down the window pane. A gust of wind broke the trails, pushing them sideways, like a hand might brush away tears. The dripping of water from the edge of the roof was the only sound. Grey was the only color. Cold was the only feeling. Mama had forgotten to light a fire in the cookstove again.

The kitchen never used to be cold like this, but then Mama never used to spend so much time in bed. Never in the middle of a Saturday morning. Mama would be busy cooking or cleaning while Thelma and Leonard played. Thelma and her brother could always think of something to do, even on rainy days like today. Splash in puddles. Build shelters of fir boughs next to the tall stumps out back. Come inside and play games. Thelma especially liked to read stories to Leonard from her first grade reader.

The rainwater blurred the window. Thelma was glad because then, even with her nose pressed against the glass, she couldn't make out the railroad track in front of the house where it happened. Why did she even want to look? Why was the house always so quiet now? And cold? Why had winter come so early?

She knew why, but what she really wondered was when it would get better. When again would Daddy come home from work, throw open the kitchen door and holler to Mama,

"What's for supper?" When would Mama have supper ready instead of coming out of the bedroom after she heard his step, surprised at how late it was, going to the cupboard and hunting for something to cook? When would they all sit and eat together at the table and talk to each other? When would Mama sing around the house as she used to?

"Telma," Mama said, startling her by suddenly coming into the kitchen as if drawn there by Thelma's thoughts. She was putting on her coat. "The ladies insist I join them for coffee this morning. I be back soon." Her voice sounded squeezed. Without looking up from buttoning her coat, she added, "Read a book or color while I'm gone." Then she picked up her umbrella and shut the door quietly behind her.

"Okay, Mama," Thelma said to the closed door.

Thelma moved from the window to the chair at the kitchen table. She rested her elbows on the unwiped oilcloth and her chin in her hands.

Yesterday Mama had been better for a while. Mrs. Craig had knocked on the door and asked them to come see her pet pig, the runt of the camp litter, she called it. Mama didn't want to go, but she dressed and they went.

Mama had smiled and even laughed a little when Thelma had trouble hanging on to the squealing, squirming baby. She hated to put it back into the box behind the stove when it was time to go, especially since Mama had acted like she was enjoying herself. And when they got home, Mama's sick headache came back, and she went into the bedroom and shut the door like she'd been doing since Leonard died.

Thelma straightened up tall in her chair. Her thoughts began to race. Maybe if she had a pig, too! She could take care of it. Play with it. Read to it. She jumped to her feet. "I'm going to get myself a pig!" she said aloud to the empty room.

She grabbed her jacket from the hook behind the door and ran from the house and down the track. Daddy said it was a mile to the company pigpens, but it didn't seem that far when she ran. Daddy also said, she now remembered, slowing her steps a little, that she must never, never go to the company pens alone because she would have to cross the high railroad trestle, and what if a train came along!

Besides, the mother pig could be dangerous if anyone came too close to her babies. Thelma quickened her steps. She would do it anyway. She had to do it!

It wasn't raining as hard now. The oily, wet ties were slick, but not too slick. Daddy was wrong about the trestle. It was easy to walk across it alone, as long as she held out both arms for balance and looked at the ties ahead and not between the ties to the canyon below.

When Thelma reached the end of the trestle, she could see the pig pen and hear the muttered grunts of the pigs.

She held her breath as she hurried closer. Part of the bad smell came from the garbage the bull cook emptied into the feeding troughs after the loggers finished their meals in the cookhouse. The camp fed the pigs well, Daddy said, because all the men liked pork chops and bacon. Thelma didn't like to think of that.

The pigs squealed louder when she leaned over the top board of the pen. It was easy to count the piglets because they were all lined up at their mother's fat belly having their dinner. Would it be all right to take one of them, Thelma wondered as she watched them nurse. There were so many, the mother wouldn't miss one. Neither would the camp, she was sure. After all, they had given one to Mrs. Craig, she reassured herself as she climbed over the top of the pen and dropped onto the trampled straw.

The heavy sow turned her big head toward the intruder in the corner. Slits for eyes blinked open, wide rubber nose snuffled, pointy feet pawed at the straw as she heaved herself to her feet, scattering squealing piglets.

Thelma knew she had to hurry. She looked for the smallest pig. None was as small as Mrs. Craig's. Any piglet now. She grabbed for one. It squealed and ran. They were all racing, like ants did when she poked their hills with a stick.

The sow's loaded underside dragged the straw as she turned toward Thelma. Thelma grabbed for a piglet and caught it by its tail. She scooped it up into her arms and held it against her chest, like she had held the runt.

The sow snuffled, kicked her hind legs and pushed off toward Thelma. Thelma backed against the fence, turned and scrambled over the top board just as the sow hit the fence. Thelma leaned against the outside of the rail to catch her breath. She had her pig!

It was raining harder now as Thelma and the squirming piglet approached the trestle. The wet surface of the ties reflected the grey of the clouds. She blinked the rain splatters from her eyes and thought of Mama. She wondered when Mama would stop crying and things would be right again. She remembered that Mama had smiled when she saw Mrs. Craig's pig. This would be Thelma's pig but for Mama, too.

She stopped at the edge of the trestle and shifted the pig to her other arm. She remembered her dad's warning about the trestle, but she knew there would be no trains until the end of the day when the men rode home from work. And she'd be careful.

She didn't have two free arms for balance now, but holding the pig tightly with one arm she stretched out the other arm and stepped onto the trestle. The pig clawed the air, scrambling for freedom. Thelma grabbed it with both hands, rocking on one tie until she regained her balance. Then she reached out cautiously with her foot until it rested on the next tie. She paused there, straddling the open drop below until she could breathe again. For a minute she wondered if she could really cross this trestle holding on to this squirming pig. She had to!

The pig continued to scratch the air and twist in Thelma's arms. One razor-sharp hoof caught Thelma's jacket and ripped the cloth. Another hoof dug long scratches on the inside of her wrist. The pig felt heavier now than when she started. Her arms tingled. She held on tighter. One careful step. Then another. She could hear the swollen river tumbling over the rocks below.

A few more feet and they would be across. The rain pelted down. The pig was as slick as the ties. Thelma wished its smooth little body had a collar or a handle or something to hang on to. If she squeezed too hard, it might squirt right out of her arms and into the canyon below. The piglet buried its head under Thelma's arm, probably too scared to look. And then they were across.

Now it didn't matter that the ties were slick. They were set deep in the gravel railroad bed and if she slipped, the worst that could happen would be landing on her seat on the wet ground. Thelma gripped the piglet and ran the last half mile home.

"Mama, Mama, look what I got!" she called as she ran up the back steps and opened the door. "Look, Mama!"

The house was still cold. The corner that held Mama's umbrella was empty. Mama was still at coffee.

She dropped to the floor and cradled the pig in her lap, rocking it gently, touching her cheek to its damp snout. From where she sat, she reached a towel and rubbed the piglet dry like Mama used to do with her after her bath. They wouldn't wait for Mama, she decided. They'd go find her.

Rainwater squished in her shoes as she ran out to the front porch. She looked down the length of the track at the row of houses. On a porch at the far end of the row, a cluster of open umbrellas touched edges, like black mushrooms growing out of the forest floor. Thelma tucked the warm, dry pig under her jacket and ran. Mama will be so happy to see us, Thelma told the piglet between breaths.

Thelma pushed the umbrellas aside with her foot to make her way to the front door. Holding her bulging jacket tightly against her with one hand, she knocked on the door with the other. She could hear the chatter. She knocked harder. She heard someone say, "Now who could that be? We're all here." Laughing. Then the door opened.

"Well, Telma! Come in!" Everyone turned to look at her. "Why, you're all wet. Soaked through, it looks like. What..."

"Mama..."

The pig slipped. Out from under the jacket, it slid. It hit the floor, feet spinning. It squealed. The ladies squealed. It ran, tipping over a table with a coffee cup on it. It shot between Mrs. West's feet and back across the room.

"Telma!" Mama shouted above the confusion. "Where did you get the pig?"

"From the pigpen, Mama. It's going to be our pet!" Thelma lunged across the room and grabbed the piglet.

"From the company pigpen?" Mrs. Box cried. Thelma tucked the pig back under her jacket. "She stole a pig from the company pigpen!" she said to the ladies.

No one spoke. Thelma buried her face in her jacket. She felt very tired and alone. Then Mama was at her side. Thelma felt her wet hair being gently pushed back from her forehead.

"Mama," she started again. "It can be our pet, like Mrs. Craig's. We can keep it in a box behind the stove," the words tumbled out. No one else spoke. She didn't want to cry so she held her breath.

"Telma," Mama said quietly as if they were alone in the room, "Mrs. Craig was asked to take care of the runt of the litter. It would have died. It wasn't getting enough food because the mother had too many babies," she explained. "We just can't—"

"But, Mama," Thelma interrupted, "I could play games with it and read stories to it, like I did with Leonard. Please, don't you see?" She clutched her bulging jacket and bit her lip.

Mama looked at the scratches on Thelma's wrist.

"It's okay, Telma. I can see," she said. "When Daddy gets home from work, he can go with you to take the little pig back." She helped Thelma to her feet.

"Then while you're gone," Mama went on, "I'll build a fire in the cookstove and when you and Daddy get back, we'll sit down to a nice supper."

Someone patted Thelma on the shoulder. She didn't look to see who it was, but it didn't matter because Mama was holding her like she used to. The little pig could go back. She didn't need it now.

CHAPTER 9: SPRING AND SUMMER 1925

Roughneck

Spring helped. It had been a long, bleak, joyless winter, but this morning Tilda saw tiny, green buds sprouting on a little bush next to a stump in their back yard, and a robin tugging a fat angleworm out of the rain-softened ground. It was raining now, but the drops were soft, gentle, almost warm. Grass had begun to poke up at the edge of the railroad bed, she noticed, as she hurried down the track toward the bunkhouses.

Work helped, too. This was her third Friday of changing the beds at the bunkhouses. Matt Johannson, the bedmaker, had pneumonia and probably wouldn't be back on the job for a month, they told her. She was glad to do it because she needed to keep busy. And, besides, the fifty cents she earned for each day's work could be put away towards their trip home to Finland.

For some reason, losing Leonard made her miss her family more. Her father, and Ivar. Ivar's oldest boy Birger would be nine now; Edvin, eight; and Ture, six. She would like to see them, and her sister Alma in Massachusetts and her boy. Charlie said they could stop and see Alma on their way to Finland. Tilda was so thankful that at least Ida lived nearby.

She picked up her step when the rain started to come down harder. She should have brought her umbrella. "Mrs. Lind," John Westbloom called from his filing shack by the track. "You're in a hurry this morning."

"**God morgon**," Tilda smiled. "You're working with the door open today."

"Ya, I like to smell the spring rain. By the way, that little girl of yours is really something!" He showed his gold tooth when he smiled. Always friendly. He kept an extra chair in his shack for anyone who stopped by to talk. The children especially liked to drop in after school and watch him sharpen the big saws and axes.

"Ya, she's always busy," Tilda said. "Kind of a tomboy, I'm afraid. But we are trying to learn her to be a lady. She hasn't been around bothering, has she?"

"No, I get a big kick out of her. She's no trouble."

"That's good. Well, you have to excuse me now. I'm helping out in the bunk houses, you know," she called over her shoulder as she hurried down the track.

She opened the bunkhouse door and stood for a minute until her eyes adjusted to the dim light. Some of the small windows were partly covered by the bunks that ran the full length of the long, narrow room. The light from the oil lamps hanging from the rafters didn't reach very far, but she could make out the heavy, wool work socks and patched long underwear hanging next to the big, pot-bellied stove in the center of the room. She could smell drying wool mixed with the odor of stale tobacco and the shoe grease loggers used to waterproof their caulk shoes. Tilda decided she'd better leave the door open for a while.

An accordion and a fiddle were sitting by the table next to the door. A tablet and pencil, playing cards, and a checker board lay on the table. Books with bent covers and copies of the *Police Gazette* had been dropped on the caulk-shredded, wood floor next to some of the beds. Loose change and dice were scattered on shelves above the bunks. She'd heard that loggers liked to gamble in their spare time.

"So you're here already," Pete, the bull cook, called from the far end of the bunk house. He was sweeping up cigarette butts and sawdust. Tilda couldn't understand why a man who cut wood and filled woodboxes, washed bedding, fed the pigs, and swept out the bunkhouses was called a "bull cook." Charlie said it was probably because in early camps his first chore in the morning was to feed the oxen they used in logging, but you'd think he'd be called something else now in modern times.

"Say, that girl of yours sure can handle herself," Pete said. "No one will ever get the best of her!" He leaned on his broom as if he'd already put in his day.

Tilda pulled the sheets off the first set of bunks and piled them on the floor. Funny, she thought, this was the second person today to mention Thelma.

Tilda shook the clean, folded sheet out over the bed and let it float down onto the mattress. The sheets were more grey than white, but the loggers had it good now compared to what it used to be. She'd heard Charlie say that when he first logged, he slept on wooden planks with straw-filled mattresses. Loggers went on strike over their living conditions, and now most of the camps had bunk beds with coil springs and real mattresses. And for a dollar a week they had maid service to change the sheets. Charlie said the boys were getting spoiled, living such a soft life, but she knew he was only joking. Everyone knew a logger's life was anything but easy. She tucked in the corners of the sheet and blanket and hurried on to the next bunk. She couldn't waste time talking to the bull cook with Thelma coming home from school at three.

"Mom, I'm home!" Thelma called, slamming her books on the kitchen table. "Leonard West came home with me and we're hungry!"

"There's coffeecake in the cupboard and milk in the screen box. **Var så god**," Tilda said.

"Big Leonard's been teaching me to wrestle," Thelma said as she took a giant bite of the cake.

"It's not polite to talk with your mouth full," Tilda reminded her.

"She learned to wrestle real quick," Leonard said, reaching for his second piece of coffeecake. He was a year and a half older than Thelma, but they were in the same grade and about the same size. He never invited Thelma to his house after school because his mother was so particular about her house. She was afraid they would track in mud. Tilda sighed. If only Little Leonard were here now to track in mud...

"Want to watch us wrestle, Mom?"

"No, Telma, I been gone all day and now I have to start supper. You two go out and play. Just come home right away when I call you."

"Hey, Thelma, let's go to the timekeeper's office and spend our nickels," Big Leonard said, reaching into his pocket. "I've got two."

"I've got four nickels," Thelma said, beating him out the back door.

"Telma," Tilda called. "Where did you get money?"

They didn't hear her. She'd have to talk to Charlie about spoiling Thelma. Giving her money to waste on candy!

Sundays the camp moved at a different pace. The boys in the bunkhouses slept in and then strolled over to the cookhouse to eat a late breakfast. They talked to each other while they ate, something they didn't have time to do on a workday. They gave each other haircuts, shaved, and trimmed mustaches. They read the Sunday paper—the comics and sports, news about logging accidents, strikes, bootlegging. They talked about the new President, Calvin Coolidge, wondering what he was going to do about crime.

Some tired of talking politics and played their musical instruments—the fiddle, accordion, a harmonica or two, and maybe a jew's-harp. The fiddler would tune up and take the lead, and someone sitting on the edge of a bunk writing a letter would tap his foot in time to the music. No one offered to sing in the middle of the day. That came at night after a few bottles of home-brew or smuggled whiskey. The young whistle punk ignored everyone and read his Bible next to a window.

All of this didn't fill their needs, or their day off. By noon they'd be looking for some excitement. That's when they'd slide their change off their shelves and lay their bets.

"What time do they get here?" one asked.

"Any time now," another answered, looking toward the open door. The young boy put away his Bible and reached for his change.

"Charlie, call Telma," Tilda said. "Dinner is almost ready."

Charlie laid down the newspaper, stretched, and headed for the door. He couldn't see her from the porch, so he started down the track past the houses.

"**Goddag**, Charlie," Ole Johnson said, falling into step. "You on your way to the wrestling match at the bunkhouse?"

"**Nej**," Charlie answered. "I'm busy with other things."

"Well, I guess I know who you're betting on," Ole said, punching Charlie in the ribs with his elbow.

"I don't keep track of bunkhouse doings," Charlie said.

Ole looked at him. "Well, just listen. You can hear the boys cheering from here. Come on. Let's take in the match."

Charlie shrugged and fell into step with Ole as they strode down the track and along the wooden walk next to the bunkhouses. Might as well see what's going on, Charlie decided. They pushed their way through the crowd of men inside the door until they were close enough to see.

"Godalmighty! What's this!" Charlie hollered.

"Hi, Dad!" Thelma panted, running over to him. "Look how much I made today!" She held out a sweaty hand to show him three nickels. Her curls stuck out in tangles and the bib of her overalls was ripped. "I beat three times and Big Leonard only beat once."

Big Leonard slowly pulled himself up from the floor.

"They give the winner of each match a nickel," Thelma explained. "Want to watch the next match, Daddy?"

Charlie wasn't listening. He grabbed Thelma by her arm and hustled her out the door and down the track towards home.

"Tilda, you got a job on your hands," Charlie said as he burst into the kitchen with Thelma in tow.

"I have lots of jobs already," Tilda said, wiping her forehead with her apron.

"Well, here's a real job!" Charlie said, still gripping Thelma by the arm. "We got to do something about this roughneck!"

Chevie Surprise - June

"Mama, is Daddy going to buy a car today?" Thelma asked, plopping down on the sofa between Tilda and Ida where she'd be sure to get her mother's attention.

Ida laughed. "How many times has she asked you that since you came to Shelton this morning?"

"Too many," Tilda said. "Especially since I don't know the answer. Charlie talks about buying a car when they finish the road to camp, but that won't be for a while yet. He just wanted to see what the Chevrolet dealer here in Shelton had to offer. He'll do lots of looking before he buys something as expensive as an automobile."

"Too bad my Charlie is working. He likes to look at new cars, too, even if we're not in the market for one."

"Well, is he or isn't he going to buy a car?" Thelma persisted.

"He's not buying a car today, Telma. Go see what Artur's doing." Tilda gave her a boost off the sofa and a gentle shove toward Arthur's room.

"Tilda, I want you to see my rose garden," Ida said, jumping to her feet. "I think I could put on my own rose parade right here on Hillcrest. Remember when we were working as maids in Portland and the people gave us the morning off to go see the rose parade? I didn't think there were that many roses in the world."

That seemed like a lifetime ago to Tilda, instead of just eight years. Sometimes she wished she could turn the clock back and relive those carefree years when they first came to Portland. Like when she and Ida and other Swedish girls who worked as maids had Thursday afternoons off and gathered at the soda fountain on Washington Street to drink malts and gossip. Or when they went to the Vasa Order dances on Saturday night to meet and dance with handsome Swedish boys who'd also immigrated to America. Or when they took the streetcar to Council Crest with their dates and rode the ferris wheel and ate cotton candy.

But if she turned the clock back, she wouldn't be married to Charlie now, and she wouldn't have Thelma or...the memories of Leonard. No, in spite of the pain of losing a child, she would never trade away the five years God had given them with Leonard. Tilda sighed. She could feel her headache coming back. So many headaches...

"Tilda, come outside," Ida repeated. "My roses are beautiful this year."

Tilda followed Ida past neatly trimmed shrubs and tidy flower beds, around the corner of the house to her rose garden. Pink, yellow, deep-red roses bordered the backyard fence. Delicate buds and full blooms balanced on long stems   Tilda walked from one bloom to another, touching and breathing in their beauty. The pain of losing Leonard was assuaged more easily now, like in this rose garden, and for this she thanked God.

"We go in now," Ida said, always in charge, like when they were growing up. "I want you to see the bedspread I'm crocheting for Artur. It's for a big bed so he'll have it when he's grown up and married."

As they stepped in the back door, they saw Tilda's Charlie walk in the front door. "I'm back," he said. "Come outside a minute, both of you. I want to show you something."

Tilda and Ida followed Charlie out, but Arthur and Thelma were already at the street racing back and forth in front of a shiny, new automobile. Charlie propped one foot on the running board and reached around behind him to pat the side of the car door, like it was a young palomino he'd just ridden off the range. He smiled and waited.

"Charlie," Tilda gasped. "You didn't buy this car, did you?"

"You damn right I did," he answered.

"But, Charlie," Tilda protested, "I didn't know you were going to buy a car today!"

"I didn't either, but the dealer that showed me around was so polite, I didn't feel I could go out without buying something," he said with a wink at Ida.

Ida laughed at Charlie's joke, Thelma opened the back door and climbed in, Arthur ran around the car two times and then climbed into the front seat to blow the horn. Tilda stood and stared at the car.

"Daddy, what's this?" Thelma asked from inside the car. "There's one on each side?" She pointed to the polished metal receptacles hanging on the door frames.

"Those are vases. Ida, run pick some flowers for our vases so when we drive home tomorrow, we will look like the President and his family."

It was Thelma's turn to honk the horn.

"But, Charlie," Tilda said, "we still have no road to camp. Where will we keep the car?"

"I was going to tell you. I rented one of the garages in that bunch between Hoodsport and Potlatch. It's close to Phoenix rail line, so we just ride the train to Potlatch and then walk one mile to pick up our car. And if the train isn't running, we can walk down from camp. We done that before," Charlie smiled. "When the road to camp is finished, they'll build garages so close to the houses, we'll think we live in the city." He patted the car again.

Tilda turned to Ida. "When we moved to camp, we didn't have a house. Now Charlie gets a house for the car before he even gets a car. What do you think of that?" she laughed. Then she became serious. "But, Charlie, you don't know how to drive!"

"I drove here from town, didn't I? The dealer showed me which pedals to push and where the emergency brake was, and here I am. You'll see how good I drive when we go home tomorrow."

Charlie had no trouble starting the motor the next morning. The salesman had shown him how to crank the car if he needed to, but the day was warm and all he had to do was pull out the choke and turn the ignition key. But then every time he stepped on the gas to move ahead, the engine died.

"Did you take the brake off?" his brother-in-law asked.

"No, by George, I forgot that."

"Always have to take off the emergency brake before you step on the gas," the brother-in-law said. The new car owner grudgingly thanked him, told Tilda and Thelma to hurry up and get in and then stepped on the gas, hopping and jerking his way down the street, gripping the steering wheel as if his palomino might buck him off.

Charlie was not a patient man, but he began to feel better as soon as he drove out of the Shelton traffic and onto the open highway toward Hoodsport. He reached his garage without a problem and drove the car safely inside.

Thirty-seven years old and his first car, Charlie ruminated as he locked the garage door. Well, he would enjoy it more because it was so long in coming. And he'd be a real celebrity in camp. No one he knew had this fine an automobile. The men would be asking him all about the car, asking for rides, wanting to sit behind the wheel.

When they arrived back in camp, Bill West was waiting.

"Word travels fast," Charlie laughed.

"Ya, Westbloom was in town and saw you drive out of the dealership. He said it was a greenish-blue Chevrolet with a black top and black fenders. Is that right?"

"Ya, and a shiny, chrome, hood decoration," Charlie answered. "It has a sun shield above the windshield, and vases for flowers on the inside door frames. I think Rockefeller himself would be proud to drive this car."

West shook Charlie's hand and congratulated him again.

"Tilda, more good news! We are really coming up in the world!"

"Charlie, what is it?"

It had been a good week. Tilda had caught Charlie's excitement about the new car. She enjoyed hearing him tell their friends about it, promising them rides to the canal for picnics when the camp shut down over the Fourth of July. They would never ride in a car as nice as this one, he told them. And now he had more good news?

"What do you miss most from the Ballard house?" Charlie asked.

"The inside bathroom! You know that." She didn't even have to think about it.

"You know the three painted houses at the far end of the row? Well, one of them is going to be empty in another week, and Superintendent Carlson said we can have it."

Tilda held her breath.

"It has an inside toilet—and a bathtub! Carlson thought the new foreman should have that house," Charlie grinned.

"Charlie, what are you saying? An inside bathroom, with bathtub!" She collapsed into a chair, and then straightened up like she'd sat on a pincushion. "Foreman!" she exclaimed.

"Ya, Tilda." Charlie couldn't stop grinning. "Carlson needed a new foreman at the side where I'm working, and he offered me the job. I'll be hook tender now, in charge of the yarding and loading crew. Brings in a little more money, too. We can build our savings for the trip to the old country we've been talking about. And—"

"**Goddag**." It was West at the open back door. "Vilma and I just got back from Shelton, and I came right over to tell you. We bought a car, too."

"Glad to hear it," Charlie said and walked to him with his outstretched hand. "Congratulations. I guess we're all moving up in the world. So what kind did you get?"

"Chevrolet. Two-tone Chevrolet."

"Is that right? What colors?"

"Greenish-blue with black roof and fenders."

"That right!" Charlie repeated.

"Ya, it's exactly like yours, even the hood decoration and the vases. Figured I couldn't go wrong if I got the same car as you. I'm on my way to the bunkhouses to tell the boys about it. Thought I'd offer them rides to the canal for clam digging." He started for the door. "By the way," he said, smiling widely, "I rented the garage next to yours so we can be neighbors there, too." He waved as he jumped off the porch and strode down the track.

Charlie stood silent a moment, then slammed the door. He looked at Tilda and shook his head. "Can you beat that. That damn West did it to me again! Anything I have, he's got to have. For two cents I'd—"

"Never mind, Charlie," Tilda said, hugging him hard around the waist. "The Wests still don't have an inside toilet!"

Halcyon Days of Summer

"No, West! Get out of the back seat! Jacobsons are riding with us this time. Take your own damn car!"

"Okay, Charlie, if you say so! But Vilma don't like to get our car dirty."

Charlie had to help Mrs. West out of the back seat. A little flesh on a woman looked good, but Mrs. West had too much! Too much nerve, too. Both of them! Well, friends are friends.

"Tilda, hand me the picnic basket and get in the car. Jacobsons, there's room now. Telma," he hollered as he walked around to his side of the car, "hurry up so we get to the beach before the sun goes down."

Charlie knew he was being grumpy, but the morning was already half gone. He wouldn't have needed to holler at Thelma though. She and her friend Irene were already in the back seat ready to go.

They had ridden the speeder out of camp to pick up the cars and drive to Hood Canal for the day. They would dig clams first, and then wade in the cold, salt water to rinse the mud off their feet. The women would spread a white table-cloth over the smooth, tide-polished rocks and lay out their lunches. Seagulls would swoop low and squawk for hand-outs. The children would toss them crusts of bread while the grownups stretched out in the sun, dozing a little as they listened to the gentle lapping of the water on the beach. Now that Charlie owned his own car, they could go to the canal often, and they did.

Sun-drenched days followed one after another, trailing behind them long, warm evenings. There was time enough after work to go fishing or swimming in nearby lakes, or to picnic with friends and to pick berries. Even Tilda, often irretrievably desolate that first winter without Leonard, responded to the warmth and beauty of the mountain summer and joined in the activities.

The children celebrated summer, too. School was out and camp kids were thirsty for adventure. They climbed through the jungles of railroad trestle beams high above the canyons. They stood close to the railroad track waiting for the fireman on the lokey to blow steam at them so they could run and scream and then wave back at the engineer when he laughed. Sometimes older boys dared each other to dash under the railroad cars one more time before the train started to move.

Younger kids found high banks to slide down and towering trees to climb up. They were Tarzan when they swung to the ground on compliant branches and Goliath when they mounted their stilts from the top of a stump and clomped around after each other. They built forts from logging debris and stashed rocks inside them for protection against the enemy, whoever that might be. Sometimes they went hunting with stick rifles, alert for that monstrous black bear hiding behind the next stump.

At dusk all the children played kick-the-can and hide-and-seek, and at dark, when they couldn't see the cans or find the hiding places, they became G-men, tiptoeing around the corners of the houses to spy on anyone who stepped out on his porch for a smoke or was walking home from a card game at the bunkhouse. Finally, mothers appeared, silhouetted in lamplighted doorways, calling their children to get into the house this minute or they'd come after them with a switch.

Then on some warm evenings when the children were finally in bed, the grownups would gather on a porch to talk and smoke and watch the moon drift lazily across the fluorescent sea of stars.

"Understand the honey-farm girls are moving their bees to the canal."

"Ya, I heard that, too. Dam's about finished. Guess the power company plans to start flooding the valley in October."

Cigarette smoke drifts and curls into the darkness.

"They say the lake will be ten times the size it is now."

"And Camp Cushman, what's left of it anyway after Phoenix moves out, will all be under water. Hard to imagine!"

"They say Phoenix won't be getting all the trees out in time. Some good timber will be going to waste under the lake."

"Well, Tacoma Power won't budge on their deadline."

A bullfrog croaks in the distance.

"So how's the hook-tending going, Charlie? Had to fire anyone yet?"

Charlie smiles. "Not yet."

"Anyone been to Hoodsport for a haircut lately?"

Everyone laughs.

"Well, when a logger don't have a wife to cut his hair, he can't be too particular. Oscar was never trained, but he's the only barber we got. And when he's too drunk to stand up, he still gives a pretty good haircut."

"Ya, that's true, but did you hear Olaf went to him last week, and Oscar was so drunk that when he was sliding the straight-edge razor across Olaf's face and down his throat, he had to hold on to Olaf's nose to steady himself."

More laughter. Then quiet.

One of the women puts on her sweater.

An owl hoots from somewhere nearby.

"Wonder if my brother in Finland sees these same stars when he looks up at the night sky," Charlie says.

Then talk turns to homes half a world away, and to child-hood escapades. They speak of families left behind, and of parents growing old without them. Finally come expressions of wonder that they who grew up in neighboring villages in Finland but never met, should end up in the same little logging camp in the northwest corner of America.

Letter from Ivar

August 28, 1925

Dear Tilda,

I have received bad news. Our sister Alma died on August 2. She was forty-one. Her husband Johan did not say in his letter what caused her death. Their boy Eskil, who you knew as a baby before they moved to America, would be about twenty now. We corresponded when they first emigrated, but then we got careless about writing.

You wrote that you wanted to go through Massachusetts to see Alma when you came to Finland for a visit, so I know this news is disappointing to you. She was thirteen years older than you, so you didn't know her well and perhaps you remember her as being harsh with you and Ida. But she was young herself when Mother died and she did her best with you until Father remarried.

Father and Kajsa are well. The boys missed being with them every day when four years ago we moved to the western part of the village. But Birger and Edvin are old enough now to run see them on their own, which they do most Sundays. Kajsa gives them long-milk and bread to eat which is a treat. Kajsa seems to take well to the grandchildren and shows none of the cruelty you and I remember. Perhaps she, too, was struggling with how to care for a sudden family during such desperate times.

I mention only Edvin and Birger running to see their grandfather and Kajsa. Ture does not run with them because of a physical problem. Ester and I have grieved over his disability, but we remind each other that he is a sweet child and is never happier than when he finds ways to please us. He may never live on his own, but the whole village cares about him, so he will do well. I have come to realize that there is much in this life that we cannot understand but must accept. Perhaps this is a truth that you, too, are learning to live with.

We hope you will soon have enough savings to make the trip home. We all want to see you and meet Charlie and Thelma. She is seven now, if I calculate right, so she and our boys can have a good time playing together.

Write to us soon, and often. We must never lose touch with each other as we did with Alma.

Your brother Ivar

Tilda held the letter open on her lap. Why was she crying? She hardly knew Alma. It would have been nice to see her sister, like it's nice to visit a distant relative, a **små-kusin**, but she hardly ever thought about her. Maybe that was it. She, too, had lost touch with Alma when Alma and her family moved to America, and now it was too late. She wiped her eyes with her apron hem.

Tilda reread the letter. Forty-one was too young to die, but her time must have been up. God's will. Ivar said there was much in life we weren't meant to understand. You live with what comes. Like with Leonard. She and Charlie had to accept his death and go on. They had Thelma to think about now. She was smart and headstrong and needed lots of correcting. It wasn't going to be easy raising a girl in a rough logging camp.

CHAPTER 10: THELMA

The Red Dress - December 1925

"Ida, I'm so happy you and Charlie and Arthur are spending Christmas in camp with us this year," Tilda said, helping them off with their coats. "I hope you weren't too uncomfortable riding the train from Potlatch."

"No, we knew it would be a cold ride, so we bundled up good," Ida said, "and Artur liked riding on the logging train. We're just glad that Charlie's mill shut down for a few days so we could come."

"And you made it in time for the Christmas party at the dance hall tonight," Tilda said. "Did Charlie bring his fiddle?"

"Ya, he did—"

"**Moster**, come see the red dress Mama made for me," Thelma interrupted, taking Ida's hand and leading her into the bedroom. She pulled aside the closet curtain. "Mama, take my dress down so **Moster** can see it."

"My, it is beautiful," Ida said, feeling the material. "Wool, isn't it? So fine. A real Christmas dress, all right. Are you wearing it to the dance tonight?"

Thelma looked at her mother. "Please, Mama, can't I go? I've stayed up late before. Please let me—"

"No, Telma, we've already talked about it," Tilda said. "You and Artur will be in bed asleep by the time the party starts. Anyway, I made the dress for you to wear Christmas Eve and Christmas Day. Not tonight. Now go play with your cousin."

Tilda gave Thelma a little push out the bedroom door and then hung the dress back in the closet. "I don't know, Ida.

Thelma is a handful. She gets her mind set on something and it's hard to talk her out of it."

Ida nodded absently. "Will they be all right here by themselves while we're at the dance?"

"They won't really be alone," Tilda answered. "'Edit' next door will look in on them. And Telma knows to go to Nelsons if she wakes up and needs something. But we'll make sure Artur and Telma are asleep when we leave."

Tilda took a box of matches from the dresser drawer and lit the lamp on top of the dresser. She put the matches back and turned the wick up. "It gets dark so early now I feel like I'm burning the lamps most of the day. Wish we had electricity like the bunkhouses."

"When did they get electricity?" Ida asked.

"Two months ago. The company fixed them up with a generator, but it doesn't have enough power for the family houses, too. Maybe when the dam is finished we'll all have electricity. I'll be glad to be through with coal oil lamps."

"Ya, they don't give very good light."

"It's not that," Tilda said. "I worry about fire. Naturally, we don't let Telma light the lamps, but I'm nervous even when I carry a lighted lamp across the room."

"I can see the fire danger, all right, if you should happen to trip."

"Well, we're going to be in danger if we don't start the potatoes cooking for supper," Tilda said. "You know our menfolk," she laughed.

Mama turned the lamp down low when she tucked Thelma and Arthur into bed after supper, but still Thelma couldn't go to sleep. It seemed like bedtime came kind of quick! Probably Mama wanted them to go to sleep early so they could leave for the dance. Well, Arthur was asleep, but she was wide awake. Arthur was hogging the covers. She'd give him a kick, but he would holler and get her into trouble. Boy cousins could be a nuisance sometimes, especially if you have to sleep with them!

Thelma thought about her dress. Wish Mama had left it out where she could see it. She had helped Mama pick out the cloth last time they were in Shelton. When they got home, Mama made her stand real still while she pinned a newspaper to her, and then Mama took her big scissors and cut the newspaper to fit. Next, she laid the newspaper pieces on the cloth, and cut around them. When she sewed the pieces together, like magic, Thelma had a dress. Mama was a good sewer.

But once, Thelma remembered, things didn't turn out so good. Winter was just starting, but it was awful cold outside, so Mama sewed her a pair of bloomers out of an old coat. One afternoon when Thelma came home from school, Mama was having a coffee party. As Thelma walked into the front room, Lillian's mother, Mrs. Box, grabbed Thelma's skirt and pulled it way up and said, "Look at that, ladies. Bet you never saw bloomers made from a wool coat before." Then she laughed and laughed. Thelma couldn't remember if anyone else laughed because she ran into the bedroom and slammed the door. Mama didn't make her wear those bloomers after that.

Thelma looked at the closet and sighed. She sure wished she could put on her red dress and go to the dance.

"Shhh," Ida whispered. "They're both asleep."

"Like little angels," Tilda said. "If Artur sleeps as sound as Telma, you can be sure we won't hear from them till morning." Tilda blew out the lamp. "We can go now," she said, and they tip-toed out of the room.

Thelma was glad they left. Keeping her eyes squeezed shut for a long time was as hard as holding her breath too long, but she didn't want them to know she was awake. That would spoil her plan. She wished Mama hadn't pulled down the shades and blown out the lamp. Even with her eyes open now, the room was black. But she knew where the matches were and could find them even in the dark.

"Charlie, don't forget the flashlights," Tilda said as she slipped into her coat.

"Do we need flashlights when the moon is so bright?" Ida's Charlie asked.

"Ya, we do," Tilda answered. "The dance hall is across the trestle, so we have to shine a light right on the ties. It's a long way down to the river if we make a misstep."

"I guess you know what you're talking about," Ida's Charlie said and picked up his fiddle and the extra flashlight.

They closed the back door carefully behind them so as not to wake the children. Tilda led the way across the yard to Nelson's back door. "I want to stop here and check once more with Edit'," Tilda said, "and maybe Nelsons would like to walk with us to the dance, if they haven't already left."

Mr. Nelson came to the door. "Sure we walk with you. Mrs. Nelson will be ready in a minute. Can you sit down and wait?"

"Ya, we wait," Charlie said.

The kitchen was warm and smelled of Mrs. Nelson's Christmas baking. "Better take off your coats or you'll be cold when we go outside," Mr. Nelson said. "Say, Charlie, has Telma won any wrestling matches lately?" he smiled.

"**Nej**, we put a stop to that. She was good though, wasn't she?" Charlie laughed.

"Charlie, that isn't funny," Tilda scolded.

"What's she doing now when you won't let her wrestle?" Mr. Nelson asked good-naturedly.

"She's learning how to throw," Charlie answered. "You know the Lathom kid? Laurence? He's teaching her to throw, straight and hard. She can hit a can on a stump, dead center." He took a sip from his glass. "She's getting good! If it comes to a contest between them, I'm not sure who would win."

"He's a lot older, isn't he?" Mr. Nelson asked.

"Just a year, but he's much bigger. Got a long arm on him, too, but she could end up as good as him. When Telma decides to do something, there's no stopping—"

"Here I am," Mrs. Nelson announced as she and Edith came into the kitchen. "I'm sorry to keep you waiting. My hem came out of my dress just when I thought I was ready, so I had to sit down and sew it again. If I'd done it right the first time, I wouldn't have had to do it over," she laughed. "Edit' helped me or I wouldn't be ready now."

"Edit' is so good at those things, isn't she," Tilda said. "I try to interest Telma in sewing or some kind of handwork, but she just wants to run around outside—"

"Stop worrying about Telma," Mrs. Nelson said. "She's got her own ideas now, but she has a good head on her shoulders. She'll figure it out..."

Thelma figured it out. She'd get the matches out of the dresser drawer and light the lamp, like Mama did. She'd lift the glass chimney and lay the lighted match on the wick until it caught fire. She'd blow out the match and put the chimney back on the lamp. Then she'd push a chair and carry the lamp into the closet so she could see behind the curtain, climb onto the chair, and take down her dress.

"Well, what are we waiting for?" Mrs. Nelson smiled. "Let's go!"

Everyone found coats, hats, and mittens, and Tilda reminded Edith to check on the children.

"Too bad the dance hall isn't on this side of the trestle instead of a mile on the other side," Ida said, running to keep up. "We'll be too tired to dance when we get there."

"**Nej**, it's just far enough to get the circulation going," Tilda's Charlie said, and they all moved into a comfortable stride.

Ida took Tilda's arm. "Remember Christmas last year, in Shelton?" Ida asked. "When your Charlie dressed up like Santa Claus and came to the door and asked Artur his name?"

"I remember. Artur started stuttering and said, 'Wa-wa-wa-what was it now, Mama?'"

"That's right," Ida laughed. "Well, I don't think we can fool him this year. He's asking lots of questions."

"Ya, he's growing up," Tilda said. "And Telma is, too. She's still headstrong, but she minds better than she used to."

Ahead frost glistened on the trestle ties. "We better take hold of arms to cross," Mr. Nelson said. "It looks pretty slick. Wouldn't want to lose one of you ladies."

"Just so my fiddle makes it," Ida's Charlie joked as he took Ida's arm.

With the moon shining over their shoulders and flashlights marking off the ties, they crossed the trestle without difficulty and hurried toward the lights from the dance hall windows in the distance.

"Not much farther. I can hear the music," Mr. Nelson said. "That should help us step along."

Soon they could hear the stamping on the wood floor and the laughing. "A schottish," Tilda said. She knew they were late but it didn't really matter. It was all she could do to last a whole evening anyway. She had to really step to keep up with Charlie's long legs on the dance floor.

"After you, ladies," Mr. Nelson said with a bow as he opened the door to the dance hall.

"Thank you," Ida laughed. "You boys are treating us like we were your first dates."

Ida's Charlie followed them in and then hurried over to the corner to join the accordion player and the fiddler. Tilda looked around the room as she took off her coat and laid it on a bench with other coats. It looked like all the married folk in camp were there and some couples from Hoodsport, too. Some of the bunkhouse boys were standing together by the food table and some others next to the wood stove. They were smiling like they were having a good time, even if there were no single girls to dance with. Ida laughed and poked Tilda and pointed at two young loggers putting on a show by dancing together.

Everyone was dressed up. Clean shirts, bright suspenders. Some of the men wore bow ties. Looked like Mrs. Jensen had a new dress. Tilda could see the Wests and the Boxes and the Warners—

"God-in-heaven, Charlie! Look at that!" Tilda exclaimed.

"Look at what?"

"There! In the middle of the dance floor."

"I'll be damned! It's Telma! Dancing the polka with Irene Jacobson! We leave her home sound asleep and she beats us to the dance!"

"Hi, Mama! Hi, Daddy!" Thelma called to them and waved without missing a step.

Tilda waved back weakly and sat down on her coat. What next, she wondered as she watched the red dress whirl among the dancers.

The Runeberg Dance - June 1926

Thelma raced Arthur for the front seat, but Arthur won. Thelma wanted to sit between her dad and uncle, but, she decided, the back seat was all right, too. She could sit next to the window and watch the trees fly by. And she could listen to Mama telling **Moster** about their bad morning.

"Can you believe it, Ida," Mama was saying, "that after Gabe went to the trouble of bringing a handcar up to camp from Potlatch last night for us to use today, Wests got up early and took the handcar themselves. So we had to walk the three miles to our garage in Hoodsport carrying our suitcase."

"Well, maybe they didn't know the handcar was for you," **Moster** said.

"They knew, all right. We told them yesterday about our plans to go to the Runeberg dance in Olympia today. They knew what time we were leaving this morning. When we got to the track and the handcar was gone, we knew what happened. They'll have some excuse when we see them at the dance," Tilda sighed.

Moster shook her head and laughed. "Well," she said, "you've had your exercise for today. I guess you can thank Wests for that."

Thelma hadn't minded the walk. She'd pulled sword ferns and thrown them at imaginary bears until Mama made her stop. She'd wanted to chase a rabbit that hopped across the trail, but Mama said to try to stay clean for the Runeberg doings. Thelma had tried, but when they got to Shelton, Mama looked at her and said she had to wash her face and arms and legs all over again.

Thelma spread her full skirt out around her on the car seat. Sometimes she liked being dressed up, even if it was a lot of bother. And it pleased Mama because Mama wanted her to be a lady. She folded her hands in her lap like Mama and **Moster** were doing. There were lots of ways to do this. She could lace her fingers together or lay the left hand over the right or the right hand over the left. Thelma had noticed that Mrs. West always laid a handkerchief in her lap before she set her hands down. Mama said it was because she was heavy and her hands sweated a lot.

Thelma never did tell Mama the game she and some of the other camp kids played after coffee parties. They would sneak into the front room the minute the ladies left and feel all the chair seats. They would see who could find Mrs. West's chair first. Mrs. West's chair was always the hot one because she was so fat.

Thelma smoothed her dress over her knees with her hands and then folded them in her lap again. Mama made this dress, too, like her Christmas dress, only she sewed this one for Easter. It was blue and soft and when she lifted the skirt up in front of her face, she could see light through it. Mama said ladies don't do that, so she only did it once.

One reason she liked dressing up was because it meant something special was happening. Like today. They'd picked up **Moster** and Uncle and Arthur in Shelton and were all going to the Midsummer Festival. Mama said that each year the Runeberg Lodge decorates a pole with leaves and flowers and everyone plays games and sings and dances around the pole. Daddy said that in Finland the party lasts all night because it never gets dark there in the middle of the summer. Daddy said this party wouldn't last that long, but they would have a good time. They would sit down for a nice program and then dance and eat and visit with other Swede-Finn people who came from miles around. There would be kids her age, too, Mama said, and she would get acquainted with them in no time.

She patted the bow on the front of her dress and felt for the matching bow in her hair. It was still there. She sat back in the seat carefully so the dress wouldn't wrinkle too much. She was looking forward to the party as much as Mama and **Moster** were. She knew they were really excited because they took so long to curl their hair and powder and rouge themselves.

The hard chair in the Runeberg Hall wasn't as comfortable as the back seat of the car, and Mama had to tell her to sit still three times during the program. The speeches were long and a lady in a sparkly dress sang so high that Thelma covered her ears until Mama made her put her hands down.

"Ladies and Gentlemen, wasn't that a great show!" a man in a shiny jacket announced from the stage. Everyone clapped. Mama poked her, so she clapped, too. "And now," the man went on, "if the ladies and boys and girls will move to the edges of the hall, the men will fold up the chairs and clear the floor for dancing." Clapping again. This time Thelma joined in without being poked.

"And while the musicians are tuning up, the ladies on the refreshment committee are excused to go to the kitchen and bring out the food for the **smörgåsbord**." Then, louder yet because everyone was moving around, the shiny man shouted, "The best is yet to come!"

Thelma hoped so.

She and Arthur stood and watched the men pick up the chairs and, quick as a wink, snap them flat. Then clack, bang, the men piled the chairs on top of each other in the corner of the room. It looked easy. Thelma took hold of the front of a chair and pulled it up. It worked. She and Arthur folded two chairs flat, slid them across the floor, and started their own stack.

"Hey, you! gimme those chairs!" someone shouted, the voice cracking like that of the eighth grade boy in her school. Thelma turned around and saw a tall boy, like Laurence Lathom only fat. He was peering down at them over heavy cheeks and double chins.

"These are our chairs," Thelma said. "We folded them."

"They're not your chairs!" the boy said, circling Thelma and Arthur, sizing them up. "I said gimme those chairs!"

"Why should we?" Thelma asked.

"Because I want them, that's why! Gimme them or else!"

"Or else what?"

"Or else I'll take them," the boy sneered. He brought his fists up in front of his face and danced a little step like Thelma had seen loggers do in fun on Sunday afternoons.

Thelma watched him wave his fists. She clenched her right hand and stretched her arm back as far as it would go. Then she swung her arm in a big half-circle until her fist landed, splat, in the middle of his face. His knees wiggled, and then his whole self fell backwards like a tree in the woods.

Thelma smoothed out her dress and straightened the bow on its front. The boy picked himself up and walked away without looking back.

"Come on, Arthur," Thelma said. "Let's fold some more chairs."

Arthur followed her, looking over his shoulder at the boy. Other people in the hall were looking, too, Thelma noticed, but she didn't see Mama. Mama must have been helping in the kitchen and Thelma was glad about that. She would have hated to disappoint her again.

The Rock Fight - August 1926

"He's going to kill me!" Thelma screamed as she ran into the kitchen, grabbed her father around the waist, and spun around behind him. She peeked out from under his arm as her assailant bounded after her.

"What's going on here?" Charlie exclaimed.

"She hit me with a rock!" Laurence shouted, "and I'm getting even!" He drew his arm back to pitch the rock.

"No you don't," Charlie shouted and pried the rock loose from Laurence's grip. "I thought you two were friends. Didn't you learn Telma how to throw?"

"I did, but she's not playing fair," Laurence said, his face flushed and grimy, a trickle of blood showing at his hairline.

"It was an accident," Thelma protested.

Charlie pulled Thelma around in front of him and gave her a shake. "Haven't we told you to quit this rock fighting?"

"But I didn't mean to hit him! I threw a rock over the wood-pile and he was standing where it landed!" Thelma said, facing her father, her face blotched and dirty. "Mom," she said, turning to Tilda, "it really was an accident—"

Tilda jumped as Laurence lunged again at Thelma and Thelma darted out of reach. With one hand Charlie grabbed Laurence by the back of his shirt collar, and with the other, the straps on the back of his overalls. He turned Laurence towards the back door and sent him scrambling onto the porch and down the steps into the dusty yard.

"Just you wait till my cousin Art gets here," Thelma screamed after him. "He'll fix you good!"

"I'll fix you good, young lady, if there's any more fighting. It'll be the strop next time. You understand? Now go sit on your bed and think about that for a while!"

Thelma sat on her bed wondering what happened. Whose side were her parents on anyway?

Maybe she had it coming. She had been told often enough to be careful when she threw rocks. That it was dangerous. Someone could get an eye put out, they told her. There were other things to do in camp besides throwing rocks, they said.

But she did those other things, too. She liked playing dolls with Louise Box. They dressed them up and took them for rides in their doll buggies. And Wayne and Oliver Hamilton helped her and Louise build houses for their dolls. She did lots of things besides throwing rocks.

But she still liked playing with Laurence! He was older and stronger and could throw a rock farther than anyone. But, she had to admit, he scared her a little, too. Like today. And once he dragged Lillian Box to the railroad track and pounded her head on the rail, but Lillian probably had it coming.

Thelma swung her legs back and forth from the edge of the bed and then stopped to examine a scab on her knee. Bored with this, she stretched out on her bed and studied the green ceiling boards. She liked this house a lot, even if it was painted green inside and out. Probably the company had only one can of paint.

Guess maybe she shouldn't have thrown the rock over the woodpile. But even if she knew he was there, she didn't know the rock would hit him. The game was to throw rocks till you pinned the enemy in his fort or made him leave his fort and run for safety. She didn't mean to hurt him. But now that Laurence was planning to get even, she was glad she had thought of her cousin.

Moster, Uncle and Art were coming to camp on Saturday, and Art was a good fighter for being only five years old. He had licked her more than once. He scratched and clawed and pulled her hair till she had to give up. When Laurence met up with Art, he'd be sorry he chased her into the house with a rock!

Art arrived at camp with his parents in time for mid-morning coffee. As soon as the grownups sat up to the table, Thelma signaled Arthur to come outside.

"...and now he's going to get even with me," Thelma said in a hushed voice. "We were both throwing rocks, so why should he be so mad? So I told him that my cousin Art was coming to visit and you'd beat up on him."

Art listened carefully. Then he rose to his feet, flexed his arm muscles, expanded his chest, and looked down the track. His voice was deeper than normal when he asked, "Where is he?"

It was mid-afternoon when they finally spotted Laurence in front of his house with his little brother Kenneth. Thelma could understand why Mama liked Kenneth so much. Like Leonard, he had yellow hair and played with his toy cars in the dirt. Thelma heard Mama tell the ladies at a coffee party about the time she was hanging out her wash and Kenneth came up to her and tugged at her skirt. "Mrs. Lind," he said, "you're the fastest lady in camp." Her friends laughed, but Thelma didn't think Kenneth meant to be funny. He'd just noticed that Mama was always the first one on Monday mornings to hang her wash on the line. Grownups laughed at the strangest things.

Kenneth was playing in the dirt now, but Laurence wasn't paying any attention to him. He was throwing rocks at a tin can on a stump. Even from a distance, Thelma could see he hit the can almost every time.

"Let's go," Thelma whispered, and they started down the track, Art in the lead—eager, unafraid. Laurence must have heard them coming because he abruptly turned in their direction.

"I brought my cousin Art," Thelma said, darting ahead of Art to stand in front of Laurence.

Laurence didn't answer. Kenneth stood up to watch.

"My cousin's from Shelton," Thelma announced, "and he's here to beat you up."

Art stepped around Thelma and placed himself directly in front of his adversary. The top of Art's head came to the middle of Laurence's chest. Laurence looked down at Art and snorted.

Art looked up into Laurence's narrowed eyes. He stepped back to look again. He saw Laurence's doubled-up fists and wide stance between the rails. Neither spoke. Art took another step away, turned slowly, and walked back down the track the way he had come.

Thelma was disappointed, but she couldn't help admiring her wiry little cousin. Art was not only a good fighter when he wanted to be, but he was smart. He'd figured out real quick that fighting someone that much bigger would be a mistake, no matter what the reason.

Milky Eyes - March 1927

Tilda dropped the sheets, towels, and long underwear into the steaming boiler. She pushed them down with the heat-bleached broom handle, grown fuzzy from its weekly soakings, and then turned to the sink to scrub the stains out of the knees of Thelma's overalls. First, bar soap. Then, up and down on the washboard. She sang in Swedish to the rhythm of her scrubbing.

In a few minutes she was back at the stove, lifting the wash out of the water with the same stick and dropping it into the empty tin tub on the floor. She slid the boiler to the back of the stove so the wash water would cool down for Thelma's school clothes and her own housedresses and aprons. Charlie's work clothes and her cleaning rags she set aside for the last boiler load.

Tilda bent over the steaming wash in the tub on the floor, wrung the water out of each piece and dropped it into the big wicker clothes basket. Straightening up and stretching her back, she walked to the window, pulled aside the curtain, and wiped the steam off with her hand. It was starting to get light outside but rain still poured down. She'd have to hang the wash on the back porch and in the kitchen again instead of on the lines out in back where the breeze made everything smell fresh like the mountain air.

Tilda looked at her hands against the white curtains. They were scalded red from wringing out the hot clothes. Washday was hard work. Still, she liked washing clothes. Maybe because it felt good to make everything clean for the week, or maybe because the steamy-hot kitchen reminded her a little of the saunas back home.

Tilda hummed softly as she picked up the tall Quaker Oats box full of clothes pins and the loaded laundry basket and started for the kitchen door. She liked washdays—

"I hate washdays!" Thelma exclaimed, stomping out of the bedroom in her bare feet, her school clothes bunched under her arm..

Tilda turned and looked at her daughter. Nine years old in another month. Where had the time gone?

"Everything in the kitchen is wet," Thelma said. "Even the air is wet!"

"It's just steam," Tilda reminded her.

"I don't care what it is! Everything is foggy and drippy and I can't see through my glasses. What's the good of wearing glasses if I can't see through them? And look! I'm standing in a puddle of water!"

"Well, the wash drips on the floor when I take it out of the boiler, but it's nice soapy water and I mop it up when I'm finished. That way the linoleum gets a good washing once a week too, just like the clothes," Tilda smiled, putting down the basket and reaching into the cupboard. "Here's a towel for your feet."

Thelma piled her clothes on the table and sat down to dry the bottoms of her feet. She slipped out of her pajamas and into her undershirt and long underwear bottoms. She drew her panty-waist vest with the dangling garters over her undershirt and then started to work her long stockings over the underwear to meet the loose ends of the garters.

"When's it going to be spring so I don't have to wear all this stuff?"

"The calendar on the wall says it's spring now," Tilda said, "but it's still winter outside."

When the stockings looked smooth, Thelma slid off the chair and stood up carefully. Tilda waited for the explosion.

"Mom! They're doing it again!" Thelma cried and stamped her foot.

"Never mind, Telma. The stockings are bound to wrinkle at the knees when you stand up."

Thelma wasn't listening. She tugged at the top of her stockings and refastened them to the garters. Then she sat down and slowly stood up again.

"Mama!" she cried, stamping both feet this time, "I can't go to school with wrinkled knees!"

Tilda sighed. Why was her daughter so particular! "You'll forget about it when you get to school," Tilda said quietly.

"And my hair is frizzing up from all the steam!" Thelma wailed, putting both hands on her head.

"My, you are cranky this morning, Telma," Tilda said, getting impatient.

"Well, maybe I wouldn't be so cranky if—if I had a baby sister!" Thelma shouted, her chin thrust out at her mother.

Tilda sat down. Here it came again. She and Charlie had talked about having a baby, but they just didn't know. The pain was still so deep from losing Leonard, and life in a logging camp was so uncertain, so full of danger, and it seemed like they had their hands full raising one child.

Thelma's day at school had not gone well. They couldn't go outside for recess because of the rain. Her best friend Irene told her she was moving to Potlatch when school was out. And now Thelma had come home to a jungle of damp clothes hanging all over the back porch and kitchen.

She hung her wet coat on the nail behind the door and batted her way through the clothes into the front room. She'd just forget it all and read her book! She liked to read. She used to read to Leonard a lot. She plopped down on the davenport and opened her book at the marker.

"Telma, come in here," her dad called. "I want to show you something."

Thelma set her book down, surprised that her dad was home from work and the afternoon was gone. She ran into the kitchen in time to see him open his lunch bucket. Usually he just set it down for her to open. It was a game. She and Leonard would look for left-over cookies, and when they found one, Dad would say he didn't know how he happened to miss it when he ate his lunch.

"Look here, Telma. You, too, Tilda."

Thelma pulled the lunch bucket closer so she could see inside. Instead of a cookie, a ball of feathers rested on the bottom of the pail. Then, before she had time to think about it, the ball moved and two big, milky eyes looked up at her.

"Daddy, is it an owl?" Thelma whispered.

"Ya, that's what it is," he answered. He'd found it at the foot of an old burned-out snag, he told them. There were feathers all around as if the mother had tried to fight off a hawk. The baby must have fallen out of the nest when its mother didn't return.

Charlie picked up the owlet. It was half as big as his hand. Thelma touched it gently. Its feathers were so soft she couldn't feel them against her fingers.

"What you think, Telma?" he asked. "Think you can take care of this baby owl till it's old enough to take care of itself?"

Thelma couldn't believe her good luck. A baby owl all her own! She'd find a little box and make it a bed of leaves, or maybe moss. She could hardly wait to tell her teacher and the kids at school.

"What do you children know about owls," Mrs. Comfort asked the class when Thelma had finished telling about the owl.

"They eat fresh meat," Laurence said.

"They only see in the dark," Harold said.

Mrs. Comfort interrupted. "Laurence is right about their food, but, Harold, owls can see very well in the daylight, too. They hunt in the night because it gives them an advantage over their prey," she explained.

Irene raised her hand. "I heard that owls turn their heads all the way around."

"That's a myth, too," Mrs. Comfort said. "It looks like they do, but the owl really turns its head just three-quarters of the way and then snaps it back so quick you think it has made a complete circle."

"I have a question," Lillian said. "If Thelma really has a pet owl, why didn't she bring it to school so we could see it?"

"Because it's too little," Thelma exclaimed, forgetting to raise her hand. "When it gets a little bigger, you can all come to my house and see it."

Thelma had trouble concentrating on her lessons the rest of the morning. When lunch time came, she dashed home to look for grubs to feed her owl. She turned over rocks and pushed pieces of rotting wood aside and started filling a jar with anything that moved—except the garter snake she found behind the woodshed. She decided it was too big for the little owlet.

Even the little bugs were hard for the baby owl to swallow until Thelma used Mama's tweezers to put the food down the tiny bird's throat. It's talons were needle-sharp, and Mama had to put iodine on Thelma's scratches. But one day when Thelma put her hand in the box to add more moss, the owlet fluttered up and perched on her finger. The next day it flew out of the box and lit on the back of Thelma's chair. Before long it was flying up and landing on her dad's shoulder. But

Thelma knew it was really growing up when its milky eyes turned clear, like Mrs. Comfort said they would, and when darker, stiffer feathers started to grow under the soft, white baby feathers. It was then that Thelma decided her baby was old enough to have company.

Edith and Irene came first.

"I'll let you pick him up if you are very careful," Thelma told them. "He's still very young, you know."

"We know," Irene said. "We'll be careful."

Thelma placed the owlet in Irene's cupped hands and Irene rubbed her cheek against its soft feathers. Edith held it next. She petted it carefully and then gave it back to Thelma to put into its box.

"You are so lucky to have such a beautiful pet," Edith said. Irene nodded in agreement.

The next day at school, Thelma invited Louise Box to come see her baby owl.

"I'm coming with her," her sister Lillian said.

Thelma hesitated. Her stomach knotted.

"It's only fair," Lillian persisted.

Thelma shushed the girls as she led them into the front room. The owl heard them and fluttered out of its box and onto Thelma's shoulder. Louise petted it lightly.

"It's beautiful," she said. "So-o-o-o soft!"

Thelma walked around the room with it on her shoulder to show Louise and Lillian how tame it was.

"My turn," Lillian said and grabbed the owl from Thelma's shoulder. "I want to give it a ride, too." She held the baby owl in one hand out in front of her and spun around.

"Don't move so fast!" Thelma said. "You'll scare him."

"No I won't," Lillian said, with another quick spin.

"Stop!" Thelma cried. "You're making him dizzy!"

"Watch this!" Lillian pumped the owlet up and down as she twirled across the room. "Whee! Watch how it can fly!"

"Give me back my owl!" Thelma cried and grabbed Lillian's arm.

"Okay, if you're going to be selfish. Here!" she said, thrusting the owl into Thelma's hands.

Thelma carried the owlet against her cheek to the box and placed it carefully into its nest. The owlet tipped over onto the moss.

"It's dizzy," Louise said.

Thelma gently stood it up again and then noticed that its feather-fuzzy white head was drooping onto its breast.

"Mama!" Thelma screamed. "Something's wrong! Come quick!"

Tilda ran into the room, picked up the owlet and touched her finger to its breast. She felt of its neck. Thelma held her breath. After a long minute, Tilda said, "Telma, I'm afraid your baby owl is dead."

Thelma's hands flew to her mouth. Louise gasped and stepped back. Lillian glanced at Thelma's face and disappeared out the door.

Thelma took the baby owl from her mother and cradled it in her hands. She lifted it to her face and stroked its soft head with her cheek. She placed the warm, still bird gently on its nest of dry moss. Then she sat down at the table, laid her head on her arms, and sobbed.

"Baby" - June 1927

Thelma pushed her doll buggy along the tracks, dodging loose rocks so she wouldn't upset Baby. She'd tried wheeling her doll buggy between the tracks, but the ties were too bumpy, even with gravel packed between them. She wheeled around a boulder and then stopped to tie Baby's bonnet. She was tucking in the blanket against the afternoon breeze when she heard the ladies.

"Well, if it isn't little Thelma with her doll buggy," Mrs. Box said. "So who do we have in the buggy today?" she laughed, elbowing Mrs. Craig. "You know she told Louise that when she grows up she's going to have a million kids?"

"How is your baby today?" Mrs. Craig asked, smiling, not laughing like Mrs. Box.

"Just fine," Thelma said. "I have to keep her covered so she won't catch cold." She reached under the hood of the buggy and made another quick tuck.

"Let me see her," Mrs. Box said. She leaned over the buggy and jerked back the blanket. Baby leaped out and ran for home, trailing her bonnet in the dirt. Thelma turned the buggy around and raced after her cat.

When Thelma reached home, Baby was waiting for her on the porch. Thelma lifted her onto her lap, apologized for Mrs. Box's rudeness, and fitted the bonnet back on her head. Baby's face was beautiful, Thelma thought as she stroked her cheeks. At times Thelma almost believed her kitten was a real baby, like Carolyn Warner.

Mrs. Warner had lots of kids so she let Thelma take two-year-old Carolyn home whenever she wanted, and sometimes Thelma pretended Carolyn was her baby sister. She told Mama she liked bathing Carolyn because she could really see the difference. She liked washing Carolyn's tangled hair and then brushing the yellow strands into ringlets.

Mrs. Warner gave Thelma one of Carolyn's outgrown baby dresses and a bonnet for her doll. Thelma dressed up her doll and wheeled her up and down the railroad track, pretending it was her baby sister. Sometimes instead of dressing the doll, she dressed her cat Baby in the same clothes, like today, and Baby didn't mind at all.

Thelma stroked her kitten's back, listening to her purr, remembering how Baby came to her. Not long after owlet died, Daddy came home and told her and Mama that a stray cat had just had kittens next to the stove in the filing shack. Mr. Westbloom had asked her dad if he knew anyone that might like one of the babies after it was weaned. They could come by and pick one out any time, he said. Daddy asked Thelma if she could think of anyone who might want a kitten, and then, she remembered, he winked at Mama.

It was easy to decide which one she wanted. It was the one with the long, yellow hair, snowy-white chest and feet, a nose that was half pink and half black, and a face that really looked like a baby's.

Daddy said Baby acted more like a dog than a cat. She followed Thelma everywhere, even into the garden when Thelma had to wade out to pull last year's carrots for supper. Where the rain water was too deep for Baby to walk, she swam behind Thelma. Mama said Baby would have followed her to school if she didn't keep her in the house until Thelma was out of sight.

The cat stretched out across Thelma's lap, purring louder than ever. Thelma loved Baby, but she knew it wasn't the same as having a real baby. She'd have to talk to Mama about that again.

Thelma swept Baby off her lap and was getting up to go find her mother when she heard the whistle. She counted. Six blasts. Before she could move, she felt Mama's hands on her shoulders, and they stood and waited until they heard the speeder. In another minute the speeder was in front of the house, and Daddy was jumping off the little car and hurrying into the house without speaking. His face was as white as Baby's paws. Thelma's knees felt skinny as she followed him and Mama into the house.

"Charlie! You all right?" Mama asked.

"Another close one," she heard her daddy say. His hands were shaking. "Another damn widow-maker. A green limb big around as the biggest part of my leg."

"What happened?"

"Bill Johnson was standing right next to me when we heard the limb crash down through the branches. Before we could move, it hit."

Mama sat down beside Daddy.

"It lit on Bill's shoulder, and..." Daddy shut his eyes.

"And?" Mama whispered.

"The damn thing tore his arm off!"

Mama shook her head and twisted her hands in her lap. "Will he be all right?" she asked in a small voice.

"We think so, but he lost a lot of blood before we got him packed off to Potlatch, and it's hard to say how he'll be by the time they get him to Shelton. One thing we know. He's through logging." Daddy made a coughing noise. "A man can't log with one arm."

Daddy's hands were shaking when he reached down to unlace his caulk shoes. Mama got up and pulled the coffee pot to the front of the stove and then went to the cupboard for the coffee bread like she always did when Daddy came home a little early. When Mama sat down again, Thelma edged over to the kitchen table and sat with them. They didn't talk until they both held coffee cups in their hands.

"Sometimes, Charlie, I don't know how I can go on living like this," Mama said. "Every day, scared I'm going to hear the six blasts of the whistle and it will be you that..."

Daddy nodded and blew on his coffee. "I been pretty lucky."

"That's what worries me. What if your luck runs out?"

Daddy didn't answer. He and Mama sat so quiet Thelma could hear the alarm clock ticking in the bedroom. Then Baby jumped into Thelma's lap and helped fill the quiet with her loud purring.

"Tilda," Daddy finally said, "we been sitting here brooding, and what good does it do? We know logging is dangerous, but that's what I do. I log. And I watch out and hope for the best." He took a sip of his coffee and then looked Mama right in the face. "And you're a logger's wife and you have to do the same. Hope for the best." He reached for a piece of coffee bread.

Thelma reached for some coffee bread, too, but she saw Mama's face squeeze up. Thelma held her kitty close. She guessed she wouldn't talk to Mama today about a baby sister. She'd just do like Daddy. Eat coffee bread and hope for the best.

Swaggering - June 1928

Thelma learned to swagger. It was easy. She just watched the loggers. She wasn't supposed to hang around the bunkhouses, but sometimes on Sunday afternoons she would sit on the timekeeper's steps across the track from the bunkhouses

and watch. Some loggers played music, some boxed or
wrestled, some sat in the sun and read magazines, but there
was always someone who walked around, swaggering.

Swaggering wasn't just taking big steps. Daddy took big
steps, but he didn't swagger. Swagger was when you rocked
side to side with each step, bent your elbows away from your
body, and swung your arms as you walked.

Mostly, Thelma noticed, it was the young men who swaggered. Daddy said some of the young loggers weren't dry
behind the ears, and yet they thought they were really tough
just by putting in an honest day's work in the woods. Daddy
said they'd open their lunch buckets at noon and brag to each
other about how close they came to being killed. The older
loggers just walked away when the younger ones started brag-
ging and swaggering.

One man told about four young loggers in B.C. who dared
each other to ride the logs that slid end-first down steep sid-
ings. Daddy told Mama that he rode a log once, but it wasn't
on purpose. He was climbing over the log when it started to
slide. He lifted his feet and rode it half way down the sidehill
before it ran into another log and stopped. Daddy knew that
if it had started rolling instead of sliding, he would have been
under it and that wasn't something he liked to think about,
much less brag about.

Some kids swaggered. Laurence Lathom's desk at school
had gotten too small for him, so some days instead of going to
school, he'd go fishing. Thelma would see him swagger down
the track right past the school with his fishing pole on his shoulder. When she told Mama about it, Mama said that that was
Mr. Lathom's problem, but Thelma must never do it. Thelma
guessed Mama meant to never swagger because Mama knew
Thelma liked school too much to miss that.

Mama never swaggered. She ran. Once Thelma tried to
outrun her. Mama was going to give her a licking for something she'd done. Thelma could run faster than any kid in
camp, but she couldn't outrun Mama. Mama caught up with
her before she reached the filing shack and gave her the licking, but Thelma didn't mind getting spanked because she was

so impressed at how fast a thirty-two-year-old lady could run. Laurence's little brother was right when he said Mama was the fastest lady in camp. But Mama never swaggered. She said it wasn't ladylike.

Mama was running right now. Thelma could see that over the edge of her mush bowl. Mama was running back and forth across the kitchen and into the front room and bedroom and back again. She had to run to finish the packing in time. The dishes and the lamp chimneys and anything else that would break had to be wrapped in newspaper and put in boxes or drawers because today the lokey was going to pull their house onto the flatcar to take them to their new camp.

"Hurry and finish your breakfast, Telma, so you can help," Mama said.

Thelma found it hard to hurry mush. She never did like it, but Mama said it was good for her and made her eat it. Moving day was always exciting so she tried to poke the mush down fast.

She thought of the day the excitement began. She had been sitting on the front steps waiting for her daddy to come home from work so she could check his lunch bucket. She'd laid her ear on the track a couple of times before she finally heard the rumble of the train and knew he was on his way. When the crew train came chugging up, moving slow in front of the houses, Daddy hopped off.

"Moving day's next week," he called to Mama as he sat down on the back porch to take off his work shoes. Thelma took his lunch pail into the kitchen and opened it to look for cookies.

"That don't give us much time," Mama said.

"Well, we knew it was coming," Daddy said as he unhooked the laces at the top of his caulk shoes and then loosened them the rest of the way down. He turned his shoes upside down and banged the dirt out against the edge of the porch. He walked into the kitchen in his stocking feet.

"And where is it we're going this time?" Mama asked.

"About five miles north of here," he said. "We'll be right above Lilliwaup. An easy three mile hike to the highway this time if we get snowed in." Daddy sat back in his chair and looked around for his coffee. "Lower Camp One is being shut down and the whole shebang moved to Upper Camp One."

"Then we get to keep this house?" Mama asked. "I've gotten used to having a bathroom again."

"Ya, we keep the same house, and this time when we get settled, I'm going to build a long back porch with a bedroom at one end for Telma."

Thelma dropped the half-eaten cookie back into the lunch pail. Her own bedroom! She slammed the lunch bucket shut and ran out of the house to tell her friends.

That had been a week ago. Any minute now the locomotive would be hooking a cable to the front end of the skids under their house and pulling it onto the flat car. No wonder Mama was running. Everyone in camp was running. The young loggers wouldn't have time to do any swaggering today.

The men worked all day to load the bunkhouses, the schoolhouse and all the family houses. Finally, just before dark, their own house was pulled onto a flatcar. The lokey would start its long pull to the new camp in the morning.

Thelma looked at the stirred-up dirt and weeds where the house had sat. "Mama, where are we going to sleep tonight?" she asked.

"In our house, like always," Mama laughed. "We won't be cooking, but we'll have some bread and milk and then we'll go to sleep in our own beds. Everything will be just the same."

Thelma looked up at their house. Sitting on its skids on the flatcar, it looked as high as the second floor of the Shelton Hotel. Pale grass and spider webs hung down from its floor planks and dirt clods stuck to the bottom of the skids. She had been six years old the first time the train moved them, but she didn't remember ever seeing the underside of the house, except sometimes when she crawled after Baby, and then it was always dark under there.

"Look at this," Mama said when they climbed onto the flatcar and into the house. "I forgot to pack the coffee pot and it rode on the stove right where I left it. This move was smoother than it looked," she laughed.

Mama laughed a lot lately. Thelma guessed she must like moving because she hummed and sang a lot, too.

It was still light outside when Mama tucked her into bed, but the days were long now, so it probably really was bedtime. But something was wrong with her bed. She kept sliding to the foot!

"The house is sitting high on one side," Mama laughed, "but it's all right. Just hang on." She started to leave the bedroom, but stopped. "I'm going to tell you something exciting to take your mind off the leaning bed," she said, pushing Thelma's hair back with her soft, cool hand.

Thelma held her breath. What could be more exciting than all that had happened today?

"Two months from now, in August," Mama smiled, "we are going to have a baby in the house."

"Whose baby?" Thelma asked.

"Our baby," Mama said, and kissed her on the cheek.

Thelma pulled the covers up over her head and then whipped them down again. She didn't know what to do. She wanted to jump out of bed and run around the house and holler, but the house was high up in the air on a flatcar. She wanted to run down the track to tell her friends, but she didn't know which flatcars they were on. So she just sat up in bed and hugged Mama real tight and thought of how tomorrow, when they got settled in their new camp, she'd walk down the new track, and swagger a little. She didn't think Mama would mind just this once.

PART V - UPPER CAMP ONE
1928-1931

CHAPTER 11: NEW BEGINNING

A Fast Ride - August 4, 1928

"Is the doctor here?" Tilda asked as the nurse helped her up into the high bed.

"Not yet," the frizzy-haired woman in white answered. "We'll call him when the time gets closer."

"But I'm always so fast," Tilda protested. "Call him now. Please."

The nurse pulled the white sheet and bedspread up over Tilda's expansive stomach. She wrote something on her tablet and hung the paper at the foot of the iron bed. She adjusted her white cap on her tight permanent. "You've got lots of time," she said as she turned around to leave.

"Please don't shut the door!" Tilda pleaded, gripping the rails at the side of her bed, grimacing with a new contraction. But the nurse left and shut the door.

"Don't worry, Mrs. Lind," said a soft voice from the other bed. "I was in here nine hours before my baby came."

Tilda tried to smile at the young woman next to her. "I'm Mrs. Bensen," the woman said. "It will be nice to have someone in the room to talk to. They don't let us get out of bed for ten days, you know, so time goes slow. They bring my baby in every four hours but just long enough for me to feed him. My husband comes during visiting hours in the evening, but that time goes so fast."

Tilda turned her head away and gripped the bed rails while she waited for another contraction to pass.

"Do you live in Shelton, Mrs. Lind?"

Tilda wanted to be friendly though her pains were making it difficult. "We just moved to Upper Camp One. Phoenix Logging Company," Tilda explained. "In the Olympics. But two weeks ago I came to Shelton to stay with my sister because my babies come so fast."

"You have other children then?"

"A girl. Ten years old."

"My, that's quite a spread between children."

"We had a boy—"

"And I have a boy now, too," Mrs. Bensen smiled.

She hadn't understood.

"Bill was so happy when we had a boy. I guess every man wants a son to follow in his footsteps."

Tilda stopped listening. The contractions were getting harder and closer together. The nurse shouldn't have shut the door! What if the birth went bad and the doctor wasn't here, and something happened to the baby...

Maybe she shouldn't be having this baby in the first place. She remembered how upset Ida had been when she told her she was in a family way. Ida said she should get an abortion, that she had no business bringing a baby to the logging camp. The terrible dangers. The isolation. No doctor when the baby gets sick. Managing a new baby in a tiny, three-room shack with no electricity or hot water...

But Tilda hadn't listened. Upper Camp One was better than the first camps. It had its black stumps and snags like the other camps, but she was used to that now. Charlie'd finished building the porches on their house and started the bedroom for

Thelma, so they would have plenty of room. He planned to build a picket fence around the front of the house next summer so the baby couldn't wander onto the railroad track. And Upper Camp One was near beautiful Price's Lake. They could walk there with Thelma and the baby in the evening. Thelma loved to swim in that lake—

Tilda tightened her hold on the rails until another contraction passed.

And they'd met new people in Upper Camp One. John and Anna Carlson, newly married and starting out in their first logging camp, had come from villages not far from her own home in Finland. She'd liked Anna right away. When the train brought Carlson's davenport from Sears, Anna, seven months along and big as a house, jumped up on the flatcar and kissed the sofa pillows. Then she felt foolish and laughed at herself and invited Tilda in for coffee.

She and Anna, both in a family way, talked about being in the hospital at the same time, but Anna beat her by nine days. In a couple days, John would pick up Anna and little Edwin and take them back to camp. She and Anna planned to spend time together with their new babies.

Everything was right for this new baby, Tilda had told her sister. Charlie made a little more money now as hook tender, and Thelma had settled down since she heard a baby was on the way. Phoenix started work on the road to camp so they would soon be able to drive to Hoodsport or Shelton in an emergency.

Another contraction. Harder still. Why didn't the nurse come back and check on her? Tilda had told her how fast her babies came! If only Ida could have stayed with her, but she had to look after Thelma and Arthur. Charlie would be on his way from camp, but wouldn't get to Shelton till evening. Tilda squeezed the railings and prayed that someone would come soon, before she had the baby alone in the bed.

She thought of Mrs. Woodworth. In the spring when her time came to have Mildred, the trestles were out. Chet was working, so she walked the three miles to the highway at

Lilliwaup where they kept their car, and then drove herself to Shelton. At least Tilda was already in the hospital.

Tilda looked from the white ceiling to the white walls. The hospital was new and clean. She'd heard that the doctors and nurses were good, so she shouldn't worry. The nurse said she had plenty of time—

Tilda heard herself cry out.

"Mrs. Lind, are you all right?" Mrs. Bensen exclaimed, raising herself on her elbow.

Tilda struggled to get the words out. "The baby's coming!"

"Oh, Mrs. Lind. What can I do? Nurse!" She pounded her fist against the wall next to her bed. "Nurse, come quick! Mrs. Lind's having her baby!"

Tilda shut her eyes and gripped the railings till her knuckles turned as white as the rails.

Sounds. The click of the nurse's heels. The door opening. Heels racing back down the hall. Mrs. Bensen shouting for the nurse to come back. Her own cries...

Minutes seemed like hours. The door again. She opened her eyes. Dr. Linkletter was bending over her, telling her not to push till they reached the delivery room.

A fast ride, a hard bed, a bright light overhead, permission to push at last, and then the hearty cry of a new life. Tilda cried in happiness and relief. A healthy baby girl had been added to her list of blessings.

Deja Vu

Thelma's little sister was six weeks old now, with dimpled arms and legs just like her baby doll. When Thelma touched the baby's skin, it was like the feathers on the head of her little owlet, so soft she could hardly feel it. The only problem they'd had with the new baby was deciding on her name.

Daddy wanted to name her Jenny because, next to Mama, he loved Jenny Lind, the famous "Swedish Nightingale," best. But Mama said, what if the baby grows up and can't sing?

Then everyone will make fun of her, and he wouldn't want that to happen. When Daddy said he had a beautiful niece in the old country named "Agnes," Mama said that would be fine, and they'd pronounce it the Swedish way, "Angnes,"or "Angie" for short. And wouldn't Leona be a fine middle name...

The first two weeks out of the hospital, they stayed at **Moster's** on Hillcrest. When you have a baby, the doctor told them, you need lots of time and help until you get your strength back, but Thelma didn't think Mama looked like she needed help. She nursed the baby and changed her, and dressed and undressed her in the gowns she'd made, and every morning she gave her a bath in the dishpan on the kitchen table.

One morning when the house was a little cold, **Moster** lit the gas oven in her stove and left the oven door open to warm the kitchen before the bath. Like always, Mama sang to Angie as she moved the soapy wash cloth over her shoulders and stomach and arms and legs. Then Mama rinsed her off and lifted her carefully onto a towel, patted her with another towel, and smoothed baby oil all over her rosy, bath-warmed skin. Thelma loved to watch and so did Arthur, but on this morning, Arthur looked at the round pink shape on the table, all shiny from the oil, and at the open oven door and said, "Let's put it in the oven and cook it!"

Moster laughed first and then Mama laughed and then they both said that with her legs folded up to her stomach, she did look a little like a small turkey, but Thelma didn't think so. She didn't think it was at all funny either. If she had anything to say about it, Arthur would never be left alone with the baby. Thelma was relieved when the two weeks were over and they were safely back in camp.

Now that Angie was six weeks old, Mama sometimes let Thelma give her a bath. Mama told her to make sure her hand was under Angie's head when she lifted her in and out of the bath and that she held her close when she carried her so she wouldn't drop her. New babies can be hurt even if you don't mean to hurt them, Mama said, so Thelma followed all the rules very carefully.

Thelma kept track of all the babies in camp. Warner's Hazel was a year old; Mildred Woodworth was three months; Edwin, two months; and Angie, six weeks. Sometimes on Saturdays when the camp kids ran out of things to do, they'd stop by at the house where the newest diapers flapped on the clothes line. Irene Jacobson and Edith Nelson came by to see Angie every Saturday and sometimes during the week. The Hamilton and Warner kids had come by twice. Louise Box liked to come at bath time. Thelma showed her how to keep the soap out of Angie's eyes and how to wash in all the fat creases. "And don't forget," Thelma told Louise "that you have to support the baby's head when you lift her out of the bath or when you pick her up to carry her."

September was a beautiful month in the mountains. Leftover heat from August warmed the middle of each day, but the edges were crisp and cool and made you run fast and work hard and sleep well. Saturday, one of those special fall days, Louise Box came to the door with her doll in its doll buggy.

"Let's take our dolls for a ride," Louise said.

"Just a minute," Thelma said and ran into the bedroom to find her mother.

"Mama," Thelma whispered when she saw Angie was asleep, "Louise is here. Can I take Angie for a ride in my doll buggy? I'll be very careful."

"The fresh air will be nice for her, all right," Mama said. "Get her sweater and cap out of the drawer, and we'll dress her warm."

The dirt was packed hard next to the house, so it was easy to push the little buggies. Thelma and Louise walked side by side, stopping to tuck in the blankets whenever they felt a little breeze. Thelma wished Louise's mother could see her now. Mrs. Box wouldn't make fun of Thelma when she was pushing a real baby in the buggy. Thelma thought of Louise's sister.

"Does Lillian like high school?" Thelma asked.

"No. She hates it. She says the kids in Shelton are stuck up and won't play with her. She's home today because it's Saturday."

"Where is she?"

"Over there. Behind that stump."

Thelma felt a sudden chill. She reached down to cover Angie. "Why is she behind the stump?"

"I don't know," Louise said. "Maybe she wants to see the baby."

Thelma's skin felt prickly. She wheeled ahead of Louise, but then stopped and sat down on the end of a log. "Tell her she can see Angie if she wants."

Lillian must have heard because she came out from behind the stump and was looking in the buggy before Louise could turn to call her. She reached in and felt Angie's cheek. "She's real all right," Lillian said.

"Of course she's real," Thelma said.

"Can I hold her?" Lillian asked politely.

"Mama doesn't want you to hold her if you haven't washed your hands," Thelma said.

"I washed them," Lillian said.

"When?"

"This morning."

"That doesn't count. It has to be right before."

"Oh, I forgot. I just washed them."

Thelma looked at Lillian. She looked clean. "Okay. But just for a minute," Thelma said. She started to tell her to put one hand under the baby's head, but before she had a chance, Lillian reached into the buggy, grabbed Angie in her blanket, and ran back to the stump.

"Lillian!" Louise gasped.

For an instant Thelma couldn't move. Then she streaked after Lillian. Lillian spun around once with Angie at arms' length and then ran around the stump, holding her out in front of her. Thelma stopped and started around the other way. Lillian climbed on top of the stump and sang in a high-pitched, sing-song voice, "We're higher than any—one. Can't catch u—us."

Thelma froze. She knew she could climb that stump and knock Lillian off in a second, but what would happen to Angie?

Lillian spun around again. Then with the baby under her arm, jumped off the stump, darted to the next stump, and clambered to the top. Thelma ran after her but stood helpless as Lillian held the baby out in front of her and went into another spin. Angie's head wobbled back and forth. Thelma shut her eyes and saw Lillian spinning the baby owl.

"Lillian, you set her down this minute or...or..."

"Or what?" Lillian laughed. She had Angie under her arm again, but now the blanket was hanging loose and Angie's feet were sticking out.

Thelma didn't know "or what." If she chased Lillian, Lillian might drop Angie. Thelma shut her eyes again and this time she saw the baby owl's head lying limp on its chest...

Thelma didn't know she was screaming or how long she screamed, but when she opened her eyes, Lillian was handing her the crying baby and Mama was running out of the house.

"Time to go home," Lillian said to Louise.

"No!" Louise said. She was four years younger than her sister, but she drew herself up tall and said, "You go home."

Thelma held Angie tight and carried her to the buggy. She patted and stroked and comforted her sister, and then laid her down carefully, adjusting the blanket to cover her legs. As she leaned closer to look at Angie's face, she felt Louise and Mama at her shoulder.

"Angie," Thelma whispered. "It's okay."

Angie stopped crying, hiccupped twice, and looked up at Thelma.

"It's okay," Thelma repeated. Angie's chin quivered when she tried to smile.

Thelma laughed and cried at the same time. Mama asked what had happened. Thelma told her Lillian didn't know how to hold a baby, but everything was all right now because she'd gone home. Louise hurried over to her own buggy to check on her "baby."

"Don't drive too fast now," Mama warned as the girls began pushing the buggies.

"We won't," both girls answered in unison.

"I know you'll be careful," Mama smiled. "You are showing Angie such a good time this afternoon."

First Birthday - 1929

The early morning sun filled the kitchen doorway and spilled onto the linoleum. Tilda loved the sunshine. She knew she should feel a little guilty for enjoying it so much when they needed rain, but she was too busy and happy today to worry about the dry spell. She hummed and sang as she cradled the mixing bowl in her lap and creamed the butter and sugar. Tilda would let Angie lick the bowl this time because this was going to be her birthday cake. Angie was one year old today.

"'There's a long, long trail a'winding,'" Tilda sang, *"'Into the land of my dreams, Where the nightingale is singing and my heart sings—'* **Gud i himlen**! Charlie!" she screamed and jumped to her feet, sending the bowl flying. She backed against the cupboard and raised up on her toes to get away. A chicken with half its head cut off was darting back and forth across the kitchen floor.

"Sorry, Tilda," Charlie apologized as he ran into the room and cornered the chicken behind the table. He grabbed it by the legs and carried it upside down with its wings flapping, back to the chopping block to finish the job. "It jerked its head back just as I brought down the axe," Charlie explained when Tilda peeked out the door, "and I threw it before I saw what happened." He wiped his hands on his pants. "Scare you a little?" he grinned.

Tilda managed a half smile and turned back to the kitchen. The bowl had landed right side up and the batter hadn't spilled. She set the bowl on the table, swept up the feathers and mopped up the blood spatters, hurrying to get rid of the mess before Angie woke up.

"Hoover promised us a chicken in every pot and a car in every garage," Charlie exclaimed and looked around the supper table from Tilda to John and Anna Carlson and back to Tilda. "And, by God, I think he can do it!" Tilda wished he wouldn't holler and get so red in the face when he talked politics.

"Well, you have a car in your garage, but from what Tilda told us a while ago, the chicken almost got away," John laughed.

That helped. Everyone laughed. Thelma took a last bite of supper and slid out of her chair to play on the floor with the babies, Angie and Edwin, until time to bring out the birthday cake.

Charlie wasn't through. "Prices have gone sky high, but people think they have to buy anyway. When they don't have the cash to pay for what they want, they put it on credit! Wages aren't going up as far as I can see. How are they ever going to get out of debt? That's the problem."

"I agree with you there," John said.

"People are even borrowing money to buy stocks. So the stock market goes up and up. Where's it all going to end? It's crazy!"

John nodded. Charlie kept shaking his head. Tilda decided this was a good time to change the subject.

"Thelma, bring over the cake and let's start our birthday party," Tilda said, picking Angie up off the floor. Mrs. Carlson lifted Edwin onto her lap.

Both babies tried to help Thelma light the candle, and Thelma helped Angie blow it out. Everyone sang "Happy Birthday," and Tilda poured the coffee and hoped they were through with politics for the evening.

In camp that fall and winter, when people weren't talking politics, they were talking about the weather. No one could remember when they had gone so long without rain. Tilda read in the paper that farmers and ranchers everywhere in the West were suffering because of the drought. San Francisco had barely enough drinking water and Seattle and Tacoma had declared a state of emergency.

"The rains will start in September," a neighbor told Tilda. When September passed without rain, another neighbor said, "Always it rains in October. No later."

October was still dry. "Maybe by Thanksgiving..."

By the end of November, the water level at Cushman Dam was down sixty feet. Charlie told Tilda that a section of the

Skokomish River had completely dried up and forty steelhead trout, weighing sixteen to eighteen pounds each, had to be lifted out of the pool under the power house and taken to a higher lake. Trees that had been under water since the dam was built and the valley flooded, now stuck up high above the surface of the lake like a rice crop in a flooded field.

Cushman Power Plant couldn't put out enough electricity for Tacoma, so the city had to close down its factories and turn off the signs that ran on electricity. They turned their street lights down low and ordered people to burn no more than one light bulb in their homes at night. Tilda felt sorry for city people who were used to electricity and now, suddenly, had to do without.

Tilda had missed having electricity when they first moved to camp, but she soon discovered that the stars and moon shown brighter when there were no street lights, and that coal oil lamps burned with a softer, warmer glow in the evening than any electric light bulb. But the people in the city wouldn't know this, and they wouldn't have lamps.

In the middle of December, Tilda read in the newspaper that President Hoover was ordering the Navy to move its carrier Lexington from the shipyard at Bremerton to Tacoma so they could use one of its generators to light the city. This worked, and the city was grateful. Three weeks later the rains started and the emergency was over. The drought had ended.

The camp people welcomed the first rains, too. It meant the fire danger was over for another year, that streams would soon run full, and that the water level behind Cushman Dam would return to normal. But the celebration was half-hearted. While everyone had been worrying about the drought, something bad had happened to America.

Most people blamed the stock market crash on Hoover. Charlie blamed it on Americans spending money they didn't have. Buying automobiles "on time," and then losing their cars because their jobs ended. Without an income and no savings, they had to go "on the dole." Millions of them, Charlie read, and think of what that was costing the country!

"It's the beginning of a long Depression, anyone can see that," Tilda heard Charlie tell John Carlson over a cup of coffee. "If people didn't spend money like drunken sailors, the country wouldn't be in this fix. If they saved a little out of every pay check, they would have something to fall back on. Put your money in the bank where it's safe, that's what I say!"

Hide-and-Seek - June 1930

"We'll sit outside," Mrs. Hill said, "where we get a little breeze. Such a warm day for June." She wiped her forehead with her handkerchief. "Carl, bring some chairs from the kitchen and we'll sit here in the shade of the house. A chair for Telma, too. My, she's growing up. Tall like her daddy."

Carl brought the chairs and Tilda sat down by her friend. The men stood apart to smoke a cigarette.

"Ya," Tilda said, "she's only twelve, but another year and she'll be moving to Shelton to go to high school. I'm glad I still have a little one at home."

"Angie was just a baby when I saw you last," Mrs. Hill said. "It was time you came to see us." She lifted Angie onto her lap and tweaked her cheek. "I put the coffee on when I saw your car drive up. You must be tired after the long, rough ride from Camp One."

"Ya, I thought that road would never end. This is the first time I've been to Simpson's Camp Four."

"Well, it's like all the other camps. Snags and stumps everywhere you look. But we don't have to look," Mrs. Hill laughed. "We drink coffee and visit, and then we have some lunch."

"You always make us feel so welcome," Tilda said.

"You should see how welcome they make you feel in Finland," Mr. Hill said as he and Charlie joined them. "People there have so little, but what they have, they share. They treat family from America like royalty."

"That's one reason we came today. We want to hear about your trip," Charlie said, "and if you had time to look up our relations? My mother and brother?"

"We wanted to, but time went so fast," Hill said, "and no one had gasoline to take us around. But, Charlie, I did learn a lot about your brother Vilhelm. Did you know about 'Ville's secret'?"

"No," Charlie laughed. "I sure didn't know he had a secret. We don't do much letter writing. I know he started hunting seals when he was fourteen, and he's still at it from what I hear."

"Ya, he is," Hill said. "In fact, he spends six months a year in his small boat out on the water and ice of the Bothnia Sea. Other seal hunters like and respect Ville, but they especially admire him for his marksmanship."

"That don't surprise me," Charlie said. "He was a good hunter on land when we needed meat for our table, but what is his "secret"?

"His secret is his ability to adjust his hunting rifle so it always shoots straight, even in cold, wet conditions on the ice. And Ville is happy to adjust any other man's rifle. All they have to do is ask."

"But why is that called a 'secret'?"

"Because," Hill laughed, "he won't tell anyone how he does it."

Charlie laughed, too. "I would sure like to see my brother. I think we'd get along good."

"You still have family in Närpes, don't you, Tilda?" Mrs. Hill asked.

"Ya, father and brother, and brother's family that I never met," Tilda said.

"Then you should make the trip," Hill exclaimed. "The price for tickets is good now with the depressed times."

"And the years go by so fast," Mrs. Hill added. "We told ourselves that one day father and mother will be gone, and we need to make the trip now. How long have you been in this country, Charlie?"

"Since 1906. I was eighteen when I came."

"Twenty-four years. Just think how your mother must want to see you."

Mrs. Hill gave Angie's cheek another quick tweak. Angie wiggled off her lap and ran behind her chair. Mrs. Hill laughed. "How old is Angie now?"

"She'll be two in August, and she really keeps me busy. She scared us half to death a couple of weeks ago when—"

"Just a minute," Mrs. Hill interrupted. "I'll run get our coffee and then you tell us what happened."

"A couple weeks ago," Tilda repeated when they all had their coffee cups in their hands, "a brush fire started close to camp. All the men left to fight the fire. I was so busy watching from our porch that I didn't notice right away that Angie was missing."

"Oh, my," Mrs. Hill said.

"Charlie had built a picket fence around the yard, but Angie is a climber and must have gone over the gate. All the women and children in camp helped us look."

"Where'd she go?" Mr. Hill asked.

"We didn't know. The trestle and the canyon seemed too far away for a toddler, but when flames started shooting up through the smoke at the edge of the camp clearing, we jumped over logs and ran around the stumps like we were crazy. We looked for twenty minutes, getting more scared all the time."

"Then I found her," Thelma said.

"Where, for heaven's sake?" Mrs. Hill asked.

"Under my bed!" Thelma seemed pleased to have finished the story. "She was playing hide-and-seek with us."

"The girls like to play hide-and-seek," Tilda said. "Thelma hides Angie and has us come look for her. Once Charlie and I looked and looked till we had to give up. Thelma had hidden her inside Charlie's work pants that were hanging on a hook behind the bathroom door. Angie was clear out of sight straddling the crotch of the pants like it was the crotch of a tree, and she didn't make a sound till we found her."

"What a monkey," Mrs. Hill laughed. She looked around behind her chair. "And where is she now?"

Tilda jumped to her feet. "Telma, where's Angie?"

"She was right here," Thelma said, instantly alert.

"She couldn't have gone far," Mrs. Hill said. "I'll look in the house."

"I'll check the railroad track," Carl said.

"Telma, help us look out here," Tilda said as she and Charlie fanned out from the house. "Maybe she fell behind a log. Ang-e-e-e," she called.

"She's not in the house," Mrs. Hill hollered from the porch a minute later. "I'm going to put on other shoes and come help you look."

Tilda climbed over a tangle of charred logs, dry brush, and sprawling blackberry vines. "Ang-e-e," she called. She looked at the thick woods on the far side of the logging slash and re-membered searching for Leonard when he was the same age. In no time at all, he had followed a rabbit across the clearing to the edge of the woods. Two-year-olds can move so fast—

"Here she is," Mrs. Hill called from the porch, holding the smiling little girl up high for all to see. "I went into the bed-room to get my shoes, and when I stooped over to pick them up, something under the dresser caught my eye. The toes of two little shoes side by side were looking back at me. I guess she'd been standing behind the dresser the whole time," Mrs. Hill laughed.

Tilda dropped into a chair and shut her eyes. Mrs. Hill patted her hand. "You relax now," she said. "I'll go fix lunch and you think about taking that trip to Finland.

"We'll do it!" Charlie exclaimed. "We won't put it off."

It was Sunday again, a week since they visited the Hills. Charlie must have had Carl Hill's advice on his mind, too.

"Look in the savings book," Charlie said, laying the little blue book on the table in front of her. "Look at the bottom of the page. $5,009.00. We can make that trip to the old country with a little left over for a rainy day."

Tilda couldn't believe what she saw. Five thousand nine dollars! She always tried to stretch the pocket book—shop-ping carefully and taking care of whatever she bought so it lasted. They didn't buy things they didn't need, and some-times they found they could do without things they thought they needed. They were careful with money and saved what they could, but she had no idea they had saved so much.

"This is a good time to go," Charlie went on. "The camp is shut down for fire season, and it's Thelma's summer vacation." He stopped to look in the savings book again. "Monday we go to Seattle to the Home Savings and Loan and draw out enough money for the tickets. What do you think about that?"

Tilda thought she'd better sit down.

"Hill said to get our passport pictures taken when we go through Shelton, so they'll be ready when we need them," Charlie said before she had time to answer. "Write to your brother and father and let them know we'll be there on the next boat."

CHAPTER 12: TROUBLE

Passports and Passbooks

Charlie shrugged his suit coat onto his shoulders as he walked into the kitchen. "Three piece wool suit on a hot summer day," he said. "You'd think we were dressing for a wedding or a funeral instead of passport pictures. I still don't see why we couldn't use last year's family picture."

"Hill told you," Tilda said. "A passport picture has to be serious. No smiling. And it has to be taken just before your trip." She put the sandwiches in the picnic box. No sense spending money in a restaurant when she could pack a lunch.

"Does this coat still fit?" Charlie asked.

Tilda placed the thermos in the box next to the sandwiches and turned to look. She watched him button the coat over the vest and look to her for approval. Her heart skipped a beat at his handsome appearance. "It fits fine," she said.

He gave the ends of his bow tie a quick tug, snugging it up tight to his stiff white collar. "Do you have to put so much starch in my shirts? My neck will be raw by the time we get to Seattle."

"It takes lots of starch to make them look good," Tilda said. "Anyway," she smiled, "wearing them can't be as bad as ironing them."

"You're right," Charlie admitted. "Are the girls ready?"

"Telma's been ready with her bankbook ever since I told her where we were going. She has $18.65 in her saving account now and another fifty cents to deposit today after cleaning house for Mrs. Carlson."

"Good," Charlie said and took off his suit coat. "I don't need to wear this in the car. I'll put it on for the picture. And when I do my bank business," he added with a quick smile. "Hurry up, now. If it takes this long to get ready to go to Seattle, how are we going to get ready to catch a boat to Finland?"

The closer they came to Seattle, the more excited Tilda became. It had been eighteen years since she and Ida left for America. Father had carried their grips to the ship, and as he walked away, he swiped at his eyes with the back of his coat sleeve. She knew he never expected to see his daughters again.

Tilda was not sorry she came to America, but now as they drove down the highway past vast, cultivated fields and lush pasture land, she thought of the little, rock-crusted farms in Finland. But over time, memory had softened the harsh corners of the landscape and of her girlhood there, and her heart raced in anticipation of their trip home. With her eyes closed she could imagine her father, older now, but still lean and straight, standing in the doorway of his house waiting for them. And she'd say to Thelma and Angie, "There is your grandfather," and they'd race through the tall grass to meet him—

"Tilda, are you sleeping?" Charlie asked. "Like you come to Seattle every day?" He poked her playfully in the ribs with his elbow.

"Thelma, look," he said. "There's the Smith Tower. It's the tallest building west of the Mississippi. Did you know that?"

With its pointed top reaching high above the other buildings, and with sunlight reflecting from the windows in the tower, the structure looked like a giant birthday candle, all lit up for a party.

"I've seen the Smith Tower," Thelma said, "and I can't look now because I'm carsick. I just want to see the bank building."

"We're almost there," Tilda said, turning to look into the back seat. Angie was asleep with her head in Thelma's lap.

The car was hot. She opened the window for fresh air, but exhaust fumes from the traffic poured in. She rolled the window back up. Tilda was glad they'd had their passport pictures taken in Shelton while everyone was still fresh.

"Where did all these cars come from anyway?" Charlie said as they approached the downtown area. "I thought we were in a Depression."

"I guess it takes a lot of people to run a city, Depression or not," Tilda said. "But look there." She pointed to a row of men sitting on the curb and others lined up in front of a large building. "King County Employment Office," Tilda read as they drove past. "Charlie, I guess we're lucky we live in the logging camp. We don't feel the Depression like lots of people."

Charlie nodded, keeping his eyes on the traffic.

As they neared the water front, Tilda caught glimpses between the buildings of the blue of Puget Sound. Deep blue, like the Bothnia Sea, she smiled to herself. Maybe when they were in Finland, Father would take the girls fishing...

"With this many cars on the street, I suppose we won't find a parking place," Charlie grumbled. A car behind them honked. Brakes squealed on their right as they crossed the intersection. Charlie wasn't used to all the traffic, and it was wearing on him, Tilda could see that.

"Charlie, remember why we're here," Tilda said. "We're drawing out money for a trip home to Finland. That should cheer you up!"

"You're right, Tilda," Charlie said, relaxing his grip on the steering wheel. "Nothing can spoil this day."

The traffic began thinning as they drove closer to the financial center of the city. Not so many department stores here to draw shoppers, Tilda thought.

Another couple blocks and they spotted the Home Savings and Loan building. Of solid concrete, it stood tall, strong, secure, like America itself, Charlie would say. It's windows mirrored the buildings across the street, making it look like ten buildings in one.

"We're in luck," Charlie said. "Nobody's parked in front of the bank." He drew up to the curb and shut the engine off.

Angie woke up and leaned over the front seat, her fine, straight hair sticking to her damp cheek.

"No cars in the whole block," Charlie said. "What day is this, Tilda? Is it a holiday?"

"It's not a holiday," Thelma said. "It's Monday."

"Then it must be a bank holiday," Charlie said. "Did we make this trip for nothing?"

"There's a sheet of paper tacked to the bank door," Tilda said. "And I can see a policeman down the block. Maybe he knows something."

Charlie put his hand on the door handle, but didn't open the door. Tilda looked at him. His face had paled. Drops of perspiration stood out on his upper lip.

"It's hot in the car, Telma," Tilda said. "Roll down the windows back there and I'll open this one." Angie climbed over the seat to help her mother wind down the front window. A little salt breeze stirred the air in the car. "Charlie?" Tilda said.

He opened the door then, stepped out onto the street, stood a moment, and then strode toward the bank's massive double doors.

Angie climbed into the back seat and sat on Thelma's lap. "I'm thirsty," she said.

"Mom, Angie's thirsty," Thelma said.

Tilda handed the water jar to Thelma, but her eyes stayed on Charlie, watching him read the white paper posted on the door. It took him a long time.

"What's Dad doing?" Thelma asked. "When can we go in?"

The policeman had walked over to Charlie, but Tilda couldn't hear what he was saying. The officer pointed at the white paper and shrugged his shoulders. Charlie leaned against the bank wall and watched the policeman walk away. Tilda felt her stomach knot. "Charlie," she called out to him. "Charlie, what's wrong?"

Charlie staggered a little as he walked back to the car. He slid into the seat beside her and rested his arms on the steering wheel. Then his head on his arms. The girls in the back seat stopped chattering.

"What did the note say?" Tilda asked.

"It said they were very sorry," Charlie answered without looking up. "The policeman said we should have read about it in the newspaper."

"About what?" Tilda asked quietly, wanting to scream the question.

"That the Home Saving and Loan went bankrupt. Our money is gone."

"Gone? What are you saying?"

"Our money's gone! All of it. Our life's savings. Five thousand dollars," Charlie choked.

"Mine, too?" Thelma whispered, leaning into the front seat.

"Yours, too."

"How can a big bank like that go broke?" Tilda asked, angry now. "Who took our money? I don't understand."

"People borrow money," Charlie said hoarsely. "They lose their jobs and can't pay it back." He started the car but didn't put it in gear. They sat and listened to it idle. They could hear an occasional seagull calling from the harbor.

"What do we do?" Tilda finally asked.

Charlie's voice was grim. "We forget about the trip," he said. "We go home and start over." He put the car in gear and moved ahead, making a U turn in the middle of the block. It was easy to do. There was little traffic in the financial district of Seattle.

More Bad News

March 10, 1931

Dear Tilda,

I am sorry to write you this news, but Charlie has made up his mind. We are moving back to Finland.

Charlie's father, as you know, owns a nice farm in Närpes. He was a respected town councilman in his younger days and was known as the best mechanic in the community. He trained Charlie to be a good mechanic, and they worked together from the time Charlie finished the sixth grade until he came to America in 1910. Charlie knew he could go back to the farm and work with his father any time, and he has decided that now is the time to do it.

Charlie says things couldn't be as bad in Finland as they are now in this country . Every day he reads about the crime in the cities, strikes and layoffs, the bread lines and soup kitchens for people out of work. He sees banks closing and hard-working people like you lose everything. When it looked like the Shelton mill would be shutting down, he resigned as millwright.

He has put the car and all our furniture up for sale. All we will take with us is what we can pack into a steamer trunk. Arthur did talk Charlie into letting him take the electric train we gave him for Christmas, even though it takes a lot of room.

I have to look at the good side. Charlie and I will be living on Charlie's father's big farm, and I will be close to our father and Ivar and his family. And Arthur is excited about the trip, riding a train across the country and sailing across the ocean in a big ocean liner.

The bad part is leaving you and Charlie. I hope that you will start saving again for a trip to Finland. We have to get together in Finland before the children are grown up and we are old.

We will need a ride to the train in Seattle and hope you can take us. We need to have one more good visit before we separate. I will let you know what day we are leaving as soon as we know.

Your sister Ida

CHAPTER 13: THE CANADA BOYS

Christmas in July, 1931

"Tilda, I haven't seen the Canada boys in a long time," Daddy said to Mama. "What you say we go to B.C. for a couple days next week over shutdown?" Thelma watched him settle onto the edge of the porch and set his dusty lunch bucket down with a clatter. Sweat glistened through dirt on his sunburned neck.

Thelma snapped open his lunch pail. Even though she was thirteen, she still liked to go through his lunch bucket when he came home from work.

"I don't know," Mama said. "It's a long drive to Vancouver. I remember that trip we took to Seaside last summer. Angie was carsick most of the way."

Daddy looked disappointed.

"Well, who do you think we see if we go?" Mama asked.

"Old friends I used to log with. My cousin Vilhelm will be there, I know that. The logging outfits in Canada shut down for fire season like we do, you know."

Dad unhooked and loosened the leather laces on his caulk shoes. Sometimes he let Thelma pull his boots off, but today he did it himself. Thelma could see he had something on his mind.

"Been a long time since we old loggers drank beer together," he called to Mama through the open kitchen door where she'd gone to pour his coffee. He pulled himself to his feet and stretched his back. He walked stiffly like he was still wearing his boots and sat down at the kitchen table.

Thelma watched him lift his cup and pour a little of the steaming hot coffee into the saucer. He balanced the saucer on his fingertips and blew on the coffee, like he was blowing white fluff off dandelions that had gone to seed. Then he popped a sugar lump into his mouth and drank the hot coffee through it.

Thelma hoped Daddy would talk Mama into another trip. Thelma remembered an earlier trip to Vancouver, B.C.—the stores and bright lights, and the elevator in the big hotel. That was before Angie was born. Now she could show Angie these things.

"Okay," Mama said with a little sigh. "I guess we go, but Charlie, you know—"

"Ya, I know. Not too much beer. Don't worry. I'll behave myself," he said, smiling and patting her on the hand. "It'll be good for you, too. Get your mind off Ida moving back to Finland."

Early morning in the mountains could be cold, even in July. Thelma and Angie nestled down in the back seat under the car robe. The sun broke through the ground mist as they started down the road out of camp. Thelma wished the trip didn't take all day, but the ferry ride from Bremerton to Seattle would be fun. And then when they arrived in Vancouver and found a hotel on First Avenue that didn't cost too much, the fun would really begin.

Thelma knew how much her dad liked meeting his friends and drinking beer with them. Course they had beer in camp, too, but it wasn't as good, Daddy said. Even though it was against the law to buy beer in the U.S., nobody got into much trouble for making it.

She'd watched John Carlson make home-brew. He stirred the ingredients together in a big crock and put it behind the cookstove where it was warm. Thelma was cleaning house at Carlsons one Saturday when he poured it out of the crock into bottles and put them under the house to ripen. She'd heard that one time his beer ripened too much and blew up, shooting glass and foam everywhere. Thelma wished she could have been there that day.

It was evening when they drove up in front of a hotel in Vancouver. "Wait here," Daddy said and jumped out of the car. He came back in a few minutes, opened Mama's door, and said the rooms looked fine. Thelma helped Angie out of the back seat and stood her up on the running board. Her little sister was red-faced and limp from the long, hot ride.

"Let's go," Daddy said, picking up their suitcase and leading the way to the lobby of the hotel. "We have two rooms on the third floor with a bed in each room. Here's the key, Tilda, with the room number. You take the girls up the elevator and I'll walk over to First Avenue where the boys always stay when they come to Vancouver."

Thelma caught her breath as the elevator started up. Angie grabbed onto Mama's skirt and hung on until the elevator jiggled to a stop. The elevator was one of the best parts of staying in a hotel.

Thelma thought the rooms were beautiful. High ceilings like in pictures of palaces. Walls with flowered wallpaper that was only a little bit faded. The floors were painted a shiny brown. An electric light bulb with a pull chain to turn it on and off hung by a cord from the ceiling.

Thelma led Angie over to the window and boosted her up so she could see the street below. A streetcar clanged by with its cable hooked to an overhead wire, like it was a big, friendly dog on a leash.

"Look, Angie," Thelma said, and pointed at the bustle of cars and people. A little dust shook loose from the gauze curtain when she pulled it back to see better. Angie sneezed and then pressed her nose against the pane, making a print in the film on the window.

"Stuffy," Mama said, coming up behind them and pulling up the sash. She closed the window in a hurry when a mix of noise and car fumes rushed into the room.

Mama was setting sandwiches out on the table for supper when Daddy walked in. "Vilhelm and the boys will be over tomorrow afternoon," he said. "About one o'clock. And they're bringing a little beer with them."

"But you were going to watch Angie while Telma and I went shopping," Mama said.

"I know, I know," Daddy said. "You put her down for her nap and me and the boys will take care of her."

Mama looked at Daddy like she wasn't sure, but Daddy seemed very sure, so it was settled.

The next morning Thelma and Angie rode the elevator up and down until the elevator man started to look cross. Thelma took Angie back to their room and held her up to the electric light bulb with the magical chain. Daddy finally said that that was enough magic and it was time to help Mama fix lunch from her magic box of groceries. Then it was time for Angie's nap.

Mama helped Angie into the tall bed and poked the sheet under the mattress on both sides so she wouldn't roll out. When she saw Angie was ready to sleep after her busy morning, she tip-toed out. "We'll be back in a couple hours," Mama whispered to Daddy as she picked up her pocketbook. "She should sleep till we get back if you and the boys aren't too noisy."

The stores were everything Thelma remembered. Brick and glass and lights and endless counters and shelves loaded with sweaters and stockings, lipsticks and jewelry. Boxes of shoes and racks of dresses and suits filled one whole floor, and tables of fine china filled part of another. Mama always looked at dishes even if she never bought any new ones. Thelma liked the books and games best.

Wherever they stopped to look, stylish young ladies hurried over to ask if they could help. The aisles were full of people, some buying, but more just looking, like her and Mama were.

The next store was just as big and busy as the first. Then they crossed the street to Woolworth's Dime Store which was best of all because Thelma knew that here they would buy something. Mama picked out a piece of flowered green cloth for a dress for Thelma when she started high school in the fall. She bought ribbon and buttons to match, but she didn't buy a pattern because she never used one. Then she found blue wool yarn for a sweater for Angie and bought extra so when Angie outgrew the sweater, she could unravel it and knit it again in a bigger size.

"Now it's your turn," Mama said.

Thelma had been holding a twenty-five cent piece since she left the hotel. She'd earned the money cleaning house for Mrs. Carlson and saved it for today. For ten cents she bought Angie a tiny, celluloid doll with arms and legs that moved. She found a Big-Little Book for herself for another ten cents and had five cents left over. Mama said she should save that for a "rainy day."

Mama and Daddy were very careful with their money. "A penny saved is a penny earned," she'd tell Thelma. Mama collected rubber bands on the kitchen doorknobs and kept adding pieces of string to the ball of string in the cupboard. Mom and Dad never threw anything away that could be re-used. "Waste not, want not," they said. Thelma thought they probably found those sayings in the Bible.

The afternoon went too fast. A streetcar with "First Avenue" written across the front rolled to a stop in front of them, and they climbed on.

"I hope the Canada boys were quiet," Mama said when they had settled into a seat and adjusted their packages. "Angie would be scared if she woke up to strangers."

Thelma heard it the minute she stepped out of the elevator. "Mama, listen!"

Mama held the rustling packages still and listened. They both hurried down the hall to the door of their room and listened again.

"Christmas carols?" Mama said. "In the middle of July? What's going on?"

Mama threw open the door. Cigarette smoke hung heavy, screening their view, but they could see well enough. Daddy and four other men, hats askew, sat around the room with short, brown bottles in their hands. More bottles lay at their feet. A couple of the men sat tipped back in their chairs. The man next to Charlie held Angie on his knee. All were singing in happy concert, but above their loud, scratchy vibratos, rang the bell-like voice of the child. She was singing with the others, *"Silent night, holy night, all is calm—"*

"Charlie!" Mama shouted. The big voices stopped.

"All is bright..." Angie sang on. Then giggled. "Hi, Mama. We're having fun!"

"Charlie, what's going on here!"

"Tilda, come say hello to Vilhelm and the boys," Daddy said, his smile as crooked as his hat.

Mama didn't say hello, but grabbed Angie instead.

"Angie didn't want to take a nap," Daddy explained.

"Sleep in hea-venly pea-ece," Angie sang on. Mama sniffed her breath and then turned a little white.

"She was hot and miserable and she couldn't sleep," one man said, "so I gave her a little sip of my beer."

"Ya, I could see she liked it," another said, "so I let her have a little of my beer, too."

The others grinned and tipped up their bottles.

Mama clutched Angie to her and ran for the bedroom. "Too bad Canada don't still have Prohibition," she exclaimed over her shoulder, slamming the door behind her.

Thelma wondered what to do. The big room was suddenly very quiet and the men seemed to be studying the cigarette butts on the floor. Then the bedroom door opened and Mama's arm reached out and pulled her into the bedroom, too, and slammed the door again.

Thelma listened at the door and heard the men leave. She watched Mama try to tuck Angie back into bed, but Angie kept giggling and wrestling with the cover. *"Jingle bells, jingle bells, jingle all the way..."* she sang, but gradually more slowly, winding down like a Christmas top. Finally the covers stayed tucked.

Mama and Daddy didn't have much to say to each other that evening, and, except for feeding Angie, they seemed to have forgotten about supper. Thelma was hungry, so Mama let her go down in the elevator to buy an ice cream cone with her nickel. Thelma guessed she understood now what Mama meant about saving your money for a "rainy day."

CHAPTER 14: TURNING POINT

August 1931

Tilda woke with a start and reached across the bed for Charlie. Still gone. A sliver of daylight at the edge of the window blind told her it was morning. She had been asleep after all. Sometimes when Charlie fought fire at night, she'd lie awake until he came home. He'd try to slip into the house quietly—

Heavy footsteps on the porch. Muffled talking. That's what had startled her awake! Tilda sat up in bed and listened.

More footsteps. Grunts. The sound of something being dragged... Tilda grabbed her bathrobe and ran to open the door. Ole Johnson and John Carlson stumbled into the front room, half dragging, half carrying a man she hardly recognized. They lifted him onto the couch and called for a blanket.

Thelma had heard the commotion, too, and stood in her pajamas at the kitchen door, her hands over her mouth. "Mama," she breathed, "is Daddy going to die?"

It was Charlie, all right, but not the long-striding, strong, fearless man who left for the fire line the evening before. Tilda had seen him come home from a fire, or an accident in the woods, worn and discouraged, but never sick. Never like this.

"Don't know what happened, Mrs. Lind," Ole said. "Charlie was spraying the fire with the hose from the lokey when all at once he dropped to his knees—"

"I know about that," Tilda interrupted, relieved that this was something she could deal with. "He gets leg cramps when he sprays cold water on the hot fire. He's had that before."

"Ya, we've seen that in men when they're on the fire line," Ole said, "and we asked Charlie if it was leg cramps. He was shivering so hard he couldn't talk, but he shook his head, no. He shivered so bad he couldn't hold the hose. The pressure of the water snaked the hose right out of his hands. Sprayed everything but the fire." Ole looked hard at Charlie and shook his head. "No, I never seen this in a man before."

John worked to take off Charlie's caulk shoes while Tilda and Ole tried to wrap the blanket completely around him so he couldn't shake it off. Charlie tried to say something but his teeth clattered together, shattering his words. He turned away and shut his eyes. Tilda saw trails of dried sweat in the soot on his face and neck, but now they couldn't get him warm. She kneeled beside him and wiped the black stains with the sleeve of her bathrobe.

"You think we should get back on the speeder and take him to Potlatch?" John asked. "Get him to the hospital? He's shaking himself right out of his skin."

"Let's try to warm him up first, and then see," Ole said.

"He's gonna die, isn't he, Mama?" Thelma cried, still frozen in the doorway.

Tilda knew why Thelma was so sure of this. Death was on everyone's mind. Two weeks before, Bill Hamilton disappeared on Lake Cushman. He'd started working for Tacoma Power when Phoenix cut back and laid off so many men. He was carrying supplies in a small boat to workmen on the dam the day he didn't come home. Charlie helped search for him that night. The next day they found his boat bobbing in the water next to the shore, but no sign of Hamilton.

The lake had been calm that day, so it was hard to imagine his falling overboard. Some wondered if he left his wife and children to start a new life somewhere, but Tilda knew he was too much of a family man for that. Some said he never got over being the driver of the speeder that accidently killed Leonard, and that he might have fallen overboard on purpose, but Tilda didn't believe that either. Maybe he was a victim of foul play or maybe he had a heart attack and fell out of the boat. All anyone knew for sure was that he was gone and his wife and four children were left to grieve.

Thelma went to school with his children. In May, Wayne graduated from eighth grade with her, and his sister Nadine was just a grade behind them. Oliver and Willard were a lot younger, but they all played together after school. Now their daddy was gone and Thelma had seen that fathers, like anyone else, could die.

Full daylight was flooding the front room when Tilda noticed a change in Charlie. Thelma saw it, too. He'd stopped shivering.

Tilda laid her hand on Charlie's cheek and then on his forehead. He was burning up! Sweat started running off his face and body like water. He struggled to free himself of the blanket. What was going on? Was it that influenza that killed so many when the children were little? Scarlet fever, another killer?

"We're through waiting!" John said. "Get him ready, Tilda. We're taking him to the hospital."

Tilda ran for his coat and slippers. Troubles always came in threes! They'd lost their life savings. In a way, she'd lost her sister Ida when she moved back to Finland, and now Charlie, who was never sick, lay dying in front of her eyes.

John and Ole sat him up and Tilda struggled to get his arm into a sleeve.

"Never mind," John said. "He don't need it with the fever. Just bring it along."

"It's windy on the open speeder," Tilda said. "It's bad to get chilled when you have fever." She started to lay the coat across his shoulders when he pushed her hands away and opened his eyes.

A hoarse whisper. "Tilda, it's all right."

Tilda dropped to her knees to hear him better.

"Help me to bed." He took another breath. "I just need a couple days...to get over this."

"Charlie, do you know what's wrong with you?"

"Malaria," he mouthed. "It's come back on me before...when I lived in Portland...before you knew me." He struggled to talk. "Put me to bed...need rest."

John and Ole helped him into the bedroom and Tilda ran to dampen some washcloths to cool his face and neck.

"Ya, that's so," John said when they had him on the bed. "I knew another feller who had malaria come back on him. Fever and chills and fever, but he got over it. I remember it looked worse than it was." He helped Charlie out of his work pants and shirt. Tilda pulled his clean union suit from the drawer and handed it to the men. The one he was wearing was soaked through with sweat.

"When did Charlie have malaria?" Ole whispered.

"It must have been when he first came to this country and worked for a few months in the mines in Mexico," Tilda said. "He worked in lead mines in Idaho, too, for a year, before he went back to logging, but I remember now he said he got malaria in Mexico."

"Then he's going to get better?" Thelma asked. Her hands gripped the end of the bed.

No one answered. Tilda wiped the soot from Charlie's neck and face with one of the cool washcloths. The other she folded and laid gently across his forehead.

"Ya, but that feels good," Charlie breathed. "Tell Telma it takes more than a little malaria to fell a good Swede-Finn logger."

The turning point came the next afternoon. Charlie's fever, along with the fire in the woods, was finally under control. He was too weak to get out of bed, so Tilda sat at his side while he slept in case the fever returned. Thelma and Angie came and went, but now as they started out of the room, Thelma stopped abruptly and turned to her mother.

"I have to talk to you about something," she said.

Tilda watched her tall, gangly daughter walk back into the room and lower herself to the floor, folding her long legs under her. When had her daughter grown so tall?

Tilda knew Thelma was self-conscious about her height. Anna Carlson teased her, telling her she should tie knots in her legs, or put a book on her head so she wouldn't grow any more. And people said, "My, but you're getting big!" until she felt like a freak. Charlie kept track of her height on the door frame in the kitchen. "Five feet, eight inches," he told Thelma the last time he measured. His wide grin told Thelma it was something to be proud of. Thelma told her mother she liked being tall like her daddy.

And she'd liked being taller than her teacher, too. There had been only four kids in the camp school during Thelma's eighth grade year, and all four of them were taller than Miss Mayer, and they liked to take advantage of this. But Miss Mayer, who was hardly five feet tall, was smart, Thelma told her mother. She moved their desks to the four corners of the room. She wanted her three eighth grade students—Thelma, Wayne Hamilton, and Leonard West—to be ready for high school in the fall.

High school in the fall? Where had the years gone? Tilda looked at Charlie sleeping comfortably since his fever broke. Thelma moving away. Another turning point.

"I talked to Wayne, Mama," Thelma said, breaking into Tilda's thoughts. "His mom is moving the family to Lilliwaup before school starts."

"Ya," Tilda said, "I heard that. Camp is no place for a widow with a family."

"Wests are moving to Hoodsport and Leonard gets to ride the school bus to Shelton."

"We're all moving, you know that," Tilda said. "When Phoenix shuts down Camp One next month, everyone who wants to stay with the company moves to Camp Two. Mr. West is leaving the company because he's tired of logging, not so Leonard can ride the school bus."

"Well, couldn't Dad look for a different job, too? Maybe in Shelton?"

"I guess he could, but he likes logging. He's been hook tender long enough to know he likes being foreman. He makes a good salary now, so we can build our savings. And with so many people losing their jobs, we're lucky that he has steady work."

"Okay, Mom. We're moving to Camp Two. Did you know that Camp Two is just two miles above Lilliwaup? I could hike the trail every day, easy, and ride the school bus from Lilliwaup. Wouldn't that work?"

"Thelma, what would you do in winter when it gets dark early or when the trail is buried in snow? You know that wouldn't work."

"I could spend the night, or the week, at Hamiltons. At least I'd know the people I was staying with."

"The school said that the Hepners, the people you'll be living with in Shelton, are a good Christian family—"

"Okay. That's all right. And I don't mind working for my board and room. But, Mama, Angie will grow up while I'm gone!" Thelma exclaimed, her voice cracking.

That was it! Tilda knew Thelma had looked forward to high school for a long time, but now that the time was here, she didn't want to leave her little sister.

How soon it came! Thirteen short years and Thelma was moving away. Grown tall but still a child, leaving home to go to high school. She herself had been young, barely sixteen, when she left home, but thirteen was too young!

Maybe they should have left the woods after that first year. Charlie had said it was up to her, but she had gotten used to camp life, and by the end of that year, she didn't mind not having electricity or radio or sidewalks. And though she would never get used to the whistles that announced fires and accidents, she had learned to live with that, too. But now the logging was requiring something more of them. Something she hadn't thought of. Their young daughter had to leave home if she wanted to finish her education. Angie left her play and climbed onto Thelma's lap, as if she understood what Thelma had said.

"You'll come home on weekends and holidays," Tilda said. "And summer vacation. Angie won't forget you. Daddy and I will miss you, but we won't forget you either," Tilda smiled. "You'll see it's all right."

Tilda moved quickly to tuck the blanket around Charlie and to hide from Thelma her own trembling chin.

PART VI - CAMP TWO 1931-1936

CHAPTER 15: FIRST FALL AND WINTER

Unexpected Company

Tilda hummed as she unpacked the dishes. How many times had she done this now? Lake Cushman, Lower Camp One, Upper Camp One, and now Camp Two. Four times in nine years, Tilda counted. From Lake Cushman to the foot of Dow Mountain, to Price's Lake, and now to a spot between two lakes. Charlie said this would be the best camp yet. It was just a short walk to Lake Melbourne on one side and Osbourne Lake on the other.

Tilda wiped out another cupboard and folded clean newspaper onto the shelf.

Four different camps but always the same. Camp Two, like the others, was a burned off, stump-filled clearing with tiny, unpainted houses lining a railroad track. This time tracks bordered both sides of the houses, the mainline on one side and a side line for idle rail cars on the other. But she was used to railroad tracks and burned-over camp sites, and she could always look up and see the green trees on the higher hills and the beautiful Olympic Mountains behind them.

Tilda unpacked her rolling pin, put it in a drawer and dropped the flour sifter into the big, metal-lined flour bin under the drawer. She could unpack with her eyes closed because all the kitchens, like the rest of the rooms in the camp houses, were alike. This time when Camp One was logged out, Phoenix didn't move the camp houses. Houses already stood empty in Camp Two. Orders for logs had been slow, so men had been laid off. They moved away to find work. Then orders started coming in again, and families from Camp One moved into the empty houses.

Tilda liked Camp Two. Their house had a bathroom and porches, so Charlie only needed to add a bedroom for Thelma and a fence around the yard for Angie. In the spring Tilda would plant hollyhocks and sweet peas next to the fence and a garden in back. And Carlsons told her they were going to buy a cow and sell fresh milk to the camp families.

Things were going well for Thelma, too. She liked the family she worked for, and she liked high school. Best of all, with the high school's big library, she would never run out of books to read.

Tilda ran water into a pail and rubbed soap on a rag. Whoever lived in this house before them didn't know much about housekeeping—

Angie was crying. She didn't usually cry when she woke up in the morning. Tilda hurried into the bedroom and picked her up out of the crib. Angie's arms felt rough. Tilda raised the window shade. Angie's face and neck, her entire body, was covered with red welts. She pushed back Angie's hair and felt her forehead. No fever. But something in her hair moved. She looked closer and gasped. Angie's scalp was crawling with bedbugs!

Tilda knew about the tiny, flat-bodied, stinging insects. She'd have to wash Angie's hair and scalp with kerosene and boil her pajamas and the bedding. Bedbugs could infest everything—the linens in the drawer, the rugs, the furniture. Charlie would have to go to Hoodsport for disinfectant powder.

Tilda was still hanging bedclothes on the line when Charlie came home from his hoot-owl shift. She hadn't thought about fixing their midday meal.

"Looks like we're having company," Charlie said as he walked into the yard.

"I'm not cleaning for company," Tilda said. "And, anyway, company's already here! Bedbugs! I never thought I'd see bedbugs in my house." She picked up a damp towel from the laundry basket and gave it an angry shake before pinning it to the line.

"That's not the company I'm talking about," Charlie laughed. "We got a letter in the mail."

Tilda took the letter and wondered if Charlie thought finding bedbugs in their house was funny.

"It's from Ida," Charlie said.

Tilda had heard from her sister only once since they moved back to Finland, and she'd started to worry. She ripped the letter out of the envelope.

August 15, 1931

Dear Tilda and Charlie,

It looks like we made a mistake when we moved back to Finland. Things are no better now than when we left for America in 1912. Charlie's big family farm still has no electricity or running water. Everywhere men are out of work and families are hungry.

Yesterday when I went outside to dip water from the rain barrel, I found a thin skin of ice on top. It reminded me of how short the summers are in Finland and how long and dark and cold the winters. That's when I put my foot down and told Charlie I wouldn't stay. He finally agreed to our coming home. It's funny to say 'coming home' to America, but I guess America really is our home now.

We will come to camp sometime the end of October and if it is all right, Arthur and I will stay with you while Charlie looks for work. We hope it won't take too long for him to find a job...

Tilda dropped the letter before she finished reading it and threw her arms around Charlie's neck. She couldn't believe what she read. She looked at the washing and cleaning mess around her and laughed. What were a few bedbugs compared to the news that her sister was moving back to America.

Waterdogs

The Woodworth girls and Donald Thompson beat Thelma and Angie to the lake.

They jumped onto the root end of the weathered log that had at some time in the past lost its hold on the rain-soaked bank and toppled over, burying its lofty head in the muddy bottom of Lake Melbourne.

"Yuck!" Merle screeched, pointing down at the lake shore. "Look at the mud. It looks like throw-up."

"No," Donald said. "It looks like diarrhea."

"Yea, diarrhea," Merle said. "That's what it is. Diarrhea! I dare someone to step in it. Double dare."

"I'm not scared to," her younger sister Roberta said.

Thelma felt Angie lean from her piggy-back position to see around her. Together they watched Roberta slide down the side of the weathered log and land with both feet in the brown muck. "Watch," Roberta repeated. Holding her nose, she plopped down in the orangy-brown mud, splashing it up her back and onto Thelma.

Thelma squatted down on the muddy bank so Angie could slide off her back. Angie could have walked the half mile from home, but Thelma liked to carry her, especially since she only saw her on weekends now that school had started.

"This stuff isn't really diarrhea," Thelma said when Angie drew up her legs. "The kids are just fooling. When the water is low, the muddy lake bottom shows." People called Lake Melbourne a "bottomless lake." Once Donald lowered a rock on a long rope to see if it would touch bottom, but the rock never did.

"Last one in's a rotten egg," Donald shouted and ran down the log and into the brown water. "I'll get the dugout." He splashed his way through the cattails and weeds.

Donald had found the crudely hollowed-out log moored in the tangle of wild shoots at the edge of the lake the summer before Thelma moved to Camp Two. Thelma wondered what would happen if the Indian who carved the dugout came back and found them using it, but none of the kids worried about it, so she didn't either.

"Here, Angie, hold up your arms," Thelma said. "We're going to swim in the deep water today, away from the mud. Won't that be fun?" Thelma slipped the skinny inner tube over Angie's head and wrapped it around her twice so it wouldn't be too loose. "Now remember, Angie, keep the inner tube under your arms so you won't slip through."

"You ready?" Donald called, paddling the dugout toward the girls. "Catch!" He tossed the loose end of a long rope to Thelma. Thelma tied the rope to the inner tube and led Angie through the ooze out into the water until she was floating free of the mud.

"We're ready," Thelma said.

Donald paddled the canoe away from shore until the coils of rope straightened and tightened. The inner tube jerked ahead and Thelma slipped down into the water to swim along side of Angie.

"Let's go!" Merle said as she and Roberta ran down the log and dived into the water. Thelma checked the knot to be sure it was secure, and then stroked ahead of Angie to catch up with the others as they headed for the clear water in the middle of the lake.

Tilda didn't have to go far from home to pick huckleberries. Like in the other camps, the huckleberry bushes dotted the logged-off hillsides, their sweet, deep-blue berries growing in clusters among the tiny leaves. With Thelma taking Angie to the lake this afternoon, Tilda could pick without interruption. She'd have enough berries picked and canned to make a dozen pies by the time Ida and Arthur came to stay with them.

Huckleberries reminded Tilda of her first camp friend and neighbor, Mrs. Nelson. "Huckleberries and blackberries grow

best on burned-over land," she'd said. She saw good in everything, even the charred hillsides. Tilda hated to see the Nelsons
move away when Camp One shut down.

Tilda missed other friends, too. Mrs. Hamilton and the
children, and the Lathoms with their boys. Especially the little
one that made her think of Leonard. She felt bad when
Jacobsons and their big, happy-go-lucky family moved to Potlatch instead of Camp Two. The Wests had their different ways
about them, but Tilda missed them anyway. The Boxes and
Jensens and the Woodworths, and their close friends, the
Carlsons, stayed with the camp.

Tilda rested her back against a windfall and examined her
purple fingers. She'd rub them with lemon when she got home.
Mrs. Nelson would probably have laughed and said, "Don't
worry. Purple fingers make good pie."

She did miss her old friends, but already she was getting
acquainted with the Camp Two people. Like the Webbs. Mrs.
Webb planned to start a Sunday School in the schoolhouse,
she told Tilda the first time they met, because the camp kids
really needed it. She also said not to let the children wander
from camp because an old man with long, shaggy hair and a
scraggly beard lived alone in a shack in the woods. "And they
say he's dangerous," Ann Webb had whispered to Tilda. "He
doesn't come to camp often, but when he does, he carries a
single-shot rifle."

Tilda listened politely, but she had enough to think about,
what with getting settled and keeping Angie busy so she
wouldn't miss her big sister so much. Angie was so excited
this morning when Tilda said she could go to the lake with
Thelma and the camp kids. Tilda never worried about Angie
when she was with Thelma.

It was a long way to the middle of the lake, even with the
water low. The swimmers stayed close to the dugout so they
could hang onto the sides and rest when they needed to.
Thelma grabbed the edge and turned to check on Angie. She
was startled to see how tiny Angie looked, bobbing along at
the end of the long rope with the wide spread of water around

her. The double wrap of inner tube forced her arms straight out, so she was kicking and leaning hard to the side in order to touch the water.

"Hey, you guys," Donald said. "If you're going to hang on, at least kick your feet."

"We're out far enough," Thelma said, still looking at Angie.

"Not yet," Donald said. "We're not in the middle."

The wind had come up, making the water choppy and slowing the dugout's progress. "Keep kicking," Donald said. Thelma felt uneasy. She watched Angie bouncing along in the small waves. The water washed across the inner tube and licked her in the face. Angie swallowed and coughed, but then smiled and waved at Thelma. The shore was a long ways away when Donald stopped paddling. "Okay. Let's turn it over," he said.

They all knew what to do. They rocked the dugout until it turned bottom-side up, like a dead fish floating on the surface of the water.

"Watch this!" Thelma called back to Angie. She climbed onto the overturned dugout and dived into the water. A minute later she surfaced with weeds hanging from her head and slime covering her shoulders. Roberta and Merle screamed in mock fright and ducked out of sight in the churned-up water. When they resurfaced, they, too, were draped with slick, pale weeds. They rolled their eyes and moaned like monsters returning from the dark at the bottom of the bottomless lake.

Angie threw her hands in the air and laughed. The inner tube slipped up to her chin, and the back wash from the swimmers splashed over her head. She sputtered and grabbed the sides of the tube. When she caught her breath, she looked at the monsters and laughed again.

"She isn't scared at all," Merle said.

"She knows we're playing," Thelma said.

"Let's catch waterdogs," Donald said, and they all turned from Angie to their new game.

Tilda set the full bucket down on the back porch. A cold wind had come up. Fall was in the air, all right. She'd walk to the lake and bring the girls home before they both got chilled. Thelma wouldn't want to miss school because of a bad cold.

"I caught one," Thelma shouted, swimming over to Angie and treading water. "Look at its little face. See its smile face? Isn't it cute, Angie?" Thelma was holding the smooth little waterdog up for Angie to pet when they heard the scream.

"Help, somebody! She's going to drown!"

Thelma squinted her eyes at the shore. It sounded like Mom, but they were a long way out and Thelma wasn't wearing her glasses.

"Tel-MAH!"

It was Mom all right. Thelma could recognize that rising pitch anywhere. She squeezed her eyes again. Mom was waving her arms over her head. Something must be wrong! Thelma helped Donald right the dugout and they started for shore.

The wind had picked up even more and was blowing against them. Donald paddled and Angie bounced and slipped and slid from side to side in the whitecaps. Water splashed over her, taking away her breath. Thelma heard her cough and looked back again. The waves were as high as the top of Angie's head.

"Hang on to the inner tube," Thelma called. She looked toward shore and saw her mother standing on the bank above the muddy slope to the lake.

Donald paddled harder. Roberta and Merle hung on to the edge of the dugout and kicked. Thelma grabbed the edge, rested a minute, and then swam ahead of the canoe. When she thought she couldn't swim any more, her feet touched the submerged end of the fallen tree and without breaking her overhand stroke to look up, she knew she was close to shore.

Tilda tore Angie from Thelma's arms and held her tight. The girls stood nearby, waiting to find out what was wrong.

"Telma," Tilda said when she could talk, "didn't you think? Angie could have tipped over in that inner tube, or slipped through! What if the inner tube started to leak?" Her voice rose and then broke. "Angie could have drowned!"

Thelma didn't move. She felt her face getting hot, even with the cold wind from the lake. She had been a little uneasy when the wind first came up, afraid that Angie might get scared in the choppy water, but Angie was having fun! Thelma hadn't thought of the danger, of what might happen, of the real possibility that Angie could have slipped through the inner tube and been lost forever in the bottomless lake.

Arthur Spoke Swedish - October, 1931

Days were getting shorter and leaves, crispier. They needed a good rain to settle the dust, Tilda told the girls, but the girls were concentrating on their art work and weren't concerned. Thelma had brought home a thick tablet and a box of new crayons from Woolworths and was drawing fat pumpkins with happy faces for Angie to color.

Tilda looked over Angie's shoulder. "That's very good," she said, even though the orange crayon had gone outside the lines. "Now you girls take your work to the front room so I can sweep and mop the kitchen floor. **Moster** and Uncle could be here any day now."

"Arthur, too," Thelma said.

"Of course, Artur, too," Tilda smiled. "Anyway, I want the house to be spick-and-span when they get here."

Charlie had done his part to get the house ready. He'd finished Thelma's bedroom on the back porch so Ida would have her own room, except on weekends when Thelma came home from school. Then they would share the room. Arthur could sleep in the front room on the couch—

"Look, Mama. Smoke," Angie said, pointing out the window. Tilda and Thelma turned to look. It wasn't smoke, thank God. It was dust swirling up behind an automobile that was speeding toward their house.

"They're here!" Thelma shouted and raced Angie and Tilda out the door.

Before the car completely stopped, Art leaped out and began telling Thelma how many knots an hour the ship traveled and how many hours and minutes it took for them to drive across each state in the 1929 Model A Ford they bought in New York for $250.00 that even had a rumble seat—

"You're talking Swedish," Thelma interrupted.

He stopped mid-sentence and glanced around quickly to be sure no one else had heard, and then continued his story in English.

"When does your Charlie get home?" Ida asked Tilda after the round of greetings.

"Charlie should be home any time," Tilda said, taking Ida by the arm and leading her into the kitchen. "We'll start a pot of coffee while we talk. I want to hear all about Father and Ivar and his family."

"Ivar is in good health," Ida said, sitting down at the kitchen table. "But he has to work long hours to keep food on the table for his growing boys. And Father gets along pretty good for his age. He asks when you are coming home for a visit. We seem so rich to them because we live in America. He doesn't understand why we can't just buy a ticket and sail tomorrow."

"Well, we're saving again for a trip," Tilda said. "With Father's age, we know we need to make plans, even if things don't always go like you think."

"Charlie and I know about that. The move we made was expensive. We were lucky to have enough money left to buy a car. Charlie knew he'd need a car so he could look for work. Now we worry that there won't be any work with times still so bad."

Autumn leaves dropped and winter covered them lightly with a powdering of snow. Art attended the camp school. The Model A came and went each weekend. Then on a week day in December, when the Christmas tree was trimmed and the baking for the holiday was finished, the little car roared up the road and into the yard with a loud "*a-ooga*" for all the camp to hear.

"Ya, I have a job," Charlie said in answer to their first question. "Head millwright at Clear Fir Lumber Company in Tacoma."

"Like a Christmas present!" Ida exclaimed. "When do you start?"

"Middle of January. And I rented a house. We can move in after New Year. Charlie, I think it's time we all celebrated!"

By the end of January, Ida and family were settled in Tacoma, Thelma was well into the second semester of her freshman year in high school, and Charlie was logging in three feet of snow. The letter from Ivar arrived in February.

February 9 , 1932

Kära Syster,

I am sorry to write bad news, but Father died January 26, two weeks ago today. He was seventy-one. He was sick only a short time and was alert to the last. He said goodbye to his wife and me and his grandsons and then he told me that, all in all, life for him had been good. He was proud of his children, he said. He had only one regret, and that was that he could not see you, Tilda, one more time. I tell you this so you know he thought of you...

There was more, but the words blurred as Tilda tried to read on. She'd finish the letter later. She had lots of time. No hurry now to make the trip to Finland.

CHAPTER 16: BULL OF THE WOODS

"Happy" - Spring 1932

Thelma liked swimming in Lake Melbourne best, but she liked the stumps in Osborne Lake. In the fall when the water was low, she could swim between the stumps and dive off the top of them. In the spring when the stumps were under water, she could stand on them and look like she was standing on top of the water. But on this day of her spring vacation, Thelma knew by the direction of the sun that she and Roberta had stayed at the lake too long, and they had better find the quickest way home. Instead of taking the old logging road back, they would cut through the woods.

"Look," Roberta whispered, grabbing Thelma's arm and pulling her behind a tree. "Look there, in the clearing. That's his shack."

Thelma peered around her side of the tree. A tiny structure, walled and roofed with rough cedar slabs, was all but hidden in a grove of standing cedars. A bit of sunlight filtered through the trees and reflected off a broken window. The door stood open.

"Whose shack?" Thelma asked, though she thought she knew.

"Happy's," Roberta answered. "I wonder if he's home."

"I don't see anybody," Thelma whispered, "but look at all the cats. They're walking in and out of the door like they owned the place."

"That's where Happy got his name. People said he was cat-happy, so they call him 'Happy' for short."

"A chicken just walked out of the house!" Thelma gasped. "And another one. Can you imagine our moms letting us have chickens in the house?"

Roberta laughed out loud, and then clamped her hands over her mouth and smiled at Thelma with her eyes.

"How does he live?" Thelma asked.

"He gets eggs from his chickens and sometimes he eats the chickens," Roberta said and giggled again. "My mom says he gets milk from his goat, and he grows vegetables behind his house."

"But where does he work?" Thelma asked. In her world, everyone worked or was looking for work.

Superintendent Carlson has him do odd jobs," Roberta said. "And he fires up the donkey first thing in the morning so it's full of steam when the men get to work." She looked back at the house. "I don't see his dog. He must not be home."

"Let's go look inside," Thelma said, tucking her rolled-up bathing suit and towel under her arm and pushing her way through the brush toward the leaning structure.

"Wait! Smoke's coming out of the smokestack."

Thelma ducked back behind the tree and suddenly remembered what Mrs. Webb had told Mama about Happy being dangerous. "We'd better look in the window first to be sure he's not there."

They hunched down and zig-zagged across the slash-littered clearing, scurrying between stumps and piles of split wood until they reached the house. Thelma flattened herself against the wall while Roberta cupped her hands around her eyes and pressed her face against the window.

"There's newspaper tacked on the inside of the window. We'll have to look through the door if we're going to see anything."

A black cat sauntered out of the shack and joined the calico where it lay stretched out in a patch of sun by a windfall. It turned to watch the girls creeping along next to the wall. A chicken clucked and fluttered out of the way as the girls reached the door and peeked into the dark room.

"Come in," a raspy voice called out. "I was waitin' for you."

They both jumped. "How'd he know we were here?" Roberta whispered.

"Come in, ladies," the voice repeated.

Thelma stepped forward cautiously, obediently. Roberta followed. When their eyes became accustomed to the dark, they saw the dog stretched out under the table. It looked up at them and yawned. The table held tattered magazines, yellowed newspapers, and a dirty plate and cup. A chicken sat on the table and clucked at them. Another balanced on the back of the chair. A gun leaned against the chair. A figure stepped out of the shadows.

"Nice of you to come see me," he said, his voice quieter than the first time he spoke. It was Happy, all right. Long hair and beard, dirty shirt and torn overalls, like Mama said. He moved to the back of the chair and brushed the chicken from its roost with one hand. The other he rested on the barrel of his gun.

"We—we have to go now," Thelma stammered. "Our folks will be looking for us." She grabbed Roberta's hand and spun out the door. A high-pitched laugh followed them as they raced for the sanctuary of the forest.

"That was a close one," Roberta said when they stopped to catch their breath. A vague trail, perhaps worn by Happy himself, led in the direction of camp, and they were soon within hollering distance of their own houses.

"I'll have to tell Mom what we did," Thelma said, "but it wasn't like we went hunting for Happy. We just happened to find him."

Roberta nodded, then stopped. Thelma heard it, too. Loud voices. Shouting. They ran across the clearing to the track in back of their houses. The shouts came from the direction of the bunkhouses. As they ran down the track, they heard cursing and threats, but louder yet, the vicious snarling and yipping of dogs.

"Someone stop them!" a woman cried.

"They're killing each other!" another shouted.

"I'm betting on the black one," a young logger called from the bunkhouse steps.

Thelma and Roberta slipped under elbows until they were in front of the circle of on-lookers. Superintendent Carlson's black dog, Brute, had camp foreman Oscar Smith's dog, Smitty, by the throat and was shaking him like a rag doll. Slobber and blood sprayed anyone standing too close. Oscar Smith ran back and forth around the dogs, all the time shaking his fist at Superintendent Carlson. "Call off that killer dog of yours, Carlson, or—"

"Your mutt started this fight, Smith. He needs to be taught a lesson!"

"I'll stop 'em!" someone shouted and struck the nearest dog hard with a heavy stick. Another hit Brute on the head repeatedly with a board until he dropped the smaller dog and gave his own head a shake.

Smith kneeled in the dirt beside his dog. The mutt lay still. Blood puddled under its neck.

"I'm sorry as all hell about your dog," Carlson said, holding his own panting dog back by its collar.

The hurt dog moved its feet and struggled to get up but flopped back down again. "He'll live," Smith snarled. He touched its ripped shoulder gently and then spun to his feet and ran at Carlson. His first swing connected and knocked Carlson backwards over Brute. Smith threw himself on top of Carlson, pommeling him with his fists and then grabbing him around the throat. Someone screamed. Suddenly, without warning, the long barrel of a single-shot rifle reached out of the crowd and came to rest on the back of Smith's head.

No one moved or spoke. In the stillness of the bunkhouse clearing, Thelma heard the click of the safety release.

"Let him up," a scratchy voice ordered.

Smith let go and turned slowly. His eyes followed the barrel of the rifle up past the scarred, calloused hands that held the gun, to the grizzled beard that lay against the butt of the gun, and the narrowed eye at the gun sight. Thelma watched as Smith stood up slowly, staggered over to his whimpering dog, picked him up and carried him into the bunkhouse.

When Thelma turned back to find Happy, he was gone.

"I told you that cat-happy man was dangerous," someone said.

"I don't call that 'dangerous'," someone else said. "Might have even saved Carlson's life."

"Where did he come from anyway? All of a sudden, here he was."

"Ya, and then he was gone."

Thelma saw her dad move into the milling group to help Carlson to his feet. "Lucky thing Happy was around," Dad said.

"That wasn't luck," someone else said. "He told me he'd come to see if the girls made it home through the woods all right. He said he followed them to make sure they didn't get lost, and that's when he saw Smith beating up on Carlson."

"Well," Daddy said, "it makes sense. Carlson's been pretty good to Happy, you know. Time the rest of us treated Happy with a little respect, too."

Mystery Fires - Summer, 1932

"Where's Charlie?" Superintendent Carlson exclaimed as Tilda opened the door. It was early morning, but his face was perspiring and he was out of breath. "I'll wait outside," he said, glancing down at his dusty boots.

Before Tilda could turn around, Charlie rushed from the bedroom, suspenders loose, work shirt in his hand. He'd fought fire most of the night and been asleep only a couple of hours. "What now?" he asked as he and Tilda joined Carlson on the porch.

"Another damn fire," Carlson exploded. He ripped off his hat, threw it in the dirt, and stomped on it. "First, fire breaks out in old slashings where we haven't logged for months. Then five miles up the creek, for no reason, another fire. And now, just when we're mopping up after that one, a third fire starts a couple miles from the second one, and against the wind. Make sense of that!" He jerked his handkerchief from his back pocket and wiped his forehead and neck.

"It don't make sense," Charlie said, buttoning his shirt over his union suit. "No electric storms—"

"You're right," Carlson said. "It don't make sense! Last night I told the fire crew they could pack up their gear and leave in the morning. Then I wake up to another damn fire." He picked up his hat and slapped the dirt off on his pant leg, boxed it back into shape, and set it on his head, tugging the brim into place.

"We have to get to the bunkhouse and tell the boys they aren't through yet," Carlson went on. "The way the smoke's filling the sky this morning, we're going to need them all and more besides."

"We'll get a crew," Charlie said. "Men show up at the office every day looking for work." He hoisted his suspenders over his shoulders and followed Carlson down the track.

Tilda returned to the kitchen and sat down at her sewing machine. Her throat and nostrils stung from breathing the smoky air.

Tilda slid the cloth under the sewing machine needle and dropped the presser foot, but she couldn't concentrate on her sewing. So much to think about. The fires were bad. The line of men at the office was bad. She understood why so many camps were shut down. The mills weren't buying logs because no one was buying lumber. No one was buying lumber because no one had money to build. That was the part she didn't understand. How a big, rich country like America could have suddenly become so poor.

Some blamed President Hoover. She thought of the pictures in the *Seattle Times* of "Hooverville" where thousands of families lived in homemade shelters in the middle of the city, crowded into shacks built from empty crates and scrap lumber. The people who lost their jobs and couldn't pay their rent had been pushed out to live in the streets.

There were other pictures, too. Ragged men and women standing in line at soup kitchens. Hundreds of men lined up at employment offices. Closeups of tired faces, with eyes that looked like empty windows. The paper said the only ones prospering now were the crooks and bootleggers. Even in a little town like Hoodsport, bootleggers were taking advantage of laid-off fishermen and loggers, getting away with whatever money the men had saved by selling them illegal whiskey at sky-high prices.

She was thankful to God that Charlie had been made hook tender because even when camps were down, he oversaw small cleanup crews—

"Tilda, fix me a bite to eat quick," Charlie said, bursting through the door, "and put dinner in the lunch bucket. We're taking men out to the new fire."

Tilda grabbed a bowl from the cupboard and dished up the oatmeal that simmered on the back of the stove. She ran to the screen box for milk for the mush, and cold fried trout and potato salad for the lunch bucket. She wrapped the trout in newspaper, spooned the salad into a jar, filled the thermos with coffee, and snapped the lunch bucket shut.

"Do you have enough men now?" Tilda asked, pouring coffee into a cup and setting it in front of him.

"Ya," Charlie mumbled, his mouth full. "There's always more men than we can use."

"Do you have any idea yet how these fires started?"

"Fishermen, maybe. Or campers. We don't know."

Tilda heard the speeder rattle to a stop in front of the house. Charlie grabbed his lunch bucket and tin hat and ran for the speeder.

"Everyone here?" he shouted above the noise of the idling engine.

"Everyone but Billy," one of the men answered. "He must've left camp last night when we were told we were through. His bunk wasn't slept in."

"His gear's still there," another man said.

"Wait up," someone hollered from down the track.

Tilda saw a young man sprint to the speeder and swing himself onto the rear of the car.

"You're late, Billy," Charlie hollered.

The boy, breathing hard, nodded and sat down as the speeder lurched ahead toward the black-brown smoke that billowed out of the forest and across the horizon.

That night Tilda had another fire nightmare. She dreamt that flaming trees were falling on the fire crew, that fire was sweeping through the brush at a speed faster than the men could run. She smelled suffocating smoke, felt heat from live coals landing on Charlie's back, and saw him rolling on the ground to put out the flames. Several times she awakened, soaked with perspiration, and reached across the bed for Charlie, but he wasn't there. Finally at daybreak she heard a murmur of voices at the other end of the house. She grabbed her bathrobe and ran to the kitchen. With a sigh of relief, she saw Charlie and Superintendent Carlson, eyes soot-ringed and hair sweat-plastered, sitting at the table drinking coffee.

"Be sure everyone understands his job," Carlson was saying. "You can depend on your crew, can't you?"

"No problem there," Charlie said, and then hesitated. "Except maybe for Billy Stone. Yesterday wasn't the first time he was late."

"Wasn't he the one I let go last winter when we had to cut back?"

"That's him. He was a good boy but lazy. Still, he was the first one around when we needed extra men to fight fire."

"Well, get after him," Carlson said, standing up to leave. "See that Charlie gets some rest now," he said to Tilda, tipping his hat as he went out the door.

Tilda studied the sky and prayed for rain, but none came. The air was heavy with smoke. No one went outside. The only movement in camp was that of heat waves dancing on the iron tracks and the locomotive chugging by several times a day, shuttling tanks of water to the fire site. But finally, at the end of the week, the brown smoke that shrouded the camp began to lift and Tilda caught a glimpse of blue sky. The fire had been brought under control. But when Charlie came home that night, his mouth was drawn tight and he paced the kitchen floor.

"Billy wasn't on the speeder tonight," he said. "We left Ole and Gus to look for him."

"Could he be hurt?" Tilda asked.

"No, it's happened before. He'll turn up, but, damn it, he's becoming a nuisance. We hired him to fight fires, not play hide-and-seek." He started to sit down, but stopped.

"I need to see Carlson," he said, disappearing out the door.

Tilda dished up supper for Thelma and Angie and pushed Charlie's meal to the back of the stove. The girls were in bed asleep when the back door opened and Charlie walked in. She watched him slump against the sinkboard, his ruddy face pale in the lamplight.

"It was Billy, all right," he said, barely loud enough for Tilda to hear. "Ole caught him red-handed. He was about to set another fire."

"No," Tilda gasped. "I can't believe it. Why?"

"He was up against it. He has a wife and baby to support. He couldn't find a job, so he made himself one. Every time we had a fire about licked, he started another one." Charlie took a deep breath. "So he could keep working."

Charlie sat down at the table and rested his head in his hands. Tilda turned to the stove to dish up his dinner. She'd never met Billy, but she knew what he looked like. She'd seen him in the newspaper many times. His face was the face of all those desperate young men with hollow eyes who were standing in line at the employment offices.

"What's going to happen to him?" she asked.

"The sheriff from Shelton will be here in the morning."

"Will Billy go to jail?"

"That's the penalty. Valuable timber's been burned. Lives were put in danger."

"And his wife and baby? What will happen to them?" Tilda asked, searching her husband's face.

In answer to that, Charlie could only shake his head and turn his eyes away.

"King of the Mountain"

Even Tilda's coolest housedress felt too warm on this August morning as she hurried down the track to the timekeeper's office. But today she didn't mind walking in the heat to get the mail, or worry about the dust that spurted over her shoes with each step. Charlie was taking the afternoon off, and that made this Saturday a holiday.

He had been working without a break for two weeks, ever since Carlson promoted him to foreman of all Camp Two operations, the new "bull of the woods." Smith had resigned as camp foreman in April when Carlson's dog nearly killed his dog. Carlson thought of Charlie right away as a possible replacement, he told Tilda, because Charlie had done such a good job as hook tender.

Tilda ran up the steps to the office, nodding to a group of men sitting in front of the bunkhouse across the track. As camp foreman, Charlie wouldn't have days off —

"Mrs. Lind," one of the bachelor loggers called out, "when does Charlie get off work today?"

"Maybe by noon," Tilda smiled. "Did you want to see him?"

"We'll see him," the logger laughed. "On the high spot between the tracks." The other men nodded and smiled.

The "high spot"? Tilda didn't know what that meant. Probably it had something to do with Charlie's new job. There was no end to the things expected of the camp foreman. At six in the morning he was at the cookhouse hollering, "All out for the woods." He rode with the men to the logging side and decided which trees should be felled and where they should fall. He was expected to keep his eye on the men as he worked beside them, fire anyone he saw sloughing off, and then hire the man's replacement.

Before the men finished logging a side, Charlie would look for the next place to log. He'd hunt for the tallest, straightest tree he could find for a new spar tree and then map out a setting around that tree. He would be in charge of moving the donkey and other equipment over the steep hillsides through jungles of brush to the new side and then oversee the rigging of the spar tree and the setting up of the equipment. Charlie told Tilda he'd be working longer days, but it was all right. He liked the responsibility. Tilda wondered if this would be the only afternoon for a while that he could come home a little early—

"Oh, excuse me, Mrs. Lind," Mrs. Webb said, bumping into Tilda in the office doorway.

"No, excuse me," Tilda smiled, moving out of her way.

"Tilda, are you all right?"

"Ya, you didn't hurt me," Tilda laughed.

"No, I mean are you all right about this afternoon?" Mrs. Webb said, patting Tilda's arm lightly, and then scurrying off before Tilda had time to answer. Tilda watched her friend hurry down the track.

"Nothing in the mail today, Mrs. Lind," the timekeeper said as Tilda stepped through the door. He started to say something more, but, instead, turned away and began leafing through the papers on his desk. Tilda studied his back a moment and then left for home.

Tilda turned from her midday cooking when she heard her husband's step on the porch. Through the open door she saw him sit down on the porch stool and begin to unlace his caulk shoes.

"Charlie, something's going on. What is it?" she asked. Fish and potatoes were boiling in one kettle and string beans from the garden, in another.

Before he could answer, Thelma ran onto the porch with Angie close behind. "Hey, Dad," Thelma said. "The kids say someone's going to beat up on you today. Is that true?"

Tilda caught her breath. "Beat up on you! Why?"

"Nobody's beating up on me," Charlie gruffed. "Bill Edson would like to try, that's all."

"What do you mean, 'that's all'?" Tilda exclaimed.

"He thinks Carlson should've made him the new camp foreman."

"Is there going to be a fight?" Thelma persisted.

"Looks like it," Charlie said. "He's going to make me prove I'm the best man for the job." He pulled his boots off and brushed the dirt from the tops of his socks.

"The fight's at three o'clock this afternoon," Thelma said. "That's what the kids say. On the high spot between the tracks."

The railroad tracks that edged both sides of the row of family houses also bordered a small hillock. The camp kids liked to play "King of the Mountain" there, but that was all in fun. Tilda had heard about Bill Edson and her knees felt weak.

Bill and Charlie worked together in Camp One as well as Camp Two. Bill stood half a head taller than Charlie and had arms long enough to hold off a bear. Charlie had told her that when the boys at the bunkhouse fooled around boxing on a Sunday afternoon, no one wanted to draw Bill. No one had beat him yet, and they usually had a black eye and split lip for trying.

"Superintendent Carlson picked you for camp foreman," Tilda said, unaware that the beans were boiling over on the stove. "Why does Edson think he should have the job?"

"He says he's been with Phoenix longer than me and has more experience. He says he can outfall and outbuck me any day of the week, including Sundays."

"Even if that was true, Carlson picked you to take Smith's place. That should be that!"

"Ya, but I think the men been egging him on. They like a little excitement, and I have to prove myself to them, too."

"Well, how is a fist fight supposed to prove who's the best foreman?"

"In the woods, being tough is what counts," Charlie said. "Now if you want me to stand up to Edson this afternoon, you'd better stop worrying and dish up my dinner."

The high spot was made up of gravel and loose dirt thrown there when the ground around the mound was first leveled off for the rail beds. Stringy weeds, coarse grass, and a few fir seedlings had taken root, but most of the ground was bare.

When Tilda and the girls reached the high spot, camp kids were already running around and over the mound, shadow boxing and feinting blows to the stomach and head. A few loggers stood around quietly smoking and talking. In a short time, most of the loggers in camp had gathered and were arguing and boasting and laying coins on the track rails to cover their bets. Several women joined Tilda off to the side. At three o'clock an eerie silence fell over the crowd.

Charlie appeared first. The quiet spectators drew apart as he moved through them to the top of the mound. His shirt was off, but he wore his undershirt. Red suspenders held up his stagged pants.

The women twisted their aprons and held their children back. "That's my dad," Thelma whispered to the boy standing next to her. "You watch. He'll be 'King of the Mountain.'"

"No, he won't," the boy said. "My pa says no one can beat Edson."

"My dad can," Thelma said.

"No, he can't."

"Yes, he can. Wait'll you see my dad fight!"

"My pa's seen Edson fight and says he's mean. He's the toughest man in camp. Look. Here he comes now."

The crowd separated a second time, splitting farther apart, making a wider path. Edson wore neither shirt nor undershirt. His suspenders were stretched taut over his barrel chest. He took his place at the top of the mound and looked around at the crowd. Someone waved a paper bill and shouted, "My money's on you, Edson. Go get him!"

"Save your money," someone hollered at the first man. "Lind's going to show Edson a thing or two."

"Let's get on with it," someone said.

"Yeah, on with it," someone echoed.

Edson turned back to Charlie and the two flexed their arm muscles, put up their fists, and began circling. Tilda's heart was in her throat.

Edson tested his muscles with short, quick jabs at the air. He danced forward and back. Charlie rocked in place, fists ready.

"Whatcha waiting for, Edson? Hit him!"

"Punch him, Charlie! Teach him a lesson!"

"Hit him, Daddy!" Thelma's voice rang out.

"I can't look!" Tilda cried.

The hot sun beat down on the high spot and reflected the heat back up from the gravel and packed dirt. The two men circled in one direction, and then the other, moving in closer.

Charlie's undershirt stuck to him in sweat-patches. Rivulets of perspiration ran down Edson's face, down his thick neck, and disappeared into the hair of his bare chest and back. Edson made a short, quick jab. Charlie did the same. The spectators cheered and called for more. Tilda buried Angie's face in her apron and looked away.

"Come on, mix it up!" someone shouted.

"Hit him, Charlie. Show him who's boss!"

"Knock him dead, Edson. Draw some blood!"

Edson planted his feet and drew back his right arm. He tightened his fist until his knuckles turned white and rolls of muscle threatened to break out of confining skin. His eyes narrowed. With the power of a locomotive, he swung a haymaker punch so swift it seemed invisible.

But Charlie saw it coming. He ducked and danced to the side, fist drawn back to return the punch, when his target dropped! Edson lay on the ground, groaning and twisting in the dirt.

The cheering and shouting stopped. The crowd stretched to see around each other. Charlie lowered his arms and stared at Edson writhing below him.

"My shoulder!" Edson gasped, and flayed the dirt with his feet.

Charlie dropped to his knees beside Edson, grabbed his arm and started to pull. It wasn't working. He took hold of Edson's wrist and, bracing his feet against the side of Edson's chest, jerked the arm violently. Edson screamed and then lay still.

Charlie stood up, brushing the dirt from his pants. Then he reached down and offered Edson his hand.

The spectators turned to each other. What the hell happened?...I don't get it...I don't either...

"Have to be careful with those haymakers," Charlie grinned as he pulled Edson to his feet. "If you miss, you can throw your shoulder out."

"By God, you're right," Edson said, rubbing his shoulder and looking at Charlie. "Guess this fight is one for the books."

"Now you're right," Charlie answered, his grin widening. Edson grinned back and then laughed out loud. Charlie laughed. Edson laughed till he had to rest his arm across Charlie's shoulder to support himself. The loggers around the high spot pocketed their bets and slapped each other in delight. They hadn't seen a better show in vaudeville.

"Here, Bill. Can I help you back to the bunkhouse?" Charlie asked, offering his arm for support.

"Hell, no, Charlie. It's my shoulder I threw out. Not my leg. But you can come along. I got a couple bottles of homebrew we could open..."

"Mama, was that a fight?" Angie asked as they walked toward their house.

"It was kind of a fight," Thelma answered for her mother.

"It was the kind of fight I like," Tilda said. She paused. "What you say we make some sandwiches and go to the lake this afternoon? That is, if there's still time when your daddy gets home from the bunkhouse."

The Blue Ox

"Let's play something else," Angie said, talking loud over the music and the stomping feet.

"Why?" Edwin asked, content with his perch on top of the pile of coats. "You like playing 'King of the Mountain' in camp. Even your dad plays it," Edwin grinned.

"That's different," Angie said. She wanted to push him off and be king. But even at age four, she knew better. He'd fall off and cry. Everyone's best coat would slip and slide off the bench and onto the dance floor. The powdery white chalk someone spread on the wooden floor to make it slick would get all over the coats. Probably the music would stop and everyone would look at them with pinched-up faces. Their mothers would run over, give them each a shake, set them down hard on the bench, waggle their fingers at their noses, and tell them to behave. Then the mothers would run back to their music and the dancing and leave them to sit. Angie had looked forward all day to coming to the Blue Ox, but she wasn't having much fun.

Mama had been having fun since morning. Her feet were dancing the minute they slipped out from under the covers and touched the linoleum floor. From her crib Angie could see her skip and spin as if she were already hearing the band. Angie listened for the music, but all she heard was her daddy's wake-up yawn and groaning stretch that he saved for the Saturday mornings he had off.

"Well," he said, blinking himself awake and raising up on one elbow, "tonight we go dancing at the Blue Ox." He smiled at Mama's excitement. "Do you think Thelma wants to go with us or stay home and take care of Angie?" he asked.

"She wants to come. She knows some of the young loggers and can dance with them."

"Then we have to take Angie. What will she do when we're dancing?"

"She can sit on the bench and watch like at the camp dances. Edvin will be there, so she'll have company. And they're good about not getting into things."

"Ya, they're never any trouble."

Mama didn't have to get after Angie to take her nap. Angie crawled into her crib after lunch and closed her eyes tight so she'd sleep fast. When she woke, Mama was in front of the little mirror that sat on the dresser.

Angie knew why the coal oil lamp next to the mirror was lit in the middle of the afternoon when they didn't need the light. Mama was going to fix her hair. The long, skinny curling iron hung by its handle inside the chimney of the lamp, warming above the tiny flame. Mama hummed as she set down her hairbrush and lifted the iron carefully from the thin glass and clamped it onto a piece of her short, shiny-brown hair. Angie heard the sizzle and saw the steam. Mama slipped the curling iron down a little and clamped it shut again. Then back into the chimney it went and crimp, crimp, some more until deep waves made a frame around her face.

Now Mama put down the curling iron, leaned toward the mirror, and studied her eyebrows. She stopped humming and picked up the tweezers she'd bought at the dime store in Shelton and began plucking, like she did to chickens before cooking them for Sunday dinner. When she finished, what was left looked like little pencil lines. They must have been right because she put away the tweezers and began humming again.

Angie knew what was next. A creamy, pink powder, packed hard like the damp creek bank. With a tiny, flat puff, she brushed the pink on her cheeks till she looked as if she had just come in from a fast walk down the railroad track. Next, she dipped a fluffy powder puff into a round box of powder that must have been made from ground-up flower petals, it smelled so nice. Holding back the fresh waves that curtained one side of her forehead, she dusted her face all over. No one had a prettier mother.

Daddy was getting ready, too. Angie climbed out of the crib and followed him outside. He carried a bucket of water and clean rags. He'd traded in his old Chevrolet for a brand new one and he wanted it to be clean and polished for everyone at the Blue Ox to see. Angie watched him scrub and polish until they could both see themselves in the shiny black paint.

Mama had sewed herself a fancy new dress. Thelma wore "pajamas" but not the going-to-bed kind. These came from Sears Roebuck catalog and were shiny with big, bright flowers all over and a bow in front. Thelma must have known the "pajamas" were right for the dance because she was smart, and she'd lived away from home for a whole school year. Except for her thick glasses with the black rims, she looked very nice.

"Let's go," Daddy said, and they hurried to the car.

Angie sat on her knees looking out the back window. She liked to watch the trees close in behind them and swallow up the road. When dust from the car screened the trees from view, Angie turned around and stood on the floor behind the front seat. "When will we get there, Daddy?" she asked, poking him in the back.

"We just started," he said.

"Don't ask that," Thelma whispered to Angie. "At least not very many times. It makes him cranky."

Mama unwrapped a stick of gum and folded it into her mouth. "You can play with this," she said, handing Angie the shiny silver wrapper. Angie wanted the gum, not the peel, but she knew Mama wouldn't let her have any because when the taste was used up, she always forgot and swallowed it. Angie folded the wrapper into a kite and showed it to Thelma.

"Nice," Thelma said and took hold of the door handle as they swung around another curve. The car bounced over a rock and swayed from side to side.

"I'm carsick," Angie said and laid her head in Thelma's lap.

"Me, too," Thelma said, "but don't fuss or they won't take us next time."

The worst of the curves were behind them when they reached Hoodsport and turned onto the Hood Canal highway. This road threaded its way between dark-green firs on one side and the deep-blue canal on the other. Tall madrona trees shedding curly, red bark leaned toward the beach. Mama said, "I never get tired of this part of the drive."

Angie said, "But when do we get there?" and then looked quick at Thelma to see if she was in trouble.

"Right now," Daddy said. "There it is. The biggest dance hall in this part of the state. Half the building sits on stilts over the water. They say that when the hall had its grand opening three years ago, 1500 people came from all over Washington to dance on the maple floors. And do you know why they named it 'Blue Ox'?"

He was looking for a place to park now. Angie shook her head. She could hear the music as they drew closer.

"Because the famous logger Paul Bunyan and his blue ox 'Babe' dug Hood Canal all by themselves," Daddy said and winked at Mama. Angie looked at Thelma to see if she should believe him, but Thelma told her to listen to the music.

They drove into a grassy field across the highway from the big, domed building. Dad stepped out and began dusting the car with a cloth he pulled out from under the seat. Mama took Thelma by one hand and Angie by the other, checked for cars up and down the highway, and then hurried across. Mama always gripped them too tightly when they crossed the street together. Thelma said it was because of Leonard.

"Hurry up, Charlie," Mama called. "Listen to that polka. The music don't wait."

When they first walked out of the bright daylight into the big hall, Angie couldn't see anything. Little by little she began to see better. Lots of people were dancing while some were sitting on benches around the floor tapping their feet. On one side of the room, people were sitting down and eating. Everyone was talking and having fun.

"Look, Angie, a fireplace made out of rock," Thelma said. "I guess you've never seen any kind of fireplace, have you? And look how many musicians! A big piano, an accordion like mine, and fiddles, and even a horn." Angie felt like the whole building jumped when the music started up again.

"Telma, take our coats to the bench over there and put them with the others," Mama instructed. "Take Angie, too, over where Edvin is sitting. Carlsons got here ahead of us, I see. Go now, and then you can dance."

So here they sat. Edwin on top of the coats being "king of the mountain," and Angie wanting to push him off but knowing better.

"I want to play something else," Angie repeated.

"Like what?" Edwin asked.

"Follow the leader, and I get to be leader."

"Okay," he said, sighing deeply. He slid down the pile of coats. Two coats followed him and landed on the floor. He threw them back on the pile.

"Follow me," Angie said over her shoulder as she raced along the top of the long benches that circled the dance floor, jumping off and on when someone was sitting in the way. Edwin followed until they were back where they started.

"My turn to be leader," he said, diving under the bench and crawling along under its length. Angie was close behind him when he suddenly stopped.

"Look, Angie," he said, pointing up at the underside of the bench. "Gum! Lots and lots of gum."

He crawled a little farther. Angie followed. He turned on his back and pushed himself along with his feet. Angie did the same. She could feel the floor quiver under her back from the dancing.

"Look under this bench," he whispered.

"More gum," Angie whispered back, not knowing why they were whispering. She reached up and touched one especially big lump. "Edwin," she said, "this one is still warm, and soft, too. And sticky."

"Smell this one," Edwin said. "It smells real good."

"So does this one."

"I bet it still tastes good," Edwin said.

The music stopped. Clapping. Laughing. "Another schottish," someone called out. More clapping. The music started. Angie could see the dancer's feet. One, two, three, hop. One, two, three, hop. Then around they whirled, each couple hopping in a circle until the end when they all went bumpedy-bump-bump—BUMP-BUMP with their feet.

"Let's have a waltz," a man called out, and the music started and around and around they danced till they ran out of music again.

"We better go back to the coat pile," Angie said when she saw their parents and Thelma walk out of the crowd toward the benches. Angie raced Edwin back to the coats.

"Just look," Mrs. Carlson said. "What good children! They are sitting here so nice, right where we left them."

Mama came closer and leaned down to see them better in the dim light. "Looks like someone gave you a treat," she said. "Someone give you and Edvin candy?"

"They were big pieces of candy, I can see that," Mrs. Carlson laughed. "They can't hardly close their mouths."

Angie tried to smile and a trickle of juice ran out of the corner of her mouth. "It's not candy," she said. "It's gum."

Mama stepped back. "Who gave you so much gum?"

"No one. We found it."

"And there's lots more where this came from," Edwin said, pointing under the bench.

Then everything happened at once. Thelma screeched and covered her mouth. She and Edwin lost their gum. Mama's knees dipped a little and she reached for Daddy's arm. Daddy shook off her hand and started looking for their coats, and the next thing Angie knew, they were headed for their car.

Mama and Daddy didn't say much about the dance on the way home. Maybe they didn't have as much fun as she and Edwin did. Edwin was right about the gum. It did still taste good.

Fish for Breakfast

"Oh my, Ida, Artur gets up early," Tilda said. "Here he comes across the clearing now, and it looks like he's carrying another mess of fish." Tilda reached into the screen box on the back porch for a bottle of milk. The air was cool, but the morning sun promised another warm August day. "We may have fresh fish for breakfast again."

"Ya, that's good," Ida said. "My Charlie has another week of vacation. Maybe we should stay through Labor Day, so you won't run out of fish," she laughed.

Tilda became serious. "We're all right. Charlie's job is steady, Superintendent Carlson told him. But some laid-off loggers are living on fish, all right. Fish and deer meat. How do people get along in a city like Tacoma when they don't have jobs and can't fish and hunt?"

"It's hard," Ida answered. "Our neighbor had to give up his house and car when he lost his job. The family moved in with relatives in the country. Another neighbor—"

"Look Mom," Arthur hollered as he reached the porch. "Caught the limit again. Ain't they swell?" He held up the forked willow branch on which he had strung the glistening trout. One still twitched slightly, struggling against the stick threaded through its gills. Arthur's shoes and pant legs were wet and twigs stuck out of his sweater. "Just don't make me eat them," he added.

"I never could get him to eat fish," Ida laughed, "but as long as he catches them for us, I can't complain. Come in now, boys," she called to the two Charlies who were standing by the woodpile talking and having a smoke. "Artur caught fish for breakfast again, and you can help clean them."

Tilda sliced leftover potatoes into her big, iron frying pan while her Charlie cleaned the fish at the sink. He cut off the heads and slit the silver bellies with his **puka kniv**, washed the fish clean and laid them on a newspaper next to the sink. Ida sprinkled the fish on both sides with flour and dropped them into a pan of sizzling butter.

"So, what were you talking about so serious?" Ida asked her Charlie when the men came into the kitchen.

"This damn depression," Ida's Charlie answered. "I read in the newspaper that thirteen million people are out of work and it's going to get worse. Wages dropped sixty percent since the stock market crash three years ago, and factory production is down fifty percent."

In spite of the bad news, Tilda had to smile. Art and his father were alike. They both talked in numbers.

"Ya," Tilda's Charlie said, "and now some cousin of Teddy Roosevelt is running for President on a "New Deal." Hard to say what will come of that. This country don't need more deals. It needs jobs."

"That's enough politics now," Tilda said. "Everybody, sit down at the table and think of something good that you read in the newspaper."

"I read that a lady named Amelia Earhart flew solo across the Atlantic Ocean," Thelma said.

"How many hours did it take?" Arthur asked. Thelma didn't know, so he lost interest and asked her to pass the bread. Ida's Charlie boned one of the smaller fish for Angie. Tilda passed around the potatoes.

"**Moster**," Art said to Tilda when he'd filled his plate with potatoes, "are these fish as good as the ones me and Dad and Uncle brought home from Flap Jack Lake that time. You know. Before we went to Finland."

"Almost as good," Tilda smiled, remembering well the day the fishermen had come home and the week that followed...

The two Charlies and Arthur emptied their packsacks on the kitchen floor. Ida retrieved the enamel coffee pot and began scrubbing the campfire soot off its sides and bottom while

Tilda's Charlie talked. He told about the ice on the banks of the lake and the trout that teemed in the ice cold water. The first night there, they'd fished until dark, fried their catch, and eaten by starlight.

"Two fine days of fishing," Ida's Charlie told the ladies.

"Tell what happened this morning," Arthur said, hopping around the pile of camping gear on the kitchen floor.

"Well," Tilda's Charlie said, "I put the skillet on the grill to heat for breakfast and turned away to flour the fish. When I turned back to the grill, here was a baby chipmunk warming itself in the frying pan."

"You didn't cook him, did you?" Thelma exclaimed.

"Heck, no," Arthur said. "Here he is!"

He opened his packsack and the tiny chipmunk leapt out and darted into the front room. Thelma and Angie ran to catch him but lost him behind the couch.

No one wanted to go to bed that night. It was too hot. Thelma and Art played checkers and the grownups played pinochle. Tilda left the game to check on Angie.

A streak of moonlight had found its way between the window frame and shade and reached into the crib. Angie was asleep, her hair matted with perspiration, her covers kicked to the foot of her bed. Tilda reached into the crib to take hold of her blanket and instead wrapped her hand around something warm and furry. She screeched and threw it out of the crib and across the room. Angie woke up and cried out. Everyone came running.

"Look at it go," Art said. "**Moster**, you scared it to death."

"It scared me to death," Tilda laughed.

In the days that followed, Thelma taught the baby chipmunk to eat out of her hand, and when Angie sat really still, the chipmunk would sit on her lap. Then one morning a week later, the little animal disappeared. Angie cried, but Thelma told her wild animals needed to run free.

"Well," Arthur said, scooping up a second helping of crispy, brown potatoes, "I'll bet these trout don't compare to the salmon we caught at Lilliwaup Falls, do they, Uncle?"

"Guess you never will forget that fishing trip, will you, Art?" Charlie laughed. "Those salmon were fighting their way up the falls to spawn like their lives depended on it," he told the ladies.

"Their lives did," Ida laughed, "with fishermen like you two standing on the bank."

"That's true," Charlie smiled. "Those fish know when summer is over—"

"Charlie," Tilda interrupted after a quick glance out the kitchen window, "Carlson just walked up on the porch."

Charlie didn't wait. He pushed his chair back and went to the door, stepped out, and closed the door behind him. Tilda felt her stomach knot and didn't know why. She put her fork down and stared at the closed door.

Arthur took a swallow of milk. "I don't want summer to be over, and school to start. I want to fish more than anything."

"Not me," Thelma said. "I like school better than anything."

"Better than anything? Better than Swedish hotcakes?"

"Yep," Thelma answered. She split her fish lengthwise and pulled the wispy skeleton from the meat with her fingers. She leaned close to her plate to look for stray bones. Satisfied, she laid the fillet on her bread and took a big bite.

Arthur studied her. "Do you like school better than swimming in Lake Melbourne with the little waterdogs?"

"That's right," Thelma answered.

Arthur thought a moment, pushed his empty milk glass aside and leaned toward her. "Do you like school better than huckleberry pie with ice cream on it?"

Thelma hesitated. Arthur leaned back and grinned impishly. The back door opened. Charlie walked silently back to his chair and sat down. The children stopped their bantering. Everyone turned to look at him.

"Well, I guess it was bound to happen," Charlie said.

"What?" Tilda breathed.

"Being let go." Charlie's voice broke. "Phoenix don't need a foreman when there's no one left to boss."

CHAPTER 17: HARD TIMES

August 6, 1933

Dear Ivar,

I have been poor to write lately. Maybe because there's not much good news. Times are bad here and, if anything, getting worse. Almost all loggers are out of work. Charlie hasn't logged steady in almost a year. He finds small jobs when the camp's down, but he's restless for real work. We live in the camp houses free, but it is still hard to manage without a regular paycheck. Ida and her family are fine because Charlie's mill is still running.

Thelma finished her second year of high school in May and is home for the summer. She and Angie are always busy and don't pay much attention to the hard times around them. I guess that's the way it should be when you're young.

We hope that you are all in good health. I can imagine that the boys miss their grandfather Edvard. I miss him, too, and think about how close we came to making our trip to Finland while he was still alive. It is taking a long time for me to get over the disappointment, but we can't question God's will. Now we look ahead to when this Depression is over and we've saved enough money again to buy tickets for the trip. We want to sit around Father's table and drink coffee with you and Ester, and get acquainted with the boys before they are grown up and gone from home.

Take good care of yourselves and write soon. Letters from home fill an empty spot in my heart.

Your sister
Tilda

CHAPTER 18: CLOSE CALLS

Carlson's Milk Cow - September 1933

A ngie knew she should be tough. She was five years old now, a logger's daughter, and Thelma's sister. Her dad would tell how Thelma could out-throw and out-wrestle any kid in camp except Laurence Lathom, and she could outrun him. Grownups said kids should be seen and not heard, but when Thelma talked back to grownups, Daddy laughed about it later. Thelma said she got lots of lickings, but still, Angie wished she could be more like her. Well, Angie decided, if she couldn't be tough like her sister, she could at least fool her friend Edwin into thinking she was tough.

Edwin was nine days older than Angie, but she could tell him she wasn't scared of snakes or bears or yellow jackets, and he believed her. When she heard that Carlson's new cow was mean, she told Edwin she wasn't afraid of any milk cow, even if she hadn't seen it yet.

The afternoon was hot. She and Edwin jumped from one clump of dried-up grass to another to keep from burning their bare feet on the hot dirt. Finally, they sat down on the ground in the shade of the schoolhouse and watched for grasshoppers.

"It's hot here, too," Edwin said.

"It's cool by the creek," Angie said. "Let's go fishing."

Angie had watched her dad make her fishing pole from a willow that grew by the creek. He tied a string to the end of the stick and a hook to the other end of the string. With his teeth, he pressed a small lead bead the size of a pea onto the string. For a sinker, he told her. He showed her how to thread a fat angleworm onto the hook, and how to jiggle the hook in the water.

It wasn't very far to their fishing hole. They just had to cross the pasture in the middle of the woods where Carlsons kept their cow. But if Angie made Edwin play follow the leader to get there, it took a while. Angie would go first and climb up on stumps higher than her head by sticking her toes into little splits and chinks in the bark. She would jump from the top of the stump to a log and race the length of the log, skipping over sharp knots and then leaping off over patches of stickery blackberry vines. "Bet you can't do that," she'd challenge.

Mama always said, "You two be careful now so you don't get hurt," but Angie liked to show off when she was with Edwin and didn't always remember her mother's warning. More than once when they played follow the leader, Angie had run ahead and grabbed the lower branches of the first tree they came to on the edge of the clearing and climbed high up into the tree. Edwin had stood below and begged her to come down. The more he coaxed, the higher she climbed until he finally ran back to her house crying, "Mrs. Lind! Mrs. Lind! She's up in a tree again and she won't come down!"

But today it was too hot for follow the leader. This time they would run across the clearing for the cool shade of the wooded trail.

Fir and hemlock stood tall and straight on each side of the path, like the king's guards in the storybook Thelma read to Angie. Salal brush with its big, shiny leaves, grew thick under the trees, sometimes crowding the path. In the spring white, bell-shaped flowers bloomed on the branches, and in the fall dark-blue berries took their place. Mama said that Indians used to make the berries into syrup or dried and ground them into flour for flat cakes. Angie didn't think she'd like that kind of cake. The berries weren't sweet like blackberries and huckleberries. But Angie ate a few as they walked along so she could show Edwin her blue teeth.

The path itself was a deep mulch of leaves and evergreen needles that cushioned and cooled their bare feet until they reached the pasture gate. Edwin opened the gate and closed it carefully behind him. Angie crawled between the rails of the fence. Their feet disappeared in the coarse, sun-bleached, pasture grass as they raced for the cool woods and the creek on the other side.

"There's Bossy over there," Edwin said, stopping suddenly and grabbing Angie's arm.

Even at a distance, Bossy was bigger than Angie had imagined. As Angie watched, Bossy turned her heavy head slowly toward them, jingling the bell on her neck, moving her mouth from side to side like she was chewing gum.

"My dad says not to excite her," Edwin warned. "We better walk slow the rest of the way."

"She don't scare me," Angie said, her voice louder than she expected, but she decided to do as Edwin said.

Angie could hear the creek bubbling and gurgling in the deep woods ahead, just past the huge, moss-covered log that marked the edge of the pasture. No one felled this tree, Daddy had told her. A hundred years ago lightning hit it or wind knocked it down, he said, and he was probably right because he knew a lot about trees.

Edwin made a sling with his hands and boosted Angie onto the log. She reached back down and pulled him up. They both slid down the other side, landing on the soft bank of the creek. Branches from the downed tree reached out over the stream bed and framed a quiet place in the stream. The water was as clear as Mama's kitchen window, and she could see trout darting back and forth like the kids at recess in the schoolyard next to her house. Round, shiny-grey rocks the size of playground marbles covered the bottom of the creek and looked close enough to touch.

"Here," Edwin whispered, always generous with the worms his dad kept in a box under his house. The worm wrapped itself around Angie's finger. She pulled it in two and gave half back to Edwin. Angie's half wiggled and stretched to get away, but she threaded it onto the hook like her dad showed her and dropped it into the water.

Edwin caught the first fish. It leaped and spun on the end of the line, reflecting the slivers of sun that edged their way between the tops of the trees. He landed it and strung it by its gills onto a forked stick, sliding it down to the crotch of the stick to make room for more.

Angie hooked the next one. She swung the end of her pole to the bank where she could grab the fish with both hands and take out the hook. The fish was slippery and strong and slipped out of her hands. She retrieved it from the mossy bank and stuck her thumb through its gills to hold it. With her other hand, she pulled out the hook. Then she slipped the fish onto the forked stick next to the one Edwin had caught. By the time they ran out of worms and started home, they had a string of seven fish, and the sun was setting behind the trees.

"We better hurry," Edwin said as he started across the pasture. "We could be in trouble with our moms."

"So what if we are?" Angie said, letting Edwin know how unworried she was. She swung her pole above her head and swooped back and forth around Edwin like a low-flying bird. "Anyway, when they see all the fish we caught—"

It started in the ground. Angie felt it in her feet before she heard it. A pounding. Like far-off thunder, it rolled toward her from behind. Thunder without the warning of lightning. Her feet froze. Edwin stopped mid-step. They stood like players in the game of statue until Edwin moved his head to look behind them. Angie saw his mouth drop open and his eyes widen like the fish on the forked stick.

"Run!" he screamed.

Angie glanced over her shoulder and saw the lowered head and rolling shoulders of Carlson's milk cow. Dust and grass swirled up from its flying hooves—

"Run!" Edwin shouted. "Head for the fence!"

Angie ran. The big animal coughed and snorted. Her bell clanged louder, nearer. The fence was a long way off.

"Faster," Edwin hollered, reaching back and grabbing Angie's arm as he ran, nearly pulling her off her feet. "She's gaining on us!"

The fence was within sight. Angie thought they couldn't run any faster, but when they heard Bossy's bell clang close behind them, they flew at the rails. Edwin threw his pole and the string of fish over the fence and Angie threw her pole after his. They grabbed the top rail of the fence and catapulted over. Angie's knee scraped a gnarly knot as she slid across the rail and landed on the packed ground. Edwin sprawled next to her on his stomach, spitting out fir needles and dirt.

They looked back at the pasture as they struggled to get their breath. Bossy stood quietly next to the fence, looking at them over the top rail. She snorted once more and then lowered her head to pull at the grass growing next to the fence post. Angie and Edwin stood up slowly and backed away. They picked up their poles, still backing, and looked for the string of fish.

Sticks. Needles. Dirt. Crumbled leaves. Nothing else. They looked in a wider circle. No fish. They moved carefully toward the fence, searching the ground with their eyes and their hands. They moved away from the fence and scuffed through the brush next to the path with their feet. The sun withdrew behind the canopy of trees, leaving the path in deep shadows. It was getting dark. They would have to go home without their fish.

When they broke out of the woods and into the camp clearing, they saw that the lamps in the houses were already lit. Then they saw their mothers standing in the open doorway of Angie's house. An instant later, their mothers were running toward them.

"**Gud i himlen**, Edvin! Where have you been?" Mrs. Carlson cried. She was carrying Edwin's new baby brother Melvin on one arm and waving the other arm in the air. Her voice shook.

"Angie, it's almost dark," Mama said. "We've been so worried!"

"And look at you two!" Mrs. Carlson exclaimed.

Angie looked at Edwin. He had dirt in his hair and on his face and a long scratch down his arm. She tried to brush the dirt off her own overalls and saw that one pant leg was torn and her knee was bleeding. She looked up at her mom and saw her face was tight. Angie had lost her fish, and, worse yet, she'd been a smart-alecky show-off. She brushed aside a tear with the back of her hand.

Now the moms seemed more mad than worried. Mrs. Carlson grabbed Edwin by his collar, and they disappeared down the track toward their house. Mama gripped Angie's arm and marched her toward the porch and the still-open kitchen door.

"Time you were taught a lesson," Mama said, breathing hard.

"But, Mama—" Angie started. She wanted to tell her mother that she'd already learned her lesson, but she was running so fast to keep up, she couldn't get the words out.

Sixteenth Birthday-April 21, 1934

"No, Charlie, don't do it!" Tilda cried as she leaned into the windshield.

"**Tyst nu!**" Charlie snapped, his hand resting on the emergency brake. "You think we get home if we just sit here and look at the road."

The afternoon sun glistened off frosted trees and rocks and ice-crusted puddles, but all Tilda could see was the caved-in road ahead.

"We have to go back," Thelma said, her glasses clicking against the back door window of the car as she tried to see around her dad's shoulder. "Daddy, the road is gone!"

"What you mean, 'gone'!" he barked. "The road's still there. It's just settled a few feet."

"It's not wide enough, Daddy," Thelma persisted. "Maybe the car won't fit."

"I'll soon find out," he said, his hand flexing open and shut on the brake release.

"Charlie, no!" Tilda exclaimed and gripped the seat under her. Charlie was so stubborn when he set his mind on something, but she had to blame herself for their being there in the first place. She was the one who insisted they go to Shelton to pick up Thelma because tomorrow was her sixteenth birthday.

Rivulets of melting snow trickled from the bank above the cave-in, threaded their way between the rocks on the narrow ledge that was once a road, and disappeared over the side. Tilda began to tremble. She'd traveled this way enough times to know that there was nothing between this sliver of road ahead of them and Lake Cushman three-hundred feet below.

It had been a miserable spring. When the snow finally melted, it began to rain. Then it turned cold again and froze everything. You didn't know from one day to the next if you should wear galoshes for rain, or boots for snow.

Tilda had just finished frosting Thelma's birthday cake this morning when Charlie said maybe they better not go, that it looked like things were freezing up again. Tilda reminded him there was no way to get in touch with Thelma now at the last minute. Tilda knew Thelma would have her suitcase packed and be waiting for them.

Charlie pulled the brake tight and stepped out on the running board. "We can't go back," he said. "There's no damn place to turn around, and I'm not backing down the camp road."

Tilda watched him walk around to the front of the car and size up what lay ahead. The road had been a little slippery when they drove down to Shelton, but that was all. Sometime during the day a stretch of this rain-soaked road as long as their house had given way under the weight of itself.

"Mama," Angie said, tapping her on the shoulder, "when we going to get there?"

Tilda had to smile in spite of her worry, but before she could answer, Charlie was back in the car. "I'm going to make a run for it," he said. Thelma grabbed Angie, slid down in the back seat, and covered her eyes.

Charlie released the brake and pressed the gas peddle. The back wheels spun in place briefly and then took hold. The car nosed down, leveled off, and waggled forward. Charlie eyed the steep slope leading out of the cave-in and pushed on the accelerator, but instead of moving ahead, the car slipped sideways and stopped. He swore and stepped back out on the running board. Tilda slid across the seat to look and wished she hadn't. The left back wheel was resting on the icy edge of

the road. Lake Cushman lay far below, still and grey under a
skin of spring ice.

"Get out of the car," Charlie ordered. "Stand back there,
next to the bank."

"What are you going to do?" Tilda asked.

"I'm going to gun this car out of this hole and back up on
the road, and I don't want anyone riding with me."

"Why? In case you slip off the edge? Maybe we better stay
in the car so you won't try it," Tilda said, angry now.

"We can walk from here, can't we?" Thelma asked. "We'd
still get home before dark."

Charlie wasn't listening. Tilda could see it was no use arguing with him and hurried the girls out of the car.

"Now stand back!" he shouted.

"Is Daddy mad at us?" Angie asked Thelma.

Thelma shook her head, whisked the tears from her face
with the back of one hand and held Angie's hand with the
other. "It's my fault," Thelma said. "If it hadn't been for my
birthday..."

An icy wind stirred the trees above the road. Tilda turned
Angie's coat collar up and tightened her own coat. Thelma
covered her mouth and nose with her scarf, but she couldn't
keep her teeth from chattering. Together they watched as
Charlie examined again the wheel resting on the edge of the
drop-off. Then he climbed back into the car.

Tilda pulled the girls close. She couldn't control her shaking, but it wasn't the cold. It was the three-hundred foot drop.
Lake Cushman had been a home to them. A livelihood. And
now it was about to become a grave. Any minute the edge of
the road could crumble under the weight of the car, or if the
back wheel slipped sideways on the ice, even the width of
Charlie's thumb, the car with Charlie in it would be gone.

Charlie put the car in gear. It shuddered a little. The back
wheels spun, but the car didn't move.

"Daddy, please don't," Thelma pleaded under her breath.
Tilda shut her eyes and prayed.

The rear wheels spun again. Small rocks and blue exhaust
splayed out from behind the car. Then it found its footing and

slowly moved forward. The back end fish-tailed as the car gained speed. Then the car shot up the steep slope and onto the road at the far end of the cave-in.

Tilda's knees were weak, but she took Thelma's arm and Angie's hand, and they ran to catch up. There would be a birthday celebration after all.

Funny Face - September 1934

"Mama, I'm carsick," Angie called out from the back seat.

"Are you going to throw up?" Tilda asked, turning around to look at her. The car slid on the loose gravel as they rounded another corner. "I don't know," Angie cried. Her face was white and she was swallowing hard.

"Pull over, Charlie, so she can get out and walk around in the fresh air."

"Pull over! There's no place to pull over on this crooked camp road!"

"I know. It's no wonder Angie and Thelma get carsick."

"It's all in their heads anyway," Charlie grumbled. "If we're going to go somewhere in the car, they complain they're carsick the minute they put on their coats."

Tilda nodded. That was true all right. "Maybe they can smell the car on their coats," Tilda said defensively.

"Mama!" Angie moaned.

"All right," Charlie said and pulled off the road as far as he could, scraping the side of the car against the brush. "Sure as hell we'll get hit from behind!"

Angie slid out of the back seat, and Tilda walked her around to the front of the car in case another car came by.

Sometimes there was traffic. Once the Wests met another car on the only straight stretch between camp and Hoodsport. Both cars were going fast and when they saw each other, they both took to the brush and hit head-on fifty feet from the road. Mrs. West never let Bill forget that, and Charlie laughed every time he thought of it.

Maybe she should remind Charlie of this now, Tilda thought, as she helped Angie back into the car. He needed a good laugh. The camp had been shut down again for four months. Hillier, manager of Phoenix, hired Charlie and other laid-off loggers to cut ties for new track above Lilliwaup. When Phoenix didn't need any more ties, Charlie worked on the tunnel for Cushman's second dam, but so many loggers hadn't found jobs that everyone's spirits were down. Prohibition was finally over, but, they complained, no one had a nickel for a beer.

"Angie," Tilda said as she helped her back into the car, "take off your coat and lie down on the back seat for a little nap. When you wake up, we'll be in Shelton."

Angie had insisted on wearing her new coat even though the day was warm. Tilda had made it from her own coat, but the fur collar was Charlie's idea. He butchered their rabbit, and while she canned the meat, he tanned the hide for the collar. The rabbit had been Thelma's pet, which worried Tilda, but, like Charlie said, she wasn't around to take care of it now anyway.

"It's warm for September," Tilda said, fanning herself with a road map. "Too warm in the car. Charlie, can't we open a window?"

"Not on this dusty road," Charlie said. "I just cleaned the inside."

Tilda was still fanning herself when the road leveled off and they reached the highway and the cooler air by the canal. "Hoodsport has grown," Tilda said. "I'm surprised anyone has money to build."

"A few do. People from Seattle like to settle here."

"There's West's house on the hill," Tilda said, pointing to the right, as if Charlie didn't know. "I'll bet Mrs. West is glad they don't have to drive the camp road any more."

Charlie must have remembered the accident, too, because he laughed out loud.

"Maybe we should move to Hoodsport," Tilda said. "You could take the log train to work, couldn't you?"

"I have to live in camp when I'm foreman, you know that."

Tilda watched two seagulls swoop down over the water. One picked up a clam from the beach, flew high and dropped it onto the rocks. In an instant both birds dived for the clam meat that lay exposed in the broken shell. Then the car turned away from the canal toward Shelton, and Tilda wondered which seagull got there first. She turned around to check on Angie.

"She's sound asleep. That's good," Tilda said.

The highway was wider now, its two lanes twisting high above Purdy Canyon. Maple and willow trees that bordered the river at the bottom of the canyon were turning color. Tilda was enjoying the ride.

"When do I get to meet the new school teacher?" Charlie asked, interrupting Tilda's thoughts. "I hear she's a real looker," he teased. "What's her name?"

"It's Miss James. Miss Rose James. Ya, you'd like her all right," Tilda laughed. "She has thick red hair, and light brown freckles on her face like a little girl. She's not much more than a girl. Young to be teaching school."

"I heard that when she went to get her driver's license," Charlie said, "they gave it to her without testing her driving. She told them she'd been driving to camp from Hoodsport every day since school started, and they said anyone who could drive that narrow, crooked road and cross those single board stringers over the swampy places, don't need to be tested."

"She's spunky, all right," Tilda said, "but she'd have to be to even think of teaching school in a logging camp. She's moving to camp next week, someone said. I hope she don't get too lonesome."

"Say," Charlie said, "I know what to do about that. I have just the man for her."

"Are you going to be a matchmaker?" Tilda laughed.

"Sure. Why not? You know Gunnar Sjoholm? The husky, young guy with the big laugh? Good man. He was new on my crew just before shut-down, but he plans to come back when Phoenix starts up again. Course you have to introduce me to Angie's teacher before I can introduce her to her future husband," Charlie grinned. "Say, will you look at Angie now," he said, his eyes switching back and forth between the road and the rear view mirror. "She's making funny faces at me in the mirror."

Tilda turned around. She caught her breath. Angie wasn't playing. Something was terribly wrong. Her eyes were rolled back and her face was twisted. She was struggling to sit up, reaching her arms toward them with fingers spread out and bent like eagle claws.

"Stop the car!" Tilda screamed.

Charlie slammed on the brakes and slid to the side of the highway. Tilda jumped out and opened the back door. Angie's small body was rigid and awkward, but, little by little, they worked her out of the car and stood her on the ground.

Angie gulped for air like a fish flung on a creek bank and opened her eyes wide. Then her body sagged. Charlie caught her before her knees hit the ground. When she began to cry, they were relieved, but knew they'd better get her to a doctor.

Charlie floor-boarded the car. Tilda held Angie on her lap and rocked her like she did when Angie was a baby. She sang to her in Swedish and in English, until finally, after what seemed like a very long time, they drove up to the emergency door of the Shelton hospital.

"She'll be fine," Dr. Linkletter said, removing the stethoscope from his ears. "There shouldn't be any after-effects. You were lucky though. Another minute and she might not have revived. Carbon-monoxide fumes can be deadly."

"I knew the exhaust pipe was rusted," Charlie said shaking his head. "I was going to get a new one—"

"And we had all the windows rolled up," Tilda said. "But why didn't the fumes bother us? We were all in the car together."

"You said Angie was lying down," the doctor said. "If her face was toward the back of the seat, her nose would be right above the car's exhaust pipe." The doctor helped her down from the examining table. "She's a mighty lucky girl."

A few minutes later, they drove into Hepner's driveway. "I've been waiting forever," Thelma said as she ran up to the car. "What took you so long?"

"We'll explain later," Tilda said. "Are you ready to go home for the weekend?"

"I've been ready." She looked at Angie. "Where did she get that coat?" she exclaimed.

"Mama made it," Angie said, stroking the fur and smiling. "Feel the collar."

Tilda caught her breath. What had she and Charlie been thinking when they used Thelma's rabbit to make a collar...

Thelma touched the collar. She circled Angie and studied the coat and collar from all sides. She looked at her dad.

"Ya, I tanned the rabbit skin and Mama sewed it. What you think of it?"

Tilda held her breath.

"You were really smart to make a coat like this, Mama," Thelma said. "It's the prettiest coat I ever saw. And my rabbit makes it even nicer."

Tilda let her breath out in a deep sigh of relief and smiled up at Charlie. "We're lucky," her smile said. "We made it through two close calls in one day."

CHAPTER 19: SIGNS OF SPRING - 1935

Birdhouse

Angie liked first grade. Reading and writing was easy and Miss James even made arithmetic fun. WhatAngie didn't like was recess. The kids pushed and shoved each other the minute they tumbled out the schoolhouse door. Sometimes the boys got mad and hollered logger words at each other and swung their fists. They'd hit and wrestle in the dirt and the girls would run around and scream. Everyone liked recess a lot. Except Angie.

Tilda worried about Angie. Of the nine children in the camp school, she was the youngest and the smallest. She was shy and underweight. She needed to be **skookum** to get along with other loggers' kids. When Tilda saw a magazine ad for Ovaltine that showed a skinny little girl hiding in a doorway, and then read the promises of the ad, she went to the store in Hoodsport and bought the biggest can of Ovaltine sold, but even this didn't help. Then one Friday afternoon in the spring when school was about through for the day, Tilda glanced out the kitchen window at the schoolhouse and saw Angie racing across the muddy yard for home.

"Mama," she shouted, pink-cheeked and excited as she threw open the back door, "can Daddy build me a birdhouse?"

Phoenix had started up logging operations again, so Charlie was at work. When he came home from the woods that night, Tilda told him how Angie had been studying birds at school and wanted a birdhouse. After supper Charlie took the spare lamp out to the woodshed, gathered up board ends stacked with the stove wood, and began sawing and hammering. Tilda told Angie she could stay up and watch, even if it was late.

Angie watched the little house take shape. She thought of the birds that would fly to this shelter, escaping certain death if a late winter freeze rode the wind out of the mountains and intruded into spring. Miss James said that happened some-times and birds needed protection. Spring in the mountains could be as skittish as a little rabbit, she told them. Angie thought of this as her daddy worked, but mostly she thought of how impressed the kids would be at recess when she showed them her birdhouse fastened high up on the end of her house.

"Charlie! Angie! Quit now," Tilda called from the back door. "You have the whole weekend to work on the birdhouse."

"Mama's right," Charlie said, brushing the sawdust off his mackinaw. "We stop now, but it will be ready Monday like I promised."

Charlie wished he had more time for little projects like this, but now that Phoenix was getting orders for more logs, he was working long hours again.

"Is it fun to build a birdhouse?" Angie asked her dad as he put away his tools.

"It's more fun than being bull of the woods," he answered, and playfully pushed Angie ahead of him into the house.

When Angie first heard her dad called "bull of the woods," she asked her mother what it meant. "It means he's boss," her mom had smiled. But Angie wasn't sure being the boss was something good. Sometimes he'd come home late from work and he'd talk like he was mad at somebody and bang his chair when he pulled it up to the table for his warmed-up dinner.

And once at recess Don and Teddy Thompson, the biggest kids in school, said the bull of the woods was giving their dad a hard time, and looked right at Angie. "He told our old man to get off his ass and earn his wages," Don said. Angie remem-bered she wanted to hide behind a stump till recess was over.

Miss James would not allow rudeness in the classroom, and, anyway, she kept everyone too busy to get into trouble. Almost everyone worked from different books because, except for her and Edwin and Mildred, they were all in different grades. Miss James would move around the room and listen to different ones read or check their arithmetic or spelling or penmanship. She would ask the Thompson boys to pull their long legs out of the aisle so they wouldn't trip someone, and even they would mind her. Maybe that was because they liked the way she told stories about pioneers or Presidents or even birds. Daddy said they listened to Miss James because she was so young and pretty.

Saturday morning Angie woke early. She could smell the Swedish hotcakes and hurried to the kitchen. Mama laid a hotcake on her plate and handed her a saucer of melted butter. Angie sprinkled the hotcake with sugar, rolled it up, and dipped it into the melted butter, wiping the dribbles off her chin with the back of her hand. Charlie sipped his coffee, watching her eat.

"Angie," he said when she'd finished her first hotcake, "I been thinking. What you say we hang the birdhouse on the end of the schoolhouse instead of our house? Then when we sit here at breakfast, we can see the birds come and go. If we hang it on our house, we have to go outside to see the birds." He took another sip of coffee and waited.

"Charlie, I think that's a good idea," Mama said, turning from the big, black frying pan on the stove. Her cheeks were pink from the heat. "What you think, Angie?"

Angie turned to the window. She parted the curtains, being careful not to smear butter on Mama's snow-white panels. The schoolhouse was just across the playground, twenty giant steps away. They would have a perfect view.

Angie had trouble sitting still at her desk Monday morning. No one had seen the birdhouse yet because the schoolhouse door faced the railroad track, not the play-yard and her house. She would surprise everyone at recess.

Don said it first. "What do you mean, 'my birdhouse'? That ain't your birdhouse. How can that be your birdhouse when it's hanging on the schoolhouse?"

"That's the school's birdhouse," Teddy said. "Anyone can see that."

"Yeh, that's right," Wilfred Webb chimed in. "Can't be her birdhouse." He always agreed with the older boys. His sister

Jean and the older Woodworth girls listened to the boys and giggled. Edwin looked worried.

"Saying something belongs to you that don't, that's lying," Donald said, taking a running kick at a rock. It ricocheted off the side of the school. "It ain't nice to lie. What will the bull of the woods say if he finds out his kid's a liar?"

"I'm not a liar!" Angie shouted. "My dad made it for me and hung it there so we could see it from our window." She felt everyone staring at her. Her face burned and her stomach turned over. "Don't you believe me?" she cried, looking from one to the other.

Suddenly Miss James was at her shoulder. "What's going on?" she asked. No one answered. "Recess is over. Everyone back into the classroom. Angie, wait here with me a minute."

"Miss James," Angie said when everyone had left, "I need to go home. I have a real bad stomach ache."

"First, Angie," Miss James said, kneeling beside her in the churned-up dirt of the school yard, "I heard what the children were saying. I want you to know I believe you."

"The kids don't. It's not fair," Angie said, blinking back the tears.

"I know that. Children, like grownups, aren't always fair. Ignore their bad manners and enjoy your birdhouse. Before long they'll be asking your dad to build one for them, too."

Angie nodded and looked at the little birdhouse hanging high on the schoolhouse wall. Its shake roof, damp with dew, sparkled in the morning sun. "My stomach feels better," Angie said and put her hand in Miss James' hand. They walked together back into the schoolroom.

Cookhouse Flunkies

"Look, Angie, a trillium," Tilda called. She kneeled on the wet ground and gently touched the pink-throated, white petals of the delicate lily.

"I found one, too," Angie said, checking its whorl of leaves to be sure there were three. Half hidden under dank, brown leaves next to a patch of snow at the edge of camp, the lilies had bloomed in secret, unsure of their survival in the still-cool sunshine.

Tilda was sure of their survival. She'd seen it every spring now for twelve years. Just when it seemed that winter would never end, she'd discover an angel-white trillium peeking out from under a pile of decayed leaves next to an exposed tree root. She had learned well that no matter how dark the winter, spring still came. After Leonard's death, she had thought there would never be another spring. But there was.

Now after years of hard times in camp and sometimes months of complete shut-down, Phoenix Logging Company was back in full operation. All twelve bunkhouses were full. Counting the married men, over one hundred fifty loggers were riding the flatcars out to the woods every day. For a few days they were even short-handed, especially in the cookhouse. That's when the camp superintendent asked her and Anna Carlson to help them out. She remembered that first day...

It was still dark outside when they finished setting the long tables with chipped crockery and bent knives and forks. And just in time! The sound of the triangle brought caulks pounding down the walk between the bunkhouses and the cookhouse. The door flew open and a parade of men in heavy wool shirts and stagged pants hung their mackinaws on wall pegs and found their places at the table.

As quick as the men sat down on the benches, camp flunkies appeared at the kitchen door carrying platters piled high with slices of ham and strips of bacon. Thick pancakes followed on other platters, and then came heaping bowls of fried potatoes and scrambled eggs, each with a giant spoon stuck in the middle. The platters and bowls were passed down the table from one calloused, knuckle-skinned hand to another, pausing just long enough at each place for the man's free hand to stab as much meat and as many pancakes as his fork could hold. He filled the rest of his plate with the eggs and potatoes and set slices of bread next to his plate. As quick as the serving dishes emptied, a flunky refilled them, and the men dished up second helpings.

Tilda and Mrs. Carlson ran with pots of steaming, black coffee, filling and refilling the cup at each place. The only sound at the tables was that of forks scraping plates and men blowing and sipping hot coffee. In less than ten minutes, the men left the long table and lined up at the "spike table," spearing slabs of meat and bread for their lunch buckets. Five more minutes and they were grabbing their mackinaws and filing out the door. The train whistled and they were gone.

The ladies looked at each other and then at the slicked-up plates. Not a word had been spoken by any of the men. Not a motion wasted.

"Tilda, can you believe it!" Mrs. Carlson said.

"No, never did I see so much food put away so fast."

"And without a word."

"Logging companies have a rule against talking at meals," Tilda said. "They say it wastes company time."

"No one would talk anyway," Mrs. Carlson laughed. "If he said three words, the food would be gone, and he'd go hungry."

"Good thing they didn't ask us to be flunkies in the evening, too," Tilda said. "Can you imagine serving these loggers supper after they worked hard in the woods all day?" She'd heard that when times were better, a logger would quit a company that didn't serve good food and all he could eat, including pie and cake, and a huge piece of hardtack covered with butter to take back to the bunkhouse for a snack at bedtime. If he didn't get this, he'd quit the camp and go away calling them "gut robbers" or worse. Once that reputation got out, the camp would have trouble hiring anyone to take his place.

"Mama," Angie said, tugging at her mother's arm, "there's a robin. Do you think it'll find my birdhouse?"

"I'm sure it will. Or maybe one of its friends has already found it," Tilda smiled. "We go home and see."

Things had gone well for Angie, Tilda thought, ever since Miss James explained to the children about the birdhouse. Things were going well for Thelma, too. Thelma said they would soon be getting a letter from the school about her graduating in May, salutatorian of her class. "Salutatorian" was a new word to Tilda, and she liked the sound of it even before she knew it meant "next to best in the class."

"Angie, we go by the office on our way home," Tilda said. "Maybe the letter from the high school came today."

There was a letter, but not the one Tilda was looking for. This letter was addressed in pencil to "Karl Lind." The front of the envelope was stained, the corner was torn, and there was no return address. The postmark said, "Seattle" Tilda held the envelope up to the light.

"Who's it from, Mama?" Angie asked.

"I don't know," Tilda said. "I can't see through the paper."

"Open it up."

"I can't. It's addressed to your daddy. We'll have to wait till he gets home from work tonight."

Tilda turned the letter over in her hand, examining it again. It had been a beautiful spring day and she wanted nothing to spoil it. She took Angie's hand and hurried down the track. She'd fix something extra for supper to keep herself busy. She would not let herself sit and worry about what might be in the letter.

Graduation - 1935

> *"Roll out the barrel, We'll have a barrel of fun.*
> *Roll out the barrel, We've got the blues on the run.*
> *Zing Boom, Ter-rar-o, Sing out a song of good cheer;*
> *Now's the time to roll the barrel..."*

Charlie twirled Tilda one more time and then sang out with everyone else on the dance floor, *"For the gang's—all—here!"*

Tilda hung on to Charlie's arm for balance as they joined John and Anna Carlson standing at the edge of the dance floor. She dropped into an empty chair to catch her breath and wait for the room to stop whirling.

"Mrs. Carlson," Tilda said, "that Beer Barrel Polka is too much for me. I think I'm getting too old to dance like that."

"But, Mrs. Lind," Mrs. Carlson said, "they say you're not old till you're forty."

"I'll be forty next February," Tilda sighed.

The nickelodeon drew it's magic wand to the back of the flashy case and waited for the next nickel. Through the blue haze of cigarette smoke and the settling dust of the last dance, Tilda watched several men jostle each other over choosing the next song. Another man leaned heavily on the big music box, and, with a lopsided grin, waved at Charlie. It looked like some of the boys from camp had already started their week-end in Hoodsport.

"Mrs. Lind, if you're going to be forty in a few months, you better dance now while you still have the strength," Mrs. Carlson whispered, elbowing her good-naturedly.

"What's this?" John said, standing close enough to hear. "Don't you know life begins at forty?"

"Ya, that's true," Charlie said, "unless you turn forty at the start of the Depression, like I did. At least we're through with Prohibition. John, find a table for the four of us and I'll spring for the first round of beer."

The food and drinks at the Old Mill Tavern in Hoodsport were cheap, and Tilda thought the shiny, new juke box played polkas and schottishes as good as the musicians at the Blue Ox. And when she and Charlie drove home late at night from the Old Mill, they didn't have to drive on the busy Hood Canal highway. They just crossed the highway and they were on the camp road. That road was crooked and narrow, but all the traffic on Saturday nights went towards camp, so it was safe.

John spotted an empty table and hurried the women over to it. Tilda and Anna slid into the booth and set their pocket books beside them. John elbowed his way back through the stand-up talkers and drinkers to help Charlie carry the mugs to the table.

"So, Telma graduates this spring," Mrs. Carlson said. "Where has the time gone! Tell me again what she plans to do after she graduates. Does she still want to move to Tacoma in the fall?"

"She does, and we're glad for that." Tilda wiped up the wet spots on the table with a used paper napkin. "We can't imagine her going to University when she is so young. She just turned seventeen in April, you know."

"And she'll go to Artur's high school?"

"Ya, but in the high school they have a 'Post-Graduate School.' Thelma wants to take business and science courses that she couldn't get in Shelton. And she likes the idea of living in the city with her **moster** and uncle and cousin Artur."

"Is she going to University the next year then?"

"She wants to, but we have to wait and see. It's awful expensive, you know." The nickelodeon blasted out another polka and the crowd moved back onto the dance floor. "Here come our boys now," Tilda said, and slid over in the booth to make room.

Charlie took a deep swig of his beer, and surfaced with a foam mustache over a wide grin. Tilda poked him to make him behave and Mrs. Carlson laughed. He wiped his mouth with the back of his sleeve and looked at Tilda.

"John, you should have seen her when I came home from work last night. Eyes wide, standing at the door with an envelope in her hand. She'd worked herself up because she didn't know what was in a letter addressed to me." He paused to take a sip of his beer. "Turned out it was from my cousin Vilhelm Ecklund."

"I thought he lived in Canada," John said.

"Ya, he did, only now he is logging around Seattle. Vilhelm immigrated to Canada a few years after I did. He left a wife and a boy at home, but planned to go back to Finland when he had enough money saved up to buy a farm." Charlie paused. "That's almost twenty-five years ago, but you know how it is with some of the boys. The years go by--"

" Ya, I've seen it," Mrs. Carlson said, shaking her head. "Wives wait and wait and their children grow up without papas."

"That's right," Charlie said, "but when Johannes grew up he went to Canada to find his papa. Johannes logged with him a year or two and then moved to Washington. Now Vilhelm writes that Johannes wants to come to Camp Two and work for me"

"Do you have a job for him?" John asked.

"If I don't, I'll make one," Charlie said.

"We heard he's a hard worker," Tilda said, "and a good boy. He'll live in the bunkhouse, but spend time with us. We'll be family, you know. I get excited when I think about it." Tilda smiled at Charlie.

"Well, we have to hold back the excitement," Charlie said. "He won't be here till the snow flies. Tilda, let's fly around the floor right now before the music stops," he grinned and led her back onto the dance floor.

CHAPTER 20: SEPARATION

Huckleberry Season - August 1935

"Summer went too fast," Tilda told her friends holding the other three corners of the bed sheet. She gave her own corner a gentle shake and watched the tiny, deep-blue huckleberries roll about. The ladies were standing in the warm afternoon sun, and Tilda could smell the sweet juiciness of the berries.

"Hold your corner higher, Mrs. Lind," Mrs. Carlson said. "The berries are all rolling to your side."

"Excuse me," Tilda said. "I guess I was daydreaming." She gave the sheet a quick shake, and the berries rolled back toward the center. Sticks, leaves, and most stems stayed on the higher edges of the sheet.

"Instead of sliding the huckleberries off the limbs, leaves and all," Esther Hollman, new to the camp, said, "why don't we pick each berry? Then we don't have to clean them later, like we're doing now."

"That would take too long with these tiny berries," Mrs. Carlson said. "It's so easy to separate the brush when we bounce them on the sheet. Besides, it's a good excuse to be together and visit."

"Like we needed an excuse," Mrs. Jensen laughed.

"I plan to pick again tomorrow," Tilda said. "I want to can enough to make a lot of pies when Johannes comes."

"You'd think Johannes was Prime Minister of Canada, the way Tilda talks about him," Mrs. Hollman said.

"He's better than that," Mrs. Carlson laughed. "He's family. Charlie's cousin's boy from Finland, by way of Canada. I don't blame her for being excited. Do you know yet when he'll be here, Tilda?"

"When the snow flies," Tilda laughed. "Sometime this winter is all we know. But now I need to get home if we're through cleaning the berries. Thelma is leaving for Tacoma in the morning and I want to help her pack."

The women agreed the berries were clean enough and scooped them into their picking pails and started for their houses.

Thelma was sitting on the bottom step of the back porch when Tilda walked up. Angie stood next to the steps pushing on the sides of two tomato soup cans with her feet.

"Press down harder," Thelma instructed. "Push on your feet."

"I am pushing," Angie said.

"Then jump on the cans," Thelma said.

"Are you packed?" Tilda interrupted.

"I'll finish tonight," Thelma sighed, getting to her feet. "Right now I'm trying to show Angie how to press cans onto her shoes so she can clunk around with the other kids. But she's such a lightweight."

Angie jumped on the cans again, and this time they buckled and the ends folded upward.

"That's good," Thelma said. "Now stand still and I'll hammer the ends around the soles of your shoes."

Tilda watched and thought how short a time it had been since Thelma had clomped around on cans with the camp kids. And stilts. They all had stilts and walked around like giants, racing each other across the school yard. Tilda wondered if Thelma's stilts were in the woodshed or if they'd left them behind in one of their moves. Tilda sighed. Thelma was moving farther away than Shelton this time.

Thelma had told Tilda she was looking forward to living in Tacoma. Art had said he had friends who drove their dad's cars and she could ride with them, too, and they'd all have a swell time. But Tacoma was a long ways away, and Thelma wouldn't be able to come home weekends as she had in high school. Tilda wondered if Thelma would get homesick—

"Angie said she's going to write to me while I'm gone," Thelma told her mother.

"Maybe," Angie said, resting one hand on Thelma's shoulder for balance while Thelma hammered the ends of the cans onto her shoes. "How many times do I have to write?"

"At least once before Christmas," Thelma said. She set the hammer down. "Now let's see you walk on those cans. If I did a good job, you'll still be wearing them when I sée you at Christmas."

Angie Writes a letter - December 1935

Der Thelma

    It tock a long time. For I had no tablet. Mother send for a stashnare. and a hole lot of shets that had no lins. I got all these things at motgunry ward. im sorry that I told mother to writ and tell you dint hafto writ. Becus I dint no that you going to writ.

    For one week I practes a haf an hour every day on my flute. And got 15 cents. but I dint want to play so long. so I played ten minets every day and got 5 cents.

    A few days ago there were abot 4 inches of snow. Edwin and Mildered and Wilferd the Teddy and I made a snow houes. Jean helped a little bit. But not mutch. Mildered wasent going to help. she was going to make one her self. Mildered and Jean made a gerate big snow ball. Thay dint want it so me and Edwen and Melven and Merell were going to roll it to are snow house. But as we were rolling it got biger yet. so prtty soon it was up to my wast. All four of us coud not move it. so we gave up. and berock it to peses.

    I got one A- in endglish and the erest all A. All Edwen told me was that he got B in ereding and Mildered and Jean never told me what thay got on theres.

    Mother got the butterfly qilt alredy. and it shur is patty.

    Well thats all I got to say in this letter. so goodby o pal pie with ice-cerem on. Say helo to Muster and Uncle and Art. Thelm dont writ any more questchens. for nexst time im going to writ to Art.

                                             Angie

CHAPTER 21: CANADA COUSINS

"**M**ama, he's here!" Angie shouted and ran from the window to hide behind Tilda's skirt.
"Angie, behave yourself. You've been waiting all day and now you act silly." Tilda loosened Angie's arms from around her waist and started for the door. Angie hopped along beside her, clapping her hands. Charlie sent his chair flying in his rush to get to the door.

Snowflakes drifted into the kitchen and evaporated in the warm air as Charlie stood in the open doorway and sized up the fresh-faced, strapping young man on the porch. "Come in quick," Charlie said, "before you freeze to death." He shook Johannes' hand as he pulled him into the kitchen.

"I'm in," Johannes said, pushing the door shut behind him. He took off his gloves and blew into his hands. "I'm used to cold, you know, and bunkhouses. What I'm not used to is a warm, good-smelling kitchen like this," he smiled.

Tilda had been baking cookies and cakes ever since they came home from Tacoma the day after Christmas. Angie peeled and crushed cardamom seeds for coffee bread while Tilda cut up apple slices for **fruktsoppa** and pie. It was New Year's Day, the last day of their two-week vacation. Charlie had written Johannes that he needed to get to camp by the first of the year if he planned to log for Phoenix. Johannes was right on time, a good sign.

Angie stood close to Tilda, peeking up at the snow-dusted figure.

Johannes pulled off his knit cap and held it in one hand. He ran his other hand through his matted-down hair until blond strands stuck out in all directions. Angie giggled and Johannes reached down and roughed up her hair. Everyone laughed. His high cheekbones were as red as the apples Tilda had peeled for the dessert, and when he turned to her, his eyes were as clear and blue as a morning sky.

"**Välkommen**," Tilda said. "Shake the snow off your jacket and hang it there by the door. Coffee is hot and supper is almost ready. Sit down while I check the potatoes."

"How's your papa these days?" Charlie asked when Johannes had settled into a chair.

"He's fine. He works hard and saves his money. Still plans to go home one day."

"How was it in Finland when you left? **Din mor**?"

"People are poor. Mother gets along. Tells me not to stay away—like Papa."

"What are your plans?" Charlie asked.

Johannes stood up and moved to the stove. "First to get warm," he laughed. He turned to Tilda. "I can't remember when food has smelled so good!"

Tilda poked a potato with a fork to see if it was done. Charlie said, "After we eat, I'll walk you to the bunkhouse and we can talk about your job. Your papa said in his letter that you have experience setting choker."

"That I do, and on steep sidehills, so I'm ready for your mountains."

Angie inched a little closer to where Johannes stood with his back to the stove. "My school is going to a movie in Shelton," she said, almost too softly to be heard.

Johannes took her hand and pulled her closer. "Is that right? If you're going that far, it must be a pretty good one."

"It is. Our teacher is reading it to us. It's called *Midsummer Night's Dream* and Mickey Rooney is in it."

"Mickey Rooney! He's a big movie star, isn't he? But how will you get to Shelton with all this snow?"

"We walk to Lilliwaup and then ride a bus."

"That's a pretty long walk. I know. That's the way I came today."

"No wonder the food smells good to you," Tilda said. "And it's ready. Let's all go to the table."

Tilda passed the potatoes and meatballs twice and her canned string beans three times before Johannes looked up from his plate and was ready for conversation. They talked about fishing and hunting while Tilda cleared the table and set out the desserts. Then talk turned to logging.

"You've logged in snow before," Charlie stated rather than asked.

"Two winters in Canada."

"Then you know what it is to take a step and find nothing under the snow but a big hole? And what it is to walk on icy logs too slick even for caulk shoes? You have to allow extra time—"

"I know," he said, smiling with pastry crumbs in the corners of his mouth. "I have experience. You don't have to worry about me."

"I like to hear that," Charlie said. "Anyway, the woods are safer now than they used to be. When I first went to work for Phoenix, I heard that a logging outfit called Schaefer Brothers outside of Shelton lost a man a day—either hurt or killed. They didn't take him down out of the woods until the end of the day either. That's how tough logging was." Charlie took a sip of his coffee. "The state safety board finally shut them down."

"Say, that reminds me. Clear up in Canada we heard about Haywire Tom Watson who was supposed to log somewhere around here."

"Ya," Charlie laughed, "everybody's heard of old Haywire."

"Well, is the story they tell about him true?"

"Far as I know," Charlie smiled. "They say he fell 120 feet while going up to top a fir for a spar tree. He landed in deep mud feet first. He smiled and waved at the crew when they took him off to the doctor. The doc said there was nothing wrong with him, so he put on his clothes and went back to work."

Johannes shook his head and reached for a cookie to dip in his coffee.

"A logger isn't always that lucky," Charlie said. "He has to be careful, keep a sharp lookout, and be ready to jump when he needs to."

"Remember Jake Wilson?" Tilda asked Charlie. "He was standing next to you when they were hauling in a log. Just as it went by you, it turned over and the stub of a broken-off branch caught Jake's leg and broke it bad."

"Ya," Charlie said, "and remember the day he got out of the hospital and came back to work? He was standing behind me when the top of a tree snapped off in the wind and came down on top of him. He wasn't hurt bad that time either, but he quit the woods."

Johannes was listening. Charlie leaned forward across the table. "You got to be smart about your logging, and quick, and have the luck with you," he said.

Johannes cleared his throat. "Well, I've had experience in the woods, I've got long legs and I'm quick. I can leave luck to the next guy. What you say you show me to the bunkhouse. I need to settle in so I'm ready for tomorrow."

"You bet," Charlie said, and reached for their jackets.

"Come to supper again tomorrow night," Tilda said, "so we can get better acquainted. You have lots of time to eat in the cookhouse this winter."

"I'll be happy to come," Johannes said. "I can see there's still some cookies left. And, Angie, you can tell me more about this movie you're going to see." He shrugged on his heavy jacket and waited for Charlie at the door. "**Tack igen**," he said as he went out the door.

Nights were long in late January. Tilda had fixed Angie's breakfast by lamp light and only now as she helped her with her boots and coat, did it start to get daylight.

"So, Angie, you go to school on Saturday now?" Charlie said, scuffing into the kitchen in his Christmas slippers. "And before the sun comes up," he added, pulling aside the curtain at the kitchen window.

"We aren't going to school today," Angie said. "We're meeting at the schoolhouse to go to the show. We have to go early so Miss James can give us 'structions on how to stay together on the trail, and how to behave in the show. And the movie starts at one o'clock."

"What if you get stuck in a snowdrift on the trail?" Charlie teased.

"Mr. Sjoholm will pull us out."

"Gunnar Sjoholm? I didn't know he was in Miss James' class," Charlie said and winked at Tilda.

"Charlie, that's enough. He's going along to help Miss James with the children. I feel lots better about them walking to Lilliwaup in the snow with a man along." Tilda set three coins on the table. "Pay attention now, Angie. Twenty-five cents for the bus. Ten cents for the movie. Five cents for a treat. Now I'll tie the money in my handkerchief and you put it way down in your coat pocket."

"Sure is generous of Gunnar to help out Miss James like this," Charlie smiled.

"Stop now, Charlie," Tilda laughed. "I have to think about what we're doing. Angie, pull your hat over your ears. I hope you are dressed warm enough," she fussed. "Where are your mittens?"

Angie pulled them out of her coat pocket.

"**Snälla flicka**. Here's your lunch bag. Looks like you're ready. I'll get my coat and walk with you to the schoolhouse. Kiss your daddy good-bye now."

"Is she going to Alaska?" Charlie laughed, and pushed them out the door.

Tilda was back on the porch in five minutes, stomping the snow off her feet. She hurried to the window in the kitchen. At least it wasn't snowing now and the men in camp kept the trail open, and the children were so excited they couldn't possibly get cold.

"Charlie," she said, relieved that the group was on its way, "I could use a **på tår**."

"I'm still waiting for my first cup of coffee."

"That's what happens when you sleep in," Tilda laughed and ran for the coffee pot. "But I like it when it snows and you have Saturday off." She poured his coffee and passed him the sugar lumps.

"This snow wouldn't keep us from working," Charlie said, "but the orders are down this time of year. You know, I think my cousin's boy Johannes would work if there was orders or not. Just for the fun of it. He likes logging that much."

"Sounds like he's doing a good job."

"You bet he is! You should see how he runs for the cable and throws himself down in the snow to fasten the choker around the log. If I'm anywhere around, he hops up and hollers and waves at me."

"Doesn't he ever get tired?"

"He don't seem to. Sometimes I have him work with me. He learns quick and is right there when I need him." Charlie wrapped both hands around his cup, watching the steam. "He's ambitious, but I think he tries too hard to please me. Sometimes he gets too close—"

"He wants to show you how **duktig** he is."

Charlie stood up to put another stick of wood in the stove. "I have to have a talk with him." He lifted the lid on the kettle and peered in. "Say, I'll have a talk with you if you don't get my mush dished up pretty soon."

Angie dropped her school books and coat in the corner of the kitchen and ran to the bread box. She buttered three slices of bread, sprinkled sugar over each one, and took the first bite at the sinkboard before Tilda could pour her milk. If she keeps eating like this, Tilda mused, she won't be underweight for long!

"Mama, the show was so good. One time Puck—that's Mickey Rooney—"

"Angie, I'm sure it was a good show. You told me about it every day this week."

"But when can I tell Johannes? He said he wanted to hear about the show."

"You can tell him day after tomorrow. He's having Sunday dinner with us. Eat now and let me finish mopping. I don't know how we track in so much black mud when the snow is so white." She hummed as she wrung out the mop and dipped it again into the bucket. She'd have to clamp fresh rags onto the mop next time she cleaned the floor—

Tilda straightened up and looked at Angie. Angie was looking at her. They'd both heard it. The whistle. Six quick blasts of the whistle and then six more.

Tilda stood at the kitchen window and waited. Up and down the tracks other women would be watching from their windows. She knew that without seeing them. It was what they did when six whistles blew and it was too cold to wait by the track. They would run to the track when they heard the speeder. For now, they would wait at their windows...

It wouldn't be Charlie. Charlie was lucky, she reminded herself. One day he came home and told how a haul-back line above him broke and dropped two hundred feet straight down. The end of the two inch thick metal cable just scratched his arm. Tilda hadn't slept well that night, thinking about it.

"Mama, light the lamp," Angie said "I can't see to color." Tilda moved mechanically. She found the matches, lifted the delicate glass chimney and touched a flame to the wick. How long had she been standing by the window? Where was the speeder? Was someone hurt so bad they had to take him straight to Potlatch? Then she heard it.

The speeder slowed in front of their house. Charlie jumped off and thanks be to God, he wasn't hurt. But why didn't he come in? Why was he just standing by the track in the cold...

Tilda felt the chill before she opened the door and called to him. "Charlie," she said when he stepped into the kitchen, "was it Johannes?"

Charlie nodded.

"Is he hurt bad?" Tilda felt Angie's arms around her waist. "Charlie, what happened?"

"We were working together. I left him in charge for five minutes while I checked up on something. When I came back, the men were bending over him where he lay in the snow." Charlie took a deep breath. "Damn it, I kept telling him to stand back. Don't get so close, I kept telling him." Tears swam in Charlie's eyes. Tilda hadn't seen him like this since Leonard...

"Charlie?"

"They were sending out the choker fast, highballing it like they do sometimes. But the choker caught on a stump and wound around it. Johannes ran to get it loose, but the choker spun back on its own and hit him in the chest."

Tilda waited for him to go on.

"When I got there, Johannes was having a little trouble breathing, but when we opened his shirt, all we saw was a little brown mark on his chest. He said he wasn't feeling too good so we helped him to the speeder and he laid down."

"You took him straight to Potlatch?"

"That's right."

"Someone drove him to the hospital in Shelton then? We need to go see him. First thing tomorrow—"

"Tilda, they took him to Shelton but not to the hospital. He died in the speeder on the way to Potlatch."

Tilda sat down. Angie buried her face in Tilda's lap.

"It was only a little brown mark," Charlie choked.

TWO LOGGERS DIE IN WOODS AT POTLATCH

WILLIAM H. PATTERSON OF SHELTON KILLED YESTER-DAY BY LOG; JOHN ECK-LUND HIT BY CHOKER

Two loggers of the Phoenix Logging camp at Potlatch died from accidents in the woods within four days, the first fatality of 1936 being John S. Ecklund, hit by a choker hook Friday, the second being William Howard Patterson, hit by a rolling log Monday morning.

Patterson died a few minutes after reaching Shelton hospital in an ambulance, Ecklund on the way to the hospital.

Details of the accident are meagre but Patterson is believed to have been hit by a skidding log in the snow while standing on another log. He died of internal injuries, the lower part of his body being crushed.

ECKLUND NATIVE OF FINLAND

John S. Ecklund was a native of Finland, born at Korsnes on August 21, 1910. He was hit over the heart by a flying choker block and died before an ambulance could rush him to a hospital.

He is survived by his father, William, of Seattle, his mother in Finland, and an uncle, Fred Ecklund, of Seattle. Funeral services will be held from Witsiers funeral home at 2:30 Saturday afternoon with Rev. Forrest D. Tibbitts in charge. Burial will follow in Shelton cemetery.

Vilhelm - May 1936

A soft knock on the door interrupted Tilda as she was about to dish up dinner.

"Now what," Charlie said. "Neighbors don't come by at supper time."

"Come in," Tilda called, but the knock sounded again.

"Are they deaf, when they don't come in," Charlie grumbled and stood up to answer the door.

Tilda could tell Charlie had had a hard day in the woods and hoped this wasn't another problem connected with his job. She put the lid back on the potatoes and watched as he opened the door. She couldn't see who he was talking to or hear what the man on the porch was saying, but Charlie invited him to come in and state his business.

His name was Johnson. Alex Johnson. He was from Seattle. He'd just walked up the trail from Lilliwaup and was spending the night in the bunkhouse. No, he wasn't looking for a job. He was looking for Vilhelm's cousin, Charlie.

"Well, you found him," Charlie smiled and looked relieved. "Tilda, put another plate on the table. This young fellow must be hungry."

"Thanks, no," he said. "I ate a sandwich from my packsack on the way up here."

"Then will you have some coffee?" Charlie asked.

The young man started to shake his head, but then nodded.

Tilda poured the coffee. Such a serious boy. Maybe he had been a friend of Johannes and wanted to talk about him with Charlie.

"Well, Alex, you've come from Vilhelm's camp. How is my cousin now?"

Alex rested his hand next to his coffee cup on the table.

Charlie went on. "It's been only four months since the accident, so I know he suffers. You never get over losing a boy. I know that."

The man looked away. He didn't touch his coffee.

Charlie waited. He looked at Tilda and then back at the visitor. He set his coffee cup on the table and stood up, sliding his chair backwards on the waxed linoleum. He walked around behind his chair and steadied his hands on the chair back. His voice was husky when he spoke. "If you got something to tell me..."

The boy cleared his throat. "Vilhelm, too, had an accident," he said. "It happened May seventh. Someone was going to write to you, but I was coming this way..."

Charlie waited, color leaving his face.

"The donkey released a log onto the cold deck and it rolled. Vilhelm was standing there. He didn't have a chance."

"**Nej**," Charlie said, shaking his head, denying what he heard. Then he sank back into his chair.

Tilda watched as the men talked quietly. After a time, they stood and shook hands.

"I'll come to the bunkhouse in the morning to see you off," Charlie said as he showed Alex to the door and closed it softly behind him.

Charlie stood facing the closed door, the cords in the back of his neck tight as bowstrings. Tilda could hear the clock ticking in the bedroom, like a heart beat.

"Vilhelm was forty-five," Charlie finally said without turning around. "Three years younger than me."

As Tilda started to go to him, his fist shot out and struck the door. The door chattered on its hinges as his fist bounced back. "Damn this business," he cried. "A man's crazy to be a logger!"

Little Hospital - June 1936

Tilda hummed as she arranged the tray. A bowl of vegetable soup, oatmeal bread and butter, and a cookie to go with the milk. She placed a cloth napkin and three sprigs of sweet peas from her garden next to the soup bowl. She wanted the tray to be **festlig** to cheer Thelma up.

"Come here, Angie," she called, "and open the door for me so I don't tip the tray."

Angie hopped and skipped ahead of her mother the length of the long back porch to Thelma's bedroom. She was enjoying taking care of her big sister. "Here we are," Angie announced as she opened her door.

It took a minute for their eyes to adjust to the dark room, especially when it was so bright and sunny outside. But Tilda had told Thelma she had to stay in bed with the shades pulled for two weeks, just like Angie did.

"Soup again?" Thelma fussed. "And more flowers that I can't even see in the dark!"

Angie's face fell. "Are you still mad because I gave you the measles?" she asked, leaning her elbows on the edge of the bed and resting her chin in her hands.

Thelma looked at her and smiled. "I guess I'm just crabby because I have to stay in bed. I can't even read!" She sat up in the bed and took the tray. "Thanks, Mom. It looks good."

Tilda didn't blame Thelma for being upset. Just when she had a chance to earn money for school clothes, she got sick. She was staying on in Tacoma after school ended to work in the berry fields. But the weather turned bad. She caught cold picking berries in the drenching rain. Fever followed. The doctor said it was tonsillitis and she'd have to stay in bed until the fever went away. Tilda and Charlie decided she should get her bed rest at home and drove to Tacoma to get her.

On their way back to camp, Angie complained that she didn't feel good either. When the rash broke out, Tilda knew what it was. Angie would have to stay in bed with the shades pulled for two weeks because, according to the doctor book, light can damage your eyes when you have the hard measles.

"I think our house has turned into a little hospital," Charlie said one day as he watched Tilda run from one bedroom to the other, trying to make the girls comfortable.

"I just hope they don't catch each other's sicknesses," Tilda said. The next day Thelma came down with Angie's hard measles.

"I can sit on the bed because I already had the measles. Right?" Angie asked, jumping up next to Thelma.

"Angie, you're tipping her tray! Come sit on the floor next to my chair and we visit with Thelma while she eats."

Angie jumped back onto the floor and sat cross-legged, leaning against Tilda's legs.

"Mama, what's this?" Angie asked, rubbing the top of Tilda's foot. "Why do you have a dent there?"

Tilda felt her foot. "When I was a young girl, I had an infection in my foot. They didn't know what to call it in those days, but our doctor in Seattle said it was probably tuberculosis of the bone. Anyway when the infection finally drained out, it left this dent."

"Did you have to stay in bed in a dark room?" Angie asked.

Tilda laughed. "No, nothing like that. I did spend many days in Anna Carlsen's house."

"Edwin's mom?"

"No, a different Anna Carlsen. She was our neighbor in Finland. She let me sit in her kitchen with my foot up on a chair when it ached so bad I couldn't go to school. But when it wasn't aching too hard, I helped with her little children so she and her ten year old boy August could work the farm."

"Why didn't the dad do that?" Thelma asked, her spoon poised above her bowl.

"He sailed to America and never came back."

"Did he drown?" Angie asked.

"No," Tilda smiled. "People wrote from America that they saw him here and there. Once in a logging camp."

Angie untied and tied Tilda's shoe laces. Thelma lifted her bowl and drank the rest of her soup. Tilda wondered if Anna Carlsen would still be alive. And if August had a family of his own and was farming the same land. She knew he would have fixed the fence by now...

"Vilhelm never went home either. Why?" Thelma asked.

"I don't know," Tilda sighed. "He always meant to go home, we know that. There are lots of men in the bunkhouses that are separated from their families in the old country. Sometimes it's because the wife doesn't want to come to this country, to leave family and friends. But most of the time they're separated because the husband wants to earn money to take back with him, but the years go by—

The bedroom door flew open. "What's going on here," a deep voice interrupted. Sunlight outlined the big man in the doorway.

"Oh, Daddy," Angie said. "Are you trying to scare us?"

"I thought maybe you were telling ghost stories here in the dark," Charlie said.

"We were telling stories, but not ghost stories," Tilda said. "You're home early. Is everything all right?"

"Ya, and I have a story to tell, too. Listen to this. Phoenix is closing down the Camp Two houses and sending the families to live in Potlatch."

Tilda jumped to her feet. She couldn't believe her ears. Potlatch, on beautiful Hood Canal. Electricity. Telephones. A real grocery store and post office. Roads in front of the houses instead of railroad tracks... Suddenly Tilda felt a chill and sat back down.

"Charlie, you told me once that a foreman has to live in camp. It won't be good, you living here in a bunkhouse while we live in Potlatch."

"Are we going to be separated, like Vilhelm's family?" Thelma asked.

"No," Charlie said. "Superintendent Carlson changed the rules. The camp foreman can take the speeder to work like the other family men. So it's time to start packing again."

"Our Camp Two friends will be living in Potlatch?"

"That's right. Now, Tilda, can you think of any other problem?"

"I can think of something good," Thelma said. "It will be easy to come home weekends from the University."

Tilda laughed. "Now there's another problem. Telma has her mind set, but where do we find money for University!"

PART VII - POTLATCH 1936-1939

CHAPTER 22 : THE TELEPHONE CALL

Changes - April 1937

"**M**ama, I hear the bell. Mrs. Remple is ringing the bell!" Angie cried, jumping up from the kitchen table and gulping down her milk.

"Careful! You spill on your dress!" Tilda warned. "If you weren't so pokey when you eat, you wouldn't be late for school every day. Now wipe off your mouth—Angie wait! Your lunch! You're supposed to bring your lunch today," Tilda exclaimed, but Angie was already out the door and streaking across the patchy lawn.

"Angie," Tilda called, running after her, "you forgot your lunch."

Angie spun around on the gravel road that separated their house from the school and grabbed the lunch box from her mother's hand.

"Wipe the milk off your mouth," Tilda hollered as Angie sprinted across the school yard toward the open schoolhouse door. Tilda breathed a sigh of relief when Angie disappeared into the building before the door closed. Good thing they lived next door to the school here in Potlatch, like they did in Camp Two.

Tilda lingered on the rain-dampened road and let the early morning sun warm her face and neck. Drops of rain from last night's shower sparkled on the newly-budded, delicate-green leaves of the maples. If spring in Potlatch was like spring in the mountains, she would soon find trilliums peeking up through last winter's mat of dead leaves. But what was she doing, standing here in the road like she didn't know it was Monday washday!

Tilda hurried toward the house, but then hesitated as she walked up the front porch steps. Wisps of steam rose from the damp boards where the sun's rays hit them. A bird called from a near-by tree. Tilda sat down on the top step and turned her face back up to the sun. Bathed in its warmth, she relaxed and took in the beauty of their new setting.

Trees bordered the far side of the road in front of their house and circled the schoolyard. Firs and big-leafed maples grew next to the houses in Potlatch. No need to clear-cut around the houses here. With the highway on one side and Hood Canal on the other, there was little fire danger.

She couldn't see the canal from where she sat, but when she closed her eyes and breathed deeply, she could smell its salty freshness. With her eyes shut, it was easy, too, to look back and relive the months since they moved to Potlatch. She remembered it was a hot day...

Tilda and the girls slid across the car seats toward the open windows as Charlie turned off the Hood Canal highway and onto a gravel road. The breeze from the windows felt good on the hot August afternoon, and through the open windows, they could look for their new house.

"There it is," Charlie announced, and pulled to a stop in front of a two-story, yellow house.

Tilda couldn't believe her eyes. No skids under this company house! It rested firmly on a cement foundation. Two big windows and the front door looked out at them from under the roof of a wide front porch. Charlie followed the others up the steps and stood back as Tilda, suddenly cautious, almost fearful, opened the front door.

The front room stretched before them, so big it took two room-size linoleum rugs to cover the floor. An oil-burning stove stood in one corner. Superintendent Carlson had told them about this new stove, that it could circulate enough heat to warm the whole house without their having to carry a single stick of wood.

Charlie led the way through the rest of the house. A hallway opened off the side of the front room and led to two big bedrooms with a bathroom between. They found another bedroom upstairs where Thelma could sleep when she came home weekends from University. The kitchen opened off the far end of the front room and was furnished with a new Frigidaire and an almost-new cookstove. A wringer washing machine stood in a corner of the kitchen on tall legs with wheels so Tilda could roll the machine up to the sink when she did the wash.

As soon as they moved in, Angie ran from room to room pushing the button light switches. "Just like the fancy hotel in B.C.," Thelma exclaimed. When they were ready for bed that evening, Tilda stood up on a chair to blow out the "lamp." Then she caught herself and laughed. She told Charlie it was hard to break a habit of fifteen years.

Tilda decided that having a telephone was almost as good as having electricity. The heavy, walnut-stained box hung on the kitchen wall next to the back door. The mouthpiece was attached to the front of the box. The receiver hung on one side and the handle for ringing up someone, on the other side. They heard eight different combinations of rings on their party line, but they only picked up the receiver when they heard their own long-short-long ring. It wasn't polite to listen in on other conversations, though Tilda suspected a few people did.

They placed the oak table they'd bought in Seattle and their four chairs in the kitchen and bought a new dining room set to help fill the long front room. Then they splurged on a "Sear's Best" floor-model, RCA Victor radio. Every night Charlie tuned in to the news of the world, and Angie listened to "Little Orphan Annie" followed by "Jack Armstrong, the All American Boy." If supper was ready when Angie's programs came on, Tilda let her take her plate into the front room and eat next to the radio.

Tilda's favorite shows came on in the afternoon. First, "Ma Perkins," and then, "Our Gal Sunday, the story that asks the question, 'Can a young girl from a little mining town in the West find happiness as the wife of a wealthy and titled Englishman?'" Tilda couldn't see why that should be a problem, but the people in these daytime shows were always troubling about something. She felt sorry for them, but she couldn't spend a lot of time worrying about them. She and Charlie had problems of their own to think about.

Charlie was no "wealthy and titled Englishman." They'd had to draw money from their savings to buy furniture when they moved into this big house, and now Angie was coaxing for a piano. Even if they found a good buy on a used one, they'd have to pay fifty cents a week for lessons. And then there was Thelma's tuition to University.

"Money don't grow on trees," Charlie reminded them. "So how we going to build any pension if we spend all our money now? Who do you think takes care of us if I get hurt in the woods? Or when I'm too old to work? Do you think Roosevelt has a Deal for that?"

The sun had moved behind a cloud and a cool breeze stirred the bushes next to the steps where Tilda was sitting. They'd managed, Tilda reflected. And they were putting aside a little out of each paycheck toward a piano and college tuition. Things were going good, but still she felt uneasy this morning. Why? She hugged herself to ward off the chill. She remembered what it was! It was that long distance telephone call!

Thelma had always loved school. For years she'd dreamed of going to college, of having a career. Maybe becoming a teacher or a scientist. She liked science. She'd applied too late last summer to get into the School of Pharmacy at the University of Washington, but this year she would try again, and in the meantime she was taking general courses. Their plans were all set, and then Tilda got the phone call from Charlie Cole.

Mr. Cole needed an office secretary at Shelton Gas Company where he was manager. He'd called the high school and asked them if they could recommend someone. They told him that a girl named Thelma Lind had graduated with honors and then moved to Tacoma to take a year of post-graduate courses in business. He was told that Thelma was attending the University of Washington this year, but that he could contact her parents in Potlatch and gave him the number. That's when Tilda got the phone call.

Mr. Cole asked Tilda how he could get in touch with Thelma. Tilda told him she'd be home for Easter vacation in a few days, and he said he'd call back. He asked Tilda to tell Thelma that he had a job for her and that he'd pay her $75.00 a month, but that she needed to start right away if she wanted the job.

When Tilda told Charlie about the call, he said that he never could see what business a girl had going to college anyway. She'd just get married and have kids and what good is a college education then? College was expensive. It was going to be tough to send Thelma to University and have any savings left. And what about their trip to Finland? Tilda wanted to see her brother in the old country, didn't she? It all made sense when Charlie said it, but Tilda was afraid it would make no sense to Thelma when they asked her to drop out of school.

Tilda would try to put the problem out of her mind for now and tend to her chores. She hurried into the house, rolled the washing machine up to the sink, and plugged the cord into the electrical socket. No more boiling clothes on the stove and wringing them out by hand till her skin burned red and her muscles ached. Life was easier for her in Potlatch, but not for Charlie. His days were longer than ever by having to ride the logging train to and from work. And living in Potlatch didn't make logging any safer. Tilda fed the rinsed clothes through the wringer and watched them drop, steaming and flat, into the wicker laundry basket. Even with a late start, she finished the wash by eleven o'clock. She carried the loaded basket to the back yard where Charlie had strung a clothesline between two trees. She stuck the tips of two clothes pins into her mouth while she shook out Charlie's work shirt.

Tilda could hear the cars rushing by on the highway as she worked. In the evening when she stood at her kitchen window peeling potatoes, she could look out over the clothes line and see the logging train cross the highway on its way to the log dump on the canal. Charlie would be on the train and even though she couldn't see him, she would know what kind of day he'd had by counting the loads of logs they brought out of the woods. The higher the number, the happier Charlie would be when he came home that evening.

Tilda shook out Charlie's work pants and clipped them next to his shirt. Lots of traffic on the highway this morning, she noticed, as she put two more clothespins in her mouth and reached for Angie's school dress. She paused to look when she heard the gravel crunch at the side of the highway. The bus from Shelton was slowing to a stop. Tilda stretched to see over the loaded clothesline. A young woman with a big suitcase stepped off the bus. As Tilda picked up the basket to return to the kitchen, she looked again. It was Thelma! Tilda's stomach tightened. Tonight when Charlie came home, they would have to talk to their daughter about dropping out of University.

"Thanks, Mom," Thelma said. "You remembered pot roast with potatoes and gravy was my favorite supper."

"You haven't been gone that long," Tilda smiled.

"Anyway, like I said," Thelma went on, "most of my tests were last week, so I finished my term paper on the weekend and handed it in, and here I am. Home early and ready for a vacation."

Charlie cleared his throat. "I guess we're out of coffee," he said to Tilda.

Tilda laughed as she got up from the table to get the coffee pot. Charlie had his own way of asking for something. When they were first married, it bothered her, like she wasn't keeping up with her grocery shopping, but now it had become a joke.

Charlie cleared his throat again, and this time pushed his chair back a little from the table. "Telma," he said, "we have to talk about something. Last night a man named Charlie Cole called us from Shelton. He wanted to talk to you."

"I don't know any Charlie Cole," Thelma said, spearing a chunk of meat on her plate with her fork.

"I don't either," Angie said, not wanting to be left out of the grownup conversation.

"Cole is manager of Shelton Gas Company," Charlie said, "and he called the high school and asked the principal some questions about kids who had graduated from there."

"What does that have to do with me?" Thelma asked, looking up from her plate, prepared to defend herself, whatever the accusation.

Charlie took a cookie from the plate in the middle of the table. He always finished his meals before anyone else in the family. Tilda figured it was because of the years he'd spent eating in camp cookhouses before he was married.

"Cole called the school to ask who they could recommend to work in his office."

"So who'd they recommend?" Thelma asked, taking a second helping of potatoes.

"The principal recommended you," Charlie said. "Mr. Cole will pay you $75.00 a month to be his office secretary."

"Office secretary? $75.00 a month? That's as much as you make, isn't it, Dad?" Thelma exclaimed, her fork pausing mid-air.

"Well, not quite," Charlie said, "but it's more money for office work than I ever heard of in these times, and to an eighteen year old girl."

"I'll be nineteen this month," Thelma said, sitting tall in her chair. "Will I start the job this summer when school is out?"

Tilda spoke up now. "That's the hard part," she said. "You'd have to drop out of University. Mr. Cole needs someone now."

Thelma's face went blank. She swallowed hard though she hadn't taken a bite. Tilda tried to read her face. Charlie was watching her, too. It felt like minutes were passing. Finally Thelma found her voice.

"I think it's a great idea," she exclaimed.

"You do?" Tilda asked. "I didn't think you'd give up University for anything."

"Well, I would," Thelma said. "For anything! You know when I couldn't get into pharmacy, the counselor put me into a bunch of courses I wasn't interested in, like sociology. And to get to school from where I live, I have to take two buses and a streetcar. I spend more time traveling back and forth than I do in classes that I don't care about in the first place."

Tilda and Charlie looked at each other and then at Thelma. They'd expected a fight.

"I can't believe my good luck," Thelma went on, smiling broadly, and then, "I think I've always wanted to be a secretary in a real office and work in the real world."

CHAPTER 23: LETTER FROM ESTER

September 20,1937

Dear Tilda,

Ivar was so happy to get your letter in August saying you were planning a trip home next summer. He was busy on the farm and didn't have time to write. Now I have to write for him.

Last month when the grain was dry, Ivar started the threshing. His boys, Birger and Edvin, are both in the army, as you know, but Edvin was nearby to help with the harvest. When Ivar was cutting straw to put into the threshing machine, he nicked his thumb with the knife. Just a couple drops of blood. Two days later his thumb was aching and swollen so Edvin took over the harvesting and Ivar went to the doctor in Närpes.

Dr. Niemois has a good reputation. He made three cuts into the thumb and put on a bandage. Next day the thumb was still swelling, so he had to cut the thumb off. Ivar stayed at the hospital, and Edvin, Ture, and I took care of the animals and other work on the farm. Two days later, because of infection, the doctor cut off Ivar's arm. Edvin took his father's arm and brought it to the church cemetery and buried it in Edvard's grave. September 15, two weeks after the injury took place, Ivar died. He was fifty-one.

Ivar was a good husband and father. He worried about leaving us, but we will get along. When the boys get out of the army, they will manage the farm and watch out for me. Ture helps and we take care of Ture, as Ivar wanted.

Don't cry too much, dear sister-in-law. I cry enough for all of us. God bless you and help us all.

Ester

CHAPTER 24: ANGIE'S VIEW

Dear Diary,

August 4, 1937

> *Today is my birthday and I got 9 presents. I was nine years old. My diary is a present from Mom.*

August 8, 9, 10

> *I went swimming when it was raining, and the water was swell...Elizabeth and I played a trick on Mildred...I went fishing today and caut three pogies.*

August 17

> *I got a $227.50 piaono.*

August 23

> *I took my first muisik lesson today.*

August 26

> *Carlsons has to cats. the biggets one was killed. hit by car on the Highway.*

August 27

> *Carlsons other little kitty was killed by a dog.*

August 30, 31

> *I dressed up in beads, rings, pins and all the jeolry I could find...I went out right after supper and played hopscotch till seven-thirdy.*

September 1, 2

> *I washed the school-house blackboard today...the bed room firnicher came today*

September 7, 8

> *Today was the first of school, and did I have fun...I got 100 in selling and arithmetic*

September 11, 12

> *My itch is afol today...I got 75 in spelling today.*

September 16

> *I heard gang busters over the radio and it sure was good.*

September 18

> *we went to a beer-palor today*

October 1

> *Elizbeth Mildred and I wrked on the things we are going to send to Soma* [Samoa]

September 23 to October 12

> *I could hardly go to school today, I have a sore on my seat...I got two more bowls today, in the same place...My bowls were so bad that I had to stay home from school today...I had my boul opened today...I went to school but it was hard to sit down.*

October 14

> *Mama's bruthr in finland cut his thum and died. Mama cries alot. He was my unckel but i never met him*

October 26, 29

> *It was raining hard today. Elizabeth and I had fun playing in the leaves out in the rain...I had fun at the Haloween party over at the skool house*

November 1, 3

> *my vaxanashun was afull...Elizabeth knocked the scabe off my vaxanashon.*

November 16

> *The most wonderful thing in the world happened to day. The boys played with us*

November 18

> *I gave Elizabeth a fingerwave. Then she gave me one.*

November 21 to December 3

> *I had to go to the doctor yesterday with my rash he said it was the itch. He gave mom some stuff and I had to have 4 bathes...My rash was a little better to day, but had to stay home frome school...We went to the doctor today. It was an infecshon in the itch...Mom*

started the treatments today...I got to take the badages off of my hands tonight.

December 12, 14, 15, 22

I started to go to sunday-school...I made decerashuns for a Christmas tree...I went to a taffy pull...We had a skool play today

December 25

We went to tacoma and opened the presents. I got so many it would take a big peese of papper to write it down

January 1, 1938

I heard the new years racut at 12:00 .

January 18

Ainley found the cutest little stray dog. His going to keep it too.

January 19

We wento Tacoma today. Thelma had her glass's fixed while Mom, dad and I whent to Musters befo they moved to Vancouver.

January 21

Ainleys dog had a fight with Elizabeth's dog. We were sure that it was dead but it wasn't.

January 28

I told about infantile paralysis in my weekly reader.

February 16

The boys at school let us girls play football whith them.

February 19

I was going to have my perment-wave, but my hair was to short so I saw Handy Andy with Will Roger.

February 26

Thelma had the Shelton kids come over. We played all kinds games.

March 18

Mrs. Rempel was sick so Ainley had what you woudn't but suppose to be school.

April 2

This morning at 6:00 Dad called me and told me to get ready for Vancover and we went. tonight we went to a Swedish Fin. danace in Portland.

June 13

> *I got some boxes ready to give to some poor people that lives bettwen hear and Shelton.*

June 20

> *I lost a penney behind the trunk, a dime in back of my bed, a penney under the porch and the fish I caught mom left in the sun so it was rotten.*

July 30, August 1

> *Antie and Unckel and Art came here today. We had a wenie roast down at the beach...Unckel and Art went to Annocortis. Antie staid here.*

July 5

> *Elizabeth and I had a circus tonight at 7:30 We made 14c.*

July 15

> *Arthur came here tonight. And I figring on righting a book.*

July 31

> *Went to a Swedish picnic in Portland today.*

August 4

> *Today is my birthday and I got 7 preasents. I was ten years old.*

August 9

> *I wentto the sckating ring tonight with the Babtis kids.*

August 11, 13

> *There was Bible sckool at Hoodsport today and I went...I quiet going to shows.*

August 16 to 24

> *Dad got his vacation...We went to Portland and I got a new coat...We went to fun land tonight...Mom and Dad went to the dance and Aruther and I stayed at home...We went on a picnic and I saw Boniville dam.*

September

> *I had my music lesson today. Woodworthes dog bit me an I might have rabbies.*

September 6 to 9

> *Today was the first day of school and did I have fin...I got 100 in everything...We played football. Made up three po ems somewhere around here.*

September 19

> *I got a Sunday school sertifect.*

October 3

> *Told Curnty Vents today.*

October 18, 19

> *I was playing football and I hurt my finger so bad I couldn't right...My finger was a little better but I still can't pracktis.*

October 22-24, 27

> *Art went up into the woods. Mildred and I were playing golf and the golf club hit me in the eye and hurt me badly...My eye was so swolen and funny looking I couldn't go to Sunday School...Unckle came here from Annacortis tonight...today was insutud so there isn't any school.*

November 28

> *We are going to start on our Christmas plays pretty soon. The techer is copying them down now.*

December 17

> *Mom and dad and I went to Springwater and the brother to the man dad fired was going to get even with him so he gave dad a black eye for Xmas.*

December 18

> *We had our Sunday school program in hoodsport but dad couldn't go because of his black eye so mom didn't go ether......*

Springwater Tavern - December 18, 1938

Angie woke with a start. Had she had a nightmare? She sat up in bed and peered around cautiously. The sun was slipping through the lace curtains and dancing on the wall next to her bed. Her dress for the Sunday school program was hanging starched and ready on a hook next to the closet curtain. Everything looked regular, but the house was too quiet. She slid back down in the bed, clutched the covers to her chin, and listened.

She didn't expect to hear weekday noises—Daddy snapping his lunch bucket shut and Mom sliding their cups and

saucers and mush bowls into the dishpan. Angie wasn't listening for Monday noises like the slosh-slosh of the washing
machine. Nor the Tuesday sizzle of the flatiron coming down
on the sprinkled clothes. She wouldn't be hearing Mom pump-
ing the foot treadle on the sewing machine this morning because it was Sunday. She knew that, and yet she wasn't hearing
any Sunday noises either.

She sat up in bed again and listened harder. Usually when
she woke up on Sunday, her dad was still in bed. She'd hear
Mom's heels click across the linoleum as she brought him his
coffee. Angie'd hear him boost himself up in the squeaky bed
to suck the coffee through a sugar lump, and then she'd hear
his big "Ahhhhh." Sometimes if she slept late, she'd hear him
in the creaky, wooden rocker by the window in the front room.
He'd be chuckling over the Katzenjammer Kids or Blondie and
Dagwood in the Sunday funny paper. But she wasn't hearing
anything.

Angie slipped out of bed, ran to her door, and opened it a
crack. She wanted to hear Mama humming as she clapped the
big wooden spoon against the side of the mixing bowl, and
the butter spluttering in the frying pan as it waited for the first
hotcake, but she didn't hear that either. Nothing was right!

Angie opened the door a little wider. At last she saw someone. Mama was coming out of the kitchen, tiptoeing toward
the rocking chair with a wet towel in her hand. But the rocker
wasn't by the window where it should have been. It was in
the darker part of the room. Dad was in the rocker where he
should be, but he wasn't reading the Sunday funnies. He was
leaning back in the chair holding something over one eye.

Angie dashed to the rocking chair and peeked around from
behind. Mama was laying the wet towel across his forehead
and clucking like Jacobson's banty hens next door. Angie
stepped around to see better and caught her breath. A dark-
red beefsteak lay across her dad's eye. As Angie watched,
Mama lifted a corner of the steak and looked underneath. Then
she turned the steak over like she was frying it, and laid it
back on his eye. Dad grumped at her to be more careful, and
then he moaned, and Mom clucked again just as someone
knocked on the door.

"Come in," Mama called.

Mrs. Carlson was already in. "So how is Mr. Lind this morning?" she asked as if he wasn't sitting right there.

Daddy groaned and Mama sighed.

"Wasn't that a night!" Mrs. Carlson said, shaking her head. "I thought sure Mr. Lind was going to kill Baxter before he was through." She reached into her coat pocket. "Here's Charlie's watch. John picked it up in the parking lot after you drove away. Look at the band, Tilda. Charlie doubled up his fist so tight it split the leather in four places," she laughed. Then she peeked under the steak, clucked like Mama, and left. Mama smiled a little and dropped the watch into her apron pocket.

Angie stared at Mama's pocket. It hadn't been a nightmare. It had really happened. Her throat tightened as she remembered.

It was Saturday night and Dad said he'd treat her and Mom to supper at Springwater Tavern on the canal. Thelma wouldn't be home from Shelton until late, so they would stay at the tavern and dance a while.

She and Mama ordered hot roast beef sandwiches with mashed potatoes and gravy. Dad ordered steamed clams. Angie didn't like the way they smelled, but they were pretty to look at, all opened up like pearl-winged butterflies ready to fly out of the bowl.

When Angie finished her dinner, her dad gave her a nickel for the juke box. She chose "Let Me Call You Sweetheart" because it was Mom's favorite song. When Angie ran back to the booth, her ice cream was waiting for her, and her mom and dad slid out to dance.

Angie guessed the tavern was saving on electricity like her folks were always doing because when the music started, someone turned out most of the lights. But she squinted at the dance floor through the dim, smoke-filled air and saw the Carlsons and the Jacobsons and other people she knew from Potlatch. Men leaning against the bar at the edge of the dance floor were laughing and punching each other while the man in the white apron behind the bar filled their glasses. Some of the men were wearing their caulk shoes like they had just come from work. They probably didn't plan to dance.

The cigarette smoke was making her eyes heavy, so she leaned against the pile of coats next to her in the booth. She must have slept a little because she didn't know when her folks and the Carlsons slipped into the booth with her. What woke her up was a stranger leaning over the table talking low to her dad. He was one of the men wearing caulk shoes, a skinny man with sweat on his nose and tobacco on his teeth. His eyes were red and he wasn't laughing now. Angie slid as far back in the booth as the coats allowed to get away from the man's sour breath.

"Yeh, that's what I said," he was saying. "My kid brother's looking for you."

"And who the hell are you?" Dad asked.

"Fred Baxter's brother." He pointed at the bar with his thumb. "I'm here to tell you he wants to see you outside."

None of the men at the bar were laughing now. They were watching. The big man at the end of the bar nodded at the skinny man, set his glass down, and walked outside. "Now!" the skinny one said to her dad. A drop of sweat dripped off his nose onto the table.

"Don't go, Charlie. They're drunk," Mama said, hanging on to Dad's arm as he started to get up. He jerked his arm loose and left the table. Mr. Carlson jumped up and followed him. "We're going home," Mama said and grabbed her pocket book and the coats and started for the door.

The fresh air smelled good. Only one light bulb burned above the door of this tavern, but the moon lighted the whole parking lot.

"Let's go home now, Charlie," Mom pleaded when she caught up to him. She took his arm again and tried to pull him toward the car. Daddy didn't seem to hear her and kept walking. Mom led Angie to the car, helped her in and slammed the door. Mama's face was all pinched like she was going to cry. When Angie looked out the window, the parking lot was full of people and the big man was talking.

"Tell me now, in front of my brother and my friends here, why you fired me."

"You know why, Fred," Dad said. "Besides being a lazy son-of-a-bitch, you were smoking on the job."

"There's no fire danger in December."

"There is this year. The woods are dry."

"I can handle my cigarettes. Me and my friends over there say I go back to work Monday."

"I say you don't."

"It won't happen again," the man said, opening and shutting his hands.

"That's right," Dad said, "because you won't be there."

The big man's fist shot out and landed in Dad's stomach. The skinny man pulled back his fist and started to swing, but Mr. Carlson grabbed his arm and twisted it behind his back. Two other men with caulk shoes moved toward Daddy, but Mr. Jacobson stepped in front of them.

"Keep it fair," Mr. Carlson shouted and the men moved back.

"Jobs are hard to get!" Fred hissed and punched her daddy in the face twice while he was struggling to straighten up.

Dad shook his head like he was trying to throw off the hurt. He rolled his shoulders and took a deep breath. Then, like lightening, his fist hit Fred in the chin and tipped him back on his heels. Dad lunged after him, grabbed him around the neck, backed him against the side of a car and pounded his head against the fender.

"Stop, Charlie," Mama screamed. "You'll kill him!"

"Let him go, Charlie," Carlson yelled. "He's had enough."

Dad loosened his hands from around Fred's neck and watched him slip down the side of the car onto the dirt roadway like a lizard sliding off a wet rock. Mama held the car door open for Daddy, and they drove onto the canal highway and headed for home. Angie looked out the back window and saw someone helping the big man up off the ground and into a car while the rest of the people went back inside.

"Let me see my watch, Tilda," Dad said.

Mom pulled it out of her pocket and handed it to him.

He held the watch to his ear and then turned it over in his hand, examining the leather. "Ya, it could use a new band," he said, with a flicker of a smile.

"What's going on?" Thelma interrupted, tightening the sash on her bathrobe as she walked into the room. "I planned to wait up for you last night, but got so sleepy— Dad! What happened?"

Mom answered for him. "Dad fired a man, and he and his brother tried to bully Dad into giving him his job back."

"I don't get it," Thelma said, combing her hair back with her fingers and adjusting her glasses. "I thought when you moved to Potlatch, things would be better."

"Better for me," Mama said. "But your dad's job is the same. He's still foreman and has to take the bad with the good."

"If I have to take the bad with the good, Tilda," Dad said, "maybe I should be getting something good with the bad." He lifted the steak off his eye and smiled at her. "Put this steak away for supper. It'll do a lot more good in my stomach than on my eye. A little black eye never hurt nobody so far as I know."

"Curnty Vents" - May 1939

The grade school, painted yellow like the company houses, stood larger than any building in Potlatch. A coat room with ten wall hooks—two or three more than needed for the average school population—and a stove for drying wet coats and warming gloves and galoshes divided the building in half. One room served as a gym as well as an auditorium for holiday programs, and the other room functioned as the classroom.

Student desks, hooked together by their varnished, wooden, lift-up tops and fold-down seats, formed three rows, four desks in each row, their wrought-iron feet fastened securely to parallel board runners. The teacher's desk was positioned at the front of the room with a pull-down map and the blackboard behind her desk. The alphabet in upper and lower case ran in a border above the blackboard as a reminder to the students at penmanship time each day, just how the letters should be formed. The American flag with its forty-eight stars hung from a sturdy pole in the corner of the room.

Miss Daves didn't sit at her desk very long at one time as she needed to move around to instruct individually the boys and girls in the different grades. But she started each day standing next to her desk to lead the students in the flag salute and the singing of "America." Then, because Miss Daves wished to broaden world understanding in these loggers' children, she added current events to their customary Monday routine.

Angie knew why Miss Daves thought Monday was the best day for current events. It was because the Sunday paper had more pages of news than the weekday papers. But Sunday was also a very busy day for Angie, and sometimes she didn't have time to look through the paper. She went to Sunday School in Hoodsport in the morning, then ate dinner, and sometimes Thelma came home from Shelton or they had other company, so how could she find time to look at the paper? Angie fidgeted at her desk. Today was Monday and she wasn't prepared.

"Children," Miss Daves said, breaking into Angie's thoughts, "today for current events, I'm going to ask the youngest person in class to report first and then move along to the oldest. That means we'll start with Billy Reader, our first grader. Billy, what current event are you going to tell us about today?"

"My cat had five kittens and two died," Billy said, standing up as he'd been instructed.

Everyone giggled except Don, his third grade brother. "That's exactly what happened," Don said, jumping to his feet in Billy's defense.

"I know, Don," Miss Daves said, "but he needs to report on events that are of interest to more people than your immediate family."

"His report is interesting to me," Edwin said. "My mom said she didn't want any more cats, but maybe if I tell her Billy's cat had kittens—"

"Edwin," Miss Daves said, rapping her desk with a ruler, "remember to raise your hand when you speak in class. Boys and girls, let's forget about the kittens for now. Don, you can remain standing. As a third grader, your turn to report comes next."

Don spoke quickly. "I saw a picture in the paper of some boys at the University of Washington swallowing goldfish—whole. They dared each other to do it and they did." He sat down.

Miss Daves shook her head. "Thank you, Don. Let's go on. Edwin, I believe you're the youngest of the fifth graders—"

"Angie is nine days younger than me," Edwin protested.

"Well, all right. Angie, I guess it's your turn."

Angie slid out from behind her desk top to stand in the aisle. Miss Daves said it was important to learn to talk on your feet. "My big sister Thelma has a boyfriend."

"That's not interesting to anyone but you," Don said.

Angie sat down.

Miss Daves rested her head in her hands. Angie thought she looked a little tired.

"I want to go next," Elizabeth said, jumping to her feet. "I saw a picture of the Dionne quintuplets in the newspaper. They will be five years old on May twenty-eighth."

"Thank you," Miss Daves said. "I'm afraid we are a little out of order. Edwin and Mildred are in the fifth grade like Angie and should report before you, Elizabeth, but never mind. It's all right," she sighed. "Edwin, let's get back to you. What did you read in the paper?"

"The Hindenburg, that German airship, exploded when it tried to land in New Jersey. Thirty-three people died."

"Edwin, that's not current. That happened two years ago," Miss Daves said.

"I must have looked at an old newspaper," Edwin said, chagrined. "Or maybe I heard my dad talking about it. But I can tell you about Joe Lewis. He won another heavyweight boxing match and is still the world champ."

"Thank you, Edwin. That's very timely. Now, Mildred."

"They are still looking for Amelia Earhart in the Pacific Ocean," Mildred said. "Her picture was on page five in the Sunday paper."

"And who was she?" Miss Daves asked.

"She was the lady who tried to fly around the world. But she didn't make it. She disappeared over the ocean."

"Thank you, Mildred," Miss Daves said, and then smiled at the husky boy in the back. "Now, Mark, as our eldest student and the one who is about to graduate from eighth grade, what current event did you find in the newspaper that seemed important?"

"Germany invaded Czechoslovakia," Mark said, "and my mom and dad are scared because my grandparents live in Germany. Dad says Hitler could get their whole country in trouble."

"You may be right, Mark," Miss Daves said, suddenly serious. "Europe is very unsettled now. We have to hope they find a peaceful solution to their problems. Thank you all for your fine reporting."

Angie knew she hadn't done so fine. She hadn't had time to read the paper because Thelma had brought her boyfriend home to eat dinner and they'd stayed all day. Still, Angie felt bad about not doing her assignment. She resolved to do better next week. In fact, she'd write herself a note on her tablet so she wouldn't forget.

She lifted the lid of her desk and took out her pencil. "Sunday look for CURNTY VENTS," she wrote in big letters across the front of her tablet.

CHAPTER 25: CHARLIE

"Crazy World" - June 1939

"Tilda, you cleaning house again?" Charlie asked, dropping the Sunday newspaper on the floor be side his rocker. "Ain't once a day enough?"

Tilda ran the dust cloth across the top of the piano one more time. "This dark wood shows everything, and when we have the windows open these warm days, we get all that dust from the road. Sometimes I think it was easier to keep house next to the oily railroad track."

"But why so particular today? Aren't we supposed to rest on Sunday?"

Tilda looked at the pile of newspapers at his feet and shook her head. "Did you forget Telma is bringing Don Wolfe home for dinner?"

"Again? That same, redheaded Scotchman? Why don't she bring home a nice Swede-Finn boy? What's wrong with Leonard West?"

Tilda pushed his feet aside and gathered up the newspaper. "You know we can't pick Thelma's friends."

"Ya, but a redhead! We never had no redhead in our family." He watched her fold the newspaper and slip it into the magazine rack. "And why bother folding the paper?" he asked, plainly irritated. "Remember the time you had everything all fixed up because a bunch of Telma's friends from the Baptist church were meeting here? Telma unfolded the newspaper you had just put away and dropped it here and there around the room."

"Ya, I remember," Tilda smiled. "She said I kept the house too nice. Her friends' houses weren't as neat and she wanted them to feel at home here."

Charlie shook his head. "Don't know why she has to get tied up with some damn Baptist group. Don't she know Baptists eat their young?"

Tilda laughed. "That's what we were told, all right, when we were growing up. I guess the Lutheran pastors wanted young people to stay away from the Baptist missionaries."

"Well," Charlie said, "Thelma knows we're Lutheran."

"How would she know that? We haven't lived near a church of any kind since we left Ballard."

Charlie stood up and walked to the window overlooking the road. "A redheaded Scotchman! What's his father do? They're all tight, you know. When it comes to money—"

"You're getting excited for nothing," Tilda said. "He seemed like a nice boy to me. Maybe a **på tår** would put you in better spirits."

Charlie followed her into the kitchen and found his place at the table. Tilda poured his coffee and then half-filled her own cup. If she drank half a cup at a time, she could drink more times during the day without upsetting her stomach. But she wasn't thinking of that now. She was wondering if Charlie had something troubling him besides Thelma's Scottish boyfriend.

"Tilda," he said after a couple sips, "there's so much going on at work these days..."

Tilda caught her breath. She was right. "Did you have to fire someone again?"

"**Nej**," he said. "Not since Springwater," he added, half-smiling to her. Then serious, "That's not the problem."

The clock on the kitchen wall ticked noisily. Tilda noticed the time and thought she should be shaping the meatballs and putting them on to brown. She hadn't peeled the potatoes yet, either. But she sat and watched Charlie run his finger over the edge of the cup, like he was looking for a chip.

"There's talk of Phoenix shutting down for good and gyppo loggers moving in with their log trucks," he said. "Can you imagine hauling logs out of the woods on trucks? It would take them a hundred years to do what railroad logging did in the last twenty years." He paused. "Of course they can build roads into places the railroad can't go, but I wouldn't call what they do 'logging.' Not like we know it. They're nothing but a clean-up crew."

"Then why does it worry you?" Tilda asked, but he didn't seem to hear her.

"You know what John Carlson and some of the other loggers was talking about?" He didn't wait for an answer. "Quitting the woods and buying stock in a veneer plant in Anacortes, a plant that hasn't even been built yet. $2,000 a share for a blueprint. I tell you the world has gone crazy!" he said, jumping to his feet and pacing back and forth across the kitchen.

"Ida's Charlie drives to Anacortes to work on plans for some mill. Is that the mill John is talking about?"

"Ya, that's it. Your brother-in-law bought a couple shares of their stock. I guess he don't remember the stock market crash and the banks closing. Gambling in stocks don't make sense anytime." He was raising his voice even though she was sitting right there. "If Phoenix closes down, there's other logging companies around. Simpson's a big outfit that can always use an experienced logger. I have to have a better reason for quitting the woods than chasing after some crazy, fly-by-night, plywood outfit. As long as I have the strength to log, that's what I'll do!"

Tilda's heart felt heavy. That old dread... She remembered Johannes telling Charlie not to worry about him, that, like Charlie, he had long legs and was quick. Charlie had told Johannes then, that sometimes that's not enough, that luck counts, too. Charlie had never had an accident, but what if he was pushing his luck?

"Buying stock in a damn blueprint—"

"**Tyst nu!**" Tilda whispered. "I heard a car drive up. It must be Telma and Don Wolfe. Be polite now, Charlie."

Charlie sat back down in his chair. "Damn redheaded Scotchman," he muttered. "I got enough to think about without this."

Tilda opened the door.

"Hi, Mom," Thelma sang out as she skipped onto the back porch. Her cheeks were flushed, and she had a young man with blond hair in tow.

"Mom. Dad. I want you to meet Bennie Banner. He drives a truck for the gas company and, Daddy, he has something important to ask you."

The young man, smiling widely, reached out his hand and shook Charlie's hand, and then Tilda's hand, and then Charlie's hand again. "Where can we talk?" he asked, moving restlessly from one foot to the other, but smiling unwaveringly.

Charlie pointed the way to the front room. As he turned to shut the door behind them, he nodded at Tilda. "I told you it was a crazy world," his look said.

The Cable Breaks - September 1939

Tilda pumped the treadle of the sewing machine till its wheel flew. At the end of the seam she flipped up the presser foot, pulled out the fabric, bit off the thread, and leaned back to rest her shoulders. Thelma was planning a simple wedding in the Baptist parsonage with just the family, but still there was lots to do. Tilda had to finish this dress for Angie, and Charlie needed a new suit, and when would they get to Seattle to shop with his working six days a week? If she just knew how to drive, she could go to Shelton and do some shopping for the wedding herself. Well, she decided, no use worrying. It would all get done. They really liked Thelma's young man and that was the important part.

Tilda slid the next seam under the presser foot and turned the hand wheel to lower the needle. She really shouldn't hurry so much. Once in Camp Two when she was feeding material under the foot, the needle came down and went all the way through her finger. If she could have an accident sitting at her sewing machine, it was probably good that she hadn't learned to drive, though, heaven knows, Charlie had tried his best to teach her.

She'd wanted to be like other women in America, free to take the car and drive where she wanted, but she must have waited too long to learn. Three times when they first moved to Potlatch, Charlie had taken her to an open prairie outside of Shelton where they had lots of room and no traffic, but she couldn't get through the gear shifting part without killing the engine.

Charlie told her to step on the gas a little as she let the clutch out slow, and that's what she tried to do. But when the car started to jerk, he'd holler, "Slow, I said!" and she'd get nervous and the car would hop and jump and then die.

She and Charlie had gone home mad after that last driving lesson. She never asked for another lesson, and he never again mentioned her driving. At least, not until after her toe operation a year later. When they went back to the doctor to have him check her toe, the doctor said to Charlie, "The toe has healed just fine. She can drive now."

Charlie said to the doctor, "That's good because she never could before the operation." Tilda saw the twinkle in his eye. Charlie didn't have a lot of patience, but he was quick with his jokes.

Except lately. He was coming home too tired. He was working too hard. Phoenix was getting more orders for logs than they could fill. With trouble in Europe, President Roosevelt was expanding Fort Lewis and other military bases all over the country and for that they needed lumber. Summer days were long, and Phoenix was taking advantage of the daylight hours.

Tilda bit off another thread and took the dress pieces to the ironing board to press open the seams. Two o'clock. Angie would be home from school soon, and she could fit the dress on her.

Tilda tested the face of the iron with a wet finger. She listened for the sizzle, but instead she heard heavy footsteps on the porch. Charlie wouldn't be home in the middle of the afternoon! Not unless something was terribly wrong. Another accident? Tilda held her breath as she stood beside the ironing board and waited. When she heard his chair scrape across the wooden planks on the porch, she knew he had sat down to take off his caulk shoes. She set the iron down and rushed outside.

"Charlie. What's wrong?"

He kept on loosening the laces on his caulk shoes.

"Charlie?" Tilda whispered.

A chipmunk scurried through the flower bed and up a tree. The day was warm but the little creature's instinct said that it was time to gather the cones under the firs and to deposit them in its secret storage place. A bird chirped in protest when the chipmunk disturbed its reverie.

"Charlie, tell me what happened."

Charlie pulled his boots off and hit them against the porch post, knocking the caked dirt off the caulks. The boots were dust-covered, the leather cracked, but he set them down gently next to his chair before sitting back and resting his head against the wall behind the chair. He closed his eyes.

Tilda's heart pounded as she waited for him to say something. Finally he opened his eyes.

"I started logging in the old country when I was fourteen," he began. "I worked in Mexico and then a year in a lead mine in Idaho when I first came to this country. Except for those jobs and a couple years in the cedar mill in Seattle, I been a logger. When the camps were down and I couldn't log, I hustled jobs at the dam, but most of the time I been running up and down mountain sides. Except for that malaria attack, I don't think I missed a day's work from sickness in forty years."

"That's right, Charlie, but what—"

"I fought drunk loggers and run-away fires and never quit." He stood and walked to the edge of the porch in his dust-crusted wool socks and slipped his suspenders off his shoulders to hang at his sides. "And in all this time, I never been hurt. Ain't that right, Tilda?"

Tilda nodded.

"I never had an accident, Tilda, because I kept a sharp eye out for danger, and when I saw it, I outjumped or outran it. And I been lucky," he said, sitting down again.

"I'll put on the coffee and be right back," Tilda said, hurrying into the kitchen. The stove was still hot from the baking she'd done earlier. She added a stick of wood to the firebox and slid the coffee pot to the front of the stove. When she returned to the porch, Charlie was leaning over from the side of the chair, dusting off his caulk shoes with his red handkerchief.

"Well, today, Tilda, I learned something," he said without looking up.

"What happened?" Tilda breathed.

"The cable broke. The haul-in line snapped in two and the log broke loose and started rolling down the sidehill toward me. I saw it coming. I jumped a windfall and started through the brush, but I knew all the time that I wasn't going to outrun that log."

"But you did! You're home safe."

"Ya, but not because I outran the log. One end of it hit a snag, and the log spun off in another direction. I watched it roll down the hill. It was the snag that saved me. My luck held, all right, but not my legs, and you need both in the woods. I have to face up to it, Tilda. A few years ago I could have outrun that log easy, and turned around and thumbed my nose at it, but I learned today that I can't do that any more. That's why I did what I did."

"What did you do?"

"I picked up my lunch bucket and walked down to the timekeeper's shack and turned in my time. Chet Woodworth gave me a ride out on the speeder."

Tilda leaned against the porch post.

"Tilda, I know it now. Logging is for young men."

"What will you do?" Tilda asked. What will we do? Tilda wondered.

"Hell, I'm only fifty-one. You'll see. I may get a job somewhere that has paved streets and sidewalks, like you planned on when you came to this country. They may not be paved with gold, like pastor promised you, but they won't be dusty in the summer and muddy in the winter. Maybe I'll take a look at that Anacortes mill your brother-in-law talks about. What you think, Tilda?"

Tilda's head spun. A new and different life? No more dread of the six whistles, of Charlie's footstep on the porch before he was due home, of fire on the horizon.

"What should we do, Tilda?"

Tilda took a deep breath. "Well, first we should have a cup of coffee. Then I finish Angie's dress. Then we go to Seattle and buy you a new suit of clothes for the wedding. You may need a suit anyway when you go talk to the superintendent of that Anacortes plywood mill.

Lower Camp One School

From left: Ivar Konikson, Harold & Irene Jacobson, Thelma,
Big Leonard, Lillian Box
Front: Margaret Warner, Edith Nelson.
Teacher, Mrs.Comfort.

First car, 1925 Chevrolet. Thelma in car.

Upper Camp One

Lind Family: Charlie, Tilda, Thelma, Angie

Angie, Melvin and Edwin Carlson in camp setting

Camp Two School

L.to R.: Jean Webb, Don Thompson, Wilfred Web, Angie,
Roberta and Mildred Woodworth, Teddy Thompson,
Merle Woodworth and Edwin Carlson.

Angie, Art, Thelma, Charlie C., Ida and Tilda
in Potlatch

Angie. Summer 1939

FROM TILDA'S KITCHEN

Swedish Hotcakes

In Finland these hotcakes are served in the evening
as a supper or dessert rather than at breakfast.

4 eggs	3/4 tsp. baking soda
1 1/2 cup flour	3/4 tsp. salt
1/3 cup sugar	2 1/4 to 2 1/2 c. milk

Place ingredients in bowl and mix until smooth. In hot, buttered skillet pour about 1/3 cup batter, tipping pan until batter is in thin layer. When bubbles appear (about one minute), turn. Hotcake should be light brown when ready. To eat, sprinkle with sugar. Then roll hotcake and dip in melted butter. They are also good served with jam, fresh strawberries or lingonberries and whip cream.

Fattigmand

A Christmas cookie

5 egg yolks	6 tbs. sugar
1 whole egg	6 tbs. cream
1/8 tsp. salt (opt.)	1 3/4+ c. flour

Beat eggs well. Add sugar and continue beating. Add rest of ingredients. (Add more flour as needed for easy handling.) Chill dough. Roll thin and cut into diamond shapes about three inches long. Cut slit in each diamond and pull point of diamond through the slit. Deep fry a few at a time in about two inches of hot oil (about 370 degrees), turning once when edges begin to brown. Drain on absorbent paper. Store in cold place. Before serving, dust each cookie with powdered sugar. *Fattigmand*, a bland cookie, is good with eggnog or coffee.

AFTERWORD: SHELTON 1990

ROSIE

Thelma, widowed now and still living in Shelton, greeted Ralph and me, her weekend guests, with exciting news. She'd just learned that Gunnar Sjoholm, a man who used to work for Dad, was living in town. Maybe if we went to see him, he could tell us some things about the early days in camp that would provide me with further information for my book.

A quick phone call. Yes, he remembered Thelma and would be happy to have us come see him. He and his wife Rosie didn't get out much now, and they would welcome the company.

Rosie? Could "Rosie" be my Miss Rose James? I remembered her so well. She had thick, auburn hair and freckles like a little girl, though she must have been all of twenty when she was my teacher in Camp Two.

The houses on the dirt street where Sjoholms lived were all tiny. The grass around their house was uncut and the porch steps leaned. The screen door was slivered where a pet dog must have scratched to get in, but the door itself stood open on this warm summer day.

"Come in," a husky voice called. The curtains were drawn, probably to keep the room cool, but in the shadows I could make out the figure of a thin but large-framed man sitting in a rocking chair with a cane at his side.

"Sure, I remember you," he told my sister when she reached down to shake his hand. "You were a spunky one. Kept your folks on the go," he laughed.

"This is my sister Angie," Thelma said, "and her husband Ralph."

"And this is my Rosie. Meet Rosie," Gunnar said and reached for her hand as she edged up to his chair. "Wasn't I lucky to marry the prettiest school teacher in all the camps?"

It was Miss James, all right. The thick, auburn hair that I remembered was thin now, with just a trace of color left. The freckles were the same.

"Angie?" she said, studying me through mist-coated eyes. "Little Angie." She spoke slowly, haltingly, smiling tentatively as she remembered. "You were so bashful when you started school, but a good student. I had nine students that year, I believe." She smiled. "Good children, all of you."

I learned she had Parkinson's disease. Her eyes and speech were affected, as well as her walk. Gunnar couldn't walk very well, but he had no trouble talking.

"Your dad. Now there was a man," he said after we were seated on the narrow sofa. "I was ten years younger than him, but when we were in the woods, I had to run to keep up. I'll never forget the time he fought Edson on the high spot between the tracks," Gunnar said, laughing and slapping his knee.

He related every detail of the incident as if it were yesterday. I have Gunnar to thank for the episode "King of the Mountain."

" Ya, I remember your mother," he went on. "A cute little woman, always hurrying here and there, taking care of the family.... Wasn't there a boy too? Oh, yes, I remember. Terrible accident. The whole camp grieved over that.

"And this is your little sister," he said to Thelma. "She must have been around when I worked in Camp Two, but I was too busy courting Rosie to notice." He smiled at Rosie and patted her hand where it rested on the arm of his chair.

"Didn't Charlie quit logging in '39? Not long before Phoenix closed down, if I remember right. Bought a share in some mill up near the San Juan Islands. Did all right, I heard..."

Most of the two-hundred shareholders in Anacortes Plywood were Scandinavian; many were friends of my parents from the logging camps. Tilda and her friends gathered in each other's living rooms to knit or crochet and drink coffee together. On weekends, like in camp, the men joined the ladies for **smörgåsbords**, dances, and picnics. On Sundays at the First Lutheran Church, Reverend Fosso, in the manner of any good, old-country preacher, excoriated them all for smoking, drinking and swearing, though most of them had already given up those things. But they listened to his sermons, and then hurried downstairs to visit with each other over coffee.

As Lake Cushman had been the doorway to the Olympic Mountains, so Anacortes was the doorway to the beautiful San Juan Islands. Charlie and Tilda built a home on a corner lot. Paved streets and sidewalks bordered not one, but two sides of their house, and from their breakfast nook window, they could catch a glimpse of the Guemes Channel. Charlie worked in the mill until he retired, and when he sold his share, he made enough to pay for the long-postponed trip to Finland and an adequate pension, with a little left over for a "rainy day."

"Dad liked to tell people about his job at the plywood mill," I told Gunnar and Rosie. "He sat up high on a machine called a 'clipper.' He pushed a button to release a tremendous blade that chopped and trimmed the bad spots out of long sheets of veneer that were moving past him on a wide conveyer belt. He was proud of what he did and joked about his coming up in the world to where all he needed now to earn a living was his thumb."

Gunnar slapped his knee. "You could always count on Charlie to make a joke," he laughed.

"It's true, the folks never really changed," Thelma said. "Remember, Angie, when they bought the electric range for their new house? Mom moved their old wood stove into the basement in case she needed to do some real cooking."

"And Dad planted potatoes in the empty parking strip between the sidewalk and the street," I said. "He felt good ground shouldn't go to waste."

Thelma turned to me. "Did Mom collect rubber bands on the kitchen doorknobs in Anacortes, too?"

"Yes," I answered, "and remember how she reused Christmas wrapping paper until it was as soft as cloth? They knew all about recycling!"

We both laughed then. Rosie smiled, already aware that old country frugality had become modern-day wisdom.

A fly buzzed lazily through the room, undecided about where to land. Rosie offered to make tea, but we had observed how difficult it was for her to get around and thanked her, but no, we shouldn't stay too long. Gunnar said, "They had it good, those last years. I'm glad of that."

Ralph spoke up. "When Charlie retired and they visited us in Parkrose, I encouraged them to tell about the camp days. Once after we'd talked a while, Tilda became very thoughtful. Then she said, 'Ya, those days were tough. Lots of hard work and worry, and sometimes heartache. But you know, when Charlie and I look back and really think about it, except for losing Leonard, those camp years were the best.'"

GLOSSARY

din mor, far	your mother, father
duktiga pojkar	capable boys
fattigmand	"poor man" cookie
festlig	festive
fruktsoppa	fruit soup (a dessert)
glögg	hot, wine-based punch
goddag, god morgon	good day, good morning
God Jul	Merry Christmas
Gud i himlen	God in heaven (a mild oath)
julgubbe	Christmas man (made from bread dough)
kära	dear (familiar form)
lutfisk	dish made from dried fish (usually cod)
moster	aunt (mother's sister)
nej	no
på tår	second cup of coffee
puka kniv	Finnish knife
skål	Cheers
skookum	(NW Indian jargon) strong, healthy
små-kusin	cousin other than first cousin
smörgåsbord	buffet supper
snälla flickor	good girls
sprits	butter cookie
syster	sister
tack, tack igen	thanks, thanks again
tyst nu	quiet now
välkommen	welcome
var så god	please, help yourself

BIBLIOGRAPHY

BOOKS

Anderson, Helen. *How, When, and Where on Hood Canal.*

Andrews, Ralph W. *Glory Days of Logging.* Seattle: Superior Publishers, 1956.

Andrews, Ralph W. *This Was Logging.* Seattle: Superior Publishers, 1954.

Barber, Olive. *The Lady and the Lumberjack.* New York: Thomas Y. Crowell, Co., 1952.

Bearden, Jean L. *A History of Hoodsport.* Port Angeles, Washington: Olympic Printers, Inc., 1987.

Churchill, Sam. *Big Sam.* Garden City, N.Y.: Doubleday & Co. Inc., 1965.

Churchill, Sam. *Don't Call Me Ma.* Garden City, N.Y.: Doubleday & Co. Inc., 1977.

Duncan, Don. *Washington, the First Hundred Years.*

Felt, Margaret; Hobi, Frank. *The Story of a Logger.* Bend, Oregon: Maverick Publications, 1984.

Haig-Brown; Langmere, Roderick. *Timber.* Corvallis, Oregon: Oregon State University Press, N.W. Reprints, 1993.

Holbrook, Stewart. *Green Commonwealth.* Seattle: Dogwood Press, 1945.

Holbrook, Stewart. *Holy Old Mackinaw.* New York: The Macmillan Co., 1938.

James, Dave. *Grisdale, Last of the Logging Camps.* Published by Mason County Historical Society. Fairfield, Washington: Ye Galleon Press, 1986.

Labbe, John T. & Replinger, Peter J. *Logging to the Salt Chuck.* (Over 100 years of railroad logging in Mason County, Washington,) Seattle, Washington: North West Short Line, 1990.

Morgan, Lane and Murray with Paul Dorpat. *Seattle, A Pictorial History.* Norfolk, Virginia: Donning Co., 1982.

Overland, Larry. *Early Settlement of Lake Cushman.* Belfair, Washington: Mason County Historical Society, 1981.

Shapiro, Mary J. *Gateway to Liberty.* New York: Random House, Inc., 1986.

Sorden, L. and Vallier, J. *Lumberjack Lingo.* North Word, Inc., 1986.

Warren, James. *King County and Its Queen City, Seattle.* Woodland Hills, California: Windsor Publications, 1981.

Whiteley, Opal S. *The Singing Creek Where the Willows Grow.* New York: Ticknor and Fields, 1986.

Williams, Richard L. *The Loggers.* New York, New York: Time/Life Books, 1976.

Workman, Rona M. *Just Loggin'.* Portland, Oregon: Metropolitan Press, 1936.

NEWSPAPERS AND PAMPHLETS

"Cushman Project." Tacoma Public Utilities. May, 1989.

"Passport to Ballard: The Centennial Story." *Ballard News Tribune,* Seattle, Washington: 1988.

Mason County Journal. Shelton, Washington, 1922-1925.

MUSEUMS

Nordic Heritage Museum, Ballard, Seattle, Washington.

Mason County Historical Society Museum, Shelton, Washington.

INDEX

TO ORDER

Where The Huckleberries Grow

Write or Call

Agnes Rands
Linden Press
P.O. Box 8249
Sisters, Oregon 97759
(541-595-2285)

or

E-Mail: ALinden99@aol.com

Include your name, address, city, state, zip
and a check for
$14.95
plus $2.00 for packaging and postage